Nonstoichiometric

Compounds

A symposium sponsored

by the Division of Inorganic

Chemistry at the

141st Meeting of the

American Chemical Society

Washington, D. C., March 21–23, 1962

Roland Ward, *Symposium Chairman*

ADVANCES IN CHEMISTRY SERIES **39**

AMERICAN CHEMICAL SOCIETY

WASHINGTON, D. C.   **1963**

Advances in Chemistry Series

Robert F. Gould, *Editor*

AMERICAN CHEMICAL SOCIETY

APPLIED PUBLICATIONS

CONTENTS

PREFACE

The stubborn opposition of Proust to Berthollet's contention that compounds could be of variable composition led to the acceptance of the law of constant composition by the end of the eighteenth century. The law was securely established by the superb analytical work of Stas more than a century ago. This was a necessary step in the approach to nonstoichiometry. The application of the phase rule to the study of systems in equilibrium showed that, in many binary systems, solid phases could have variable composition. Thus about a century later Berthollet's suspicions were seen to have some foundation. The advent of x-ray techniques for the study of crystalline solids contributed greatly to the construction of more detailed phase diagrams in the solidus region, revealing many more instances of nonstoichiometry.

Within the last 30 years there has developed a lively interest in the electronic properties of solids, many of which depend upon the existence of lattice defects and departures from stoichiometry.

The deviation from ideal composition in many cases was found to be well beyond the limits detectable by chemical analysis, while in other instances broad regions of homogeneity were recorded. Within recent years, the development of more refined x-ray techniques, combined with artful methods of annealing and of growing single crystals, has recealed that some hitherto board regions of homogeneity can be subdivided into rather sharply defined phases of essentially constant composition. It seemed an appropriate time to call a conference.

The symposia of the Division of Inorganic Chemistry of the American Chemical Society have usually been opened by a general lecture on the first day of the meeting, followed in subsequent sessions by more specific papers. The collection of papers presented in this volume includes the general lecture presented by J. S. Anderson. Because solid state chemists tend to become specialized in their interests, the symposium was arranged under the headings of oxides, hydrides, chalcogenides, and bronzes, although not all of the papers fall into these categories. All of the papers were by invitation, but in each of the divisions, one author was asked to give a general survey of the problem of nonstoichiometry. These were given by the following speakers: A. D. Wadsley on oxides, G. G. Libowitz on hydrides, J. S. Prener on chalcogenides, and M. J. Sienko on bronzes.

It is a pleasure to acknowledge the help given me by T. R. P. Gibb of Tufts University and Ephraim Banks of the Polytechnic Institute of Brooklyn in arranging this symposium.

ROLAND WARD

The University of Connecticut
Storrs, Conn.

Current Problems in Nonstoichiometry

J. S. ANDERSON
National Chemical Laboratory, Teddington, Middlesex, England

Four problems confronting the chemistry of solids are surveyed. From statistical thermodynamics the occurrence of nonstoichiometry can be reasonably correlated with the valence properties of the elements, but theory is obviously too crude to cover grossly nonstoichiometric compounds. Lattice energy calculations can lead to the conclusion that all nonstoichiometric phases should be metastable and numerous ordered intermediate binary phases have recently been discovered. Estimates of the endothermicity of defective structures disagree with reliable equilibrium measurements. Interactions between lattice defects are therefore considered, and attention is directed to lattice relaxation, short range ordering, and the nature of defect clusters or complexes in real systems. On this basis conflicting arguments can probably be reconciled. Attention is finally drawn to the still unresolved question of what factors limit the existence range of a phase in any specific case.

Chemical thought was dominated by the law of constant composition for 120 years, in the sense that a fixed composition and a rational formula were taken as the definitive criteria for a compound. As applied to solid compounds, the law was not a generalization from experimental fact. The controversy between Berthollet and Proust was unsatisfactory; it was settled by a dogmatic, but natural, extrapolation of the conclusions drawn by Dalton from the atomic theory. These are inherently valid for discrete molecules. Until physical scientists were ready to think of crystalline inorganic compounds as infinite three-dimensional assemblies of atoms, the stage was not set for reopening this particular aspect of the recurrent problem of the strictly quantized or the statistical and quasicontinuous description of natural phenomena.

EDITOR'S NOTE. The symbolism used in this article is that of A. L. G. Rees of the Australian Commonwealth Scientific Research Industrial Organization, while that used by other authors in the symposium is that of F. A. Kroger and H. J. Vink of Phillips Research Laboratories. This was pointed out to the author, who feels that, of the accepted symbolisms for defect solids, that of Rees is best suited to convey the chemical and structural information required.

Since about 1930, but especially in the last few years, the concept of non-stoichiometric compounds has been a stimulating influence in inorganic chemistry. It has opened up new ideas; it has led to much new work on the constitution and the valence problems of inorganic compounds; it has shed light on the mechanism of reactions taking place in the solid state. Indeed, it goes to the roots of our ideas about the definition of a chemical compound.

It has become clear, however, that some serious problems remain unsolved. A real divergence has arisen between the essentially structural and the essentially thermodynamic ideas, and the attractive clarity of our theoretical outlook has been blurred. This introductory symposium paper seeks to formulate some questions that need to be answered.

We note certain key stages in the development of the subject, which point ahead to the still unresolved problems. Kurnakov's work (1910–14) really reopened the dormant issue. Systematic studies of heterogeneous equilibria had revealed solid solutions and intermediate phases in many (especially in intermetallic) systems. By studying a range of quantitative properties across equilibrium diagrams, Kurnakov showed that singularities or turning points of values of physical properties—maxima of melting points, maxima or minima of electrical conductivity or of thermoelectric power, etc.—did not necessarily coincide with the compositions assigned to intermediate phases of rational formula. He recognized that this implied a certain indeterminacy in defining intermetallic or quasimetallic compounds, and described them as berthollides [Kurnakov, 1914 (25)]. Because he was chiefly concerned with intermetallic systems—to which it is still generally considered that one must extend a good deal of chemical license—his work did not immediately have much impact on theory.

The palladium-hydrogen system presented another long-standing anomaly. The relation of hydrogen to the metals can be given a formal thermodynamic description in terms of solid solutions, but the uniquely high sorption of hydrogen in palladium evinced evidence of highly specific—i.e., chemical—forces of interaction. This was probably the first nonstoichiometric system for which equilibrium measurements were made (Hoitsema, 1895; Gillespie, 1926), revealing two nonstoichiometric ranges which merged into a single phase above 568° C. at 20 atm. The stoichiometry of the β phase constituted a puzzle, for although Procrustean reasoning assigned to it the formula Pd_2H, its formula was irrational and dependent on the equilibrium hydrogen pressure, with isotherms rising very steeply for hydrogen contents exceeding $PdH_{0.6}$. It was early recognized that hydrogen must be present as H atoms, not H_2 molecules. With the additional evidence furnished by x-ray diffraction and, more especially, by neutron diffraction studies, it has since become clear that the palladium-hydrogen system is not peculiar, but exemplifies features—e.g., partial occupancy of crystallographic sites, the problems of composition limits and of the succession of phases of related structure—which must find a natural place in any successful theory of nonstoichiometric compounds.

Because intermetallic systems undoubtedly display certain special features that follow from their metallic binding forces, considerable importance attached to the growing evidence that the chalcogenides, the essentially ionic oxides, the nitrides, and other representative binary compounds of the transition metals were, not infrequently, both variable and irrational in composition. Schenck and Dingmann's equilibrium study of the iron-oxygen system (39) was notable in this connection: They showed that stoichiometric ferrous oxide, $FeO_{1.000}$, the oxide of an important and typical valence state, did not exist. It lay outside the broad existence field of a nonstoichiometric phase. It is, perhaps, still not certain whether the wüstite phase extends just to the stoichiometric composition at the lowest extreme of the limited range over which it is stable, but in general much accurate work on this most important system has confirmed the first conclusions. A great deal more evidence of the same kind, extending over much of the periodic system, came from the lengthy series of papers by Biltz and his coworkers on the systematic doctrine of affinity, which added an immense fund of reliable information on the dissociation equilibria and the succession of phases in the oxides, sulfides, selenides, arsenides, etc., of the metals, together with x-ray diffraction data, densities, and magnetic and other properties bearing on the existence and constitution of compounds of variable composition.

Yet more important was the publication by Schottky and Wagner (1930) of their classical paper on the statistical thermodynamics of real crystals (*41*). This clarified the role of intrinsic lattice disorder as the equilibrium state of the stoichiometric crystal above 0° K. and led logically to the deduction that equilibrium between the crystal of an ordered mixed phase—i.e., a binary compound of ionic, covalent, or metallic type—and its components was statistical, not unique and determinate as is that of a molecular compound. As the consequence of a statistical thermodynamic theorem this proposition should be generally valid. The stoichiometrically ideal crystal has no special status, but the extent to which different substances may display a detectable variability of composition must depend on the energetics of each case—in particular, on the energetics of lattice disorder and of valence change. This point is taken up below, for it is fundamental to the problems that have to be considered.

The Schottky-Wagner papers gave a background against which to view the experimental facts. Ferrous oxide and palladium hydride appeared as striking instances of a more general phenomenon; nonstoichiometry could be given an exact structural meaning. Thus the FeO_{1+x} and FeS_{1+x} phases were recognized, from their cell dimensions and densities, as iron-deficient, with an excess of cation vacancies [Jette and Foote, 1932 (*23*)] and (as far as the evidence then went) a sensibly perfect oxygen or sulfur sublattice. The work of Ehrlich (1939, 1949) (*16*) on titanium oxides and chalcogenides, and of Haraldsen (1937) (*21*) and Tengner (1938) (*44*) and others on transition metal sulfides and selenides, revealed how remarkably incomplete the occupancy of lattice sites could be.

At the other end of the composition scale, the predicted widespread occurrence of slight nonstoichiometry linked up with the mechanisms of solid state reactions and with the properties of semiconductors. To preserve electrostatic neutrality, with the creation of cation vacancies or of interstitial cations in an ionic crystal there must go a corresponding number of positive holes and electrons. To the chemist, these excess charges, localized, must correspond to some chemically and energetically reasonable species. Wagner and his pupils (1933, 1936) formulated a quantitative theory (*47*) of the kinetics of solid state reactions, and especially of the oxidation of metals, in terms of the mobility of point defects and of positive holes or electrons. As semiconductor physics has developed, it has been found that measurements of the concentrations of current carriers provide by far the most sensitive means of detecting and measuring very small deviations from stoichiometry, and of studying the dissociation equilibria of nearly stoichiometric compounds.

Problem 1.   The Occurrence of Nonstoichiometry

The observed facts fall into two groups:

1. For certain compounds, stoichiometric deviations are detectable but, in general, are very small: within the range only of special analytical experiments or of methods based on direct determination of carrier concentrations. Examples are PbS_{1+x}, Cu_2O_{1+x}, ZnO_{1-x}, alkali halides containing F-centers, etc. It is reasonable to assume that the stoichiometric deviation is small enough for the lattice defects to be isolated and randomly distributed, so that the Schottky-Wagner theoretical treatment properly applies (possibly with some correction for activities in place of concentrations).

2. At the other extreme—and it is with these that this paper and this symposium must be chiefly concerned—are the crystals which show gross departure from ideal stoichiometry—e.g., $Fe_{0.84}O$, $Ti_{0.96}O_{0.96}O_{0.69}$ to $Ti_{0.74}O_{0.98}$, $NiTe_{1.0}$ to $NiTe_{2.0}$, etc. Even a zeroth order treatment, in which the lattice defects are regarded as randomly distributed, shows that a high proportion of atoms have an incomplete coordination environment, and a high proportion of vacant lattice sites or of interstitials must be adjacent to one another. The stability of such defective crystals, as compared with alternative structures, is a serious question.

In view of the very wide differences indeed between different substances it is pertinent to inquire whether all ionic, covalent, and metallic binary phases are variable in composition, and what factors determine the quantitative differences actually observed.

Knowledge on the first point is incomplete, largely because interest has been so concentrated on a few classes of compounds—notably the oxides, hydrides, sulfides, nitrides, etc., of the transition metals—but partly for a deeper reason. Ormont (1959) (32) has pointed out that the question is not meaningful beyond a certain limit, set by the inherent properties of the stoichiometric material and by the attainable purity of experimental samples. If the vacancies or interstitials produced by nonstoichiometry are outweighed by those present as a result of intrinsic lattice disorder, or if the charged carriers created by nonstoichiometry are fewer than those conferring intrinsic conductivity, there is no means of detecting them. It appears from the available evidence that, above their Tammann temperatures—i.e., when inner equilibrium is attainable—many typical ionic compounds contain more than 10^{16} to 10^{17} defect pairs per cubic centimeter. Only methods based on counting electrons (or positive holes) would give evidence of nonstoichiometry below a mole fraction of 10^{-4} to 10^{-5}. Such compounds as the silicides, arsenides, etc., of transition metals frequently have high intrinsic electronic conductivity; stoichiometric deviations below the direct analytical limit may well be inaccessible to observation. In any case, intrinsic properties may be swamped by the effects of impurities, and especially by the variable-valence impurities such as iron. There are very few materials, outside the small range that have been intensively studied as semiconductors, for which the total impurity concentrations have been reduced to 10^{-6}. There is thus a limit beyond which fixity or variability of composition has no operational meaning.

As an example, it appears still uncertain whether the high temperature conductivity of very pure magnesium oxide, and the way it varies with the ambient oxygen pressure, involves any measure of nonstoichiometry, or whether it is wholly attributable to residual impurities [Mitoff, 1959 (29)]. At very high temperatures the conductivity of refractory oxides may be intrinsic, and may mask any displacement of stoichiometric equilibrium.

To explore the factors that determine how far nonstoichiometry may be observed in practice, we may consider the straightforward case of an oxide, MO, in which the intrinsic lattice disorder is of Frenkel type. It will be involved in simultaneous internal and external equilibria which [using the symbolism of Rees (1954) (33)] may be represented by the equations:

$$M^{2+}|\square + \Delta \rightleftharpoons \square_+ + M^{2+}|\Delta \tag{1}$$

$$M \text{ gas} + \Delta + 2 M^{2+}|\square_+ \rightleftharpoons M^{2+}|\Delta + 2 M^+|\square_+ \tag{2}$$

$$\tfrac{1}{2} O_2 + 2 M^{2+}|\square_+ \rightleftharpoons 2 M^{3+}|\square_+ + \square_+ + O^{-2}|\square_- \tag{3}$$

$$2 M^{2+}|\square_+ \rightleftharpoons M^{3+}|\square_+ + M^+|\square_+ \tag{4}$$

For convenience, Equations 2 and 3, which represent alternative ways of writing the nonstoichiometry reaction, show the positive holes or electrons as trapped at cation positions. Equilibria 2 and 3 are linked through the intrinsic disorder process (Equation 1), the intrinsic conduction equilibrium (Equation 4), and the Gibbs-Duhem relation ($n_1\delta\mu_1, + n_2\delta\mu_2 = 0$) between the thermodynamic potentials of the components in equilibrium with the crystal. Reaction 3 is usually the more convenient to translate into experimental terms.

Examination of the equilibrium conditions shows that the equilibrium constant for intrinsic disorder (Equation 1) involves only the (endothermic) energy needed to create a complementary pair of defects in the ordered, stoichiometric crystal lattice. Writing $\overline{N}^h$, $\overline{N}^i$ as the number of cation vacancies and of interstitial cations, respectively, in a stoichiometric crystal with N lattice sites in all, at an expenditure of energy denoted by E^h, E^i, respectively, then the intrinsic disorder, ζ, is given by Equation 5.

$$\zeta = \frac{\overline{N}^h}{N} = \frac{\overline{N}^i}{\overline{N}} = \text{const. exp.} -(E^h + E^i)/2kT \tag{5}$$

The energy changes in the processes represented by Equations 2 and 3 involve not only the creation or elimination of lattice defects but the essentially chemical factors:

1. The ionization energy of M, or the dissociation energy and electron affinity of the nonmetal, for the incorporation of either component in the crystal lattice.

2. A valence change on the part of cations proper to the crystal lattice—and it is here that the energetic accessibility of other valence states enters the argument and the frequent occurrence of nonstoichiometry among transition metal compounds falls into place.

3. The change in local Madelung energy resulting from changes in ionic charge, partially offsetting the energy change (2).

4. The energy of relaxation of the crystal lattice immediately around the lattice defects and, more particularly, around the altervalent ions.

In the subsequent discussion it is argued that this last merits more attention than it has, on the whole, received.

The net ΔE or ΔH for incorporation of excess of either component in the stoichiometric phase can be either negative or positive. Whether the equilibrium constants of Reactions 2 and 3 permit of significant deviations from stoichiometry therefore depends largely on the term $T\Delta S$, in which the configurational entropy of random distribution of defects is the dominant factor. Even if ΔH is large and positive, nonstoichiometry might become significant at high enough temperatures.

What determines whether nonstoichiometric behavior can readily be observed is largely the form of the dissociation pressure–composition isotherms in the equilibrium diagram. If the free energy rises too steeply with excess of either component, it may not be practicable to detect stoichiometric changes which, in principle, are taking place. The explicit relation between the stoichiometric defect (= x for the composition MO_{1+x}) and the free energy is complicated and awkward to work out, but the relative pressure $p(x) / p(0)$ [where $p(x)$ is the equilibrium pressure over MO_{1+x}, and $p(0)$ is the equilibrium pressure of the stoichiometric phase, $MO_{1.000}$] is rather simple, and depends only on the intrinsic properties of the stoichiometric crystal: the equilibrium constants for Reactions 1 and 4. Bloem and Kröger (1956) (9) and Brouwer (1954) (14, 15) have refined the treatment of the defect equilibria to take account of the ionization of defects. Figure 1, based on their treatment, shows the $(p(x)/p(0), X)_T$ relations for some hypothetical, but representative, cases: (i) intrinsic lattice disorder, ζ, very small, intrinsic electronic conductivity ($\overline{n} = \overline{p}$ electrons or positive holes per cc.) very small; (ii) ζ in the range typical of ionic compounds at the Tammann point, $\overline{n}$ very small; (iii) ζ large as in ii but $\overline{n}$ of comparable magnitude; (iv) ζ as in ii, $\overline{n}$ large; and (v) ζ large and n large.

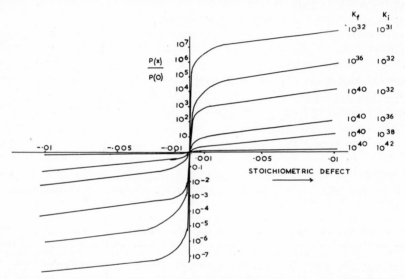

Figure 1.   Reduced pressure, $p(x)/p(0)$ for phase AB_{1+x} as dependent on stoichiometric defect

K_f. *Equilibrium constant for intrinsic lattice disorder (Equation 1)*
K_i. *Equilibrium constant for intrinsic current carriers (Equation 4)*

It is clear that for most typically electrovalent compounds, built up from inert-gas type cations of low electron affinity and inert-gas type anions of high ionization potential—e.g., compounds of the A subgroup metals, and the halides of the metals in general—the free energy curve must rise very steeply for small departures from ideal composition. Nevertheless, because the creation of lattice defects in such crystals is highly endothermic, the intrinsic disorder, ζ, must increase steeply with temperature and nonstoichiometry can be expected to be observable at high enough temperatures: "High" is to be defined here in terms of the properties of the substance considered. Thus many of the oxides of stable valence states of the metals show n-type conductivity at moderately high temperatures, without analytically detectable changes of composition. Thorn and Ackermann (1961) (45) have shown that some of the most stable oxides lose oxygen and vaporize incongruently at 2400° to 2800° K.—e.g., $ZrO_{1.96}$, $ThO_{1.95}$. Sawyer (1960) (38) has shown that, in contrast to its existence limits at lower temperatures, uranium dioxide in equilibrium with the metal becomes oxygen-deficient at 2500° to 3000° K. The composition ranges which thus become appreciable at the highest temperatures are as compatible with the straightforward Schottky-Wagner conception as is, for example, the behavior of zinc oxide at 1200° K., or potassium chloride in equilibrium with potassium vapor at 800° K.

Intrinsic lattice disorder may well be higher in crystals where the binding forces are largely covalent than in purely ionic crystals. Although the creation of a vacancy involves the severance of bonds and a change in hybridization of the atoms adjacent to the vacant site, the bonds in many structures are inherently electron-deficient because of the high coordination number of each atom. Cohesive energy lost in breaking bonds may be partly compensated by an increase in the bond order of the other bonds formed by atoms adjacent to the vacancy. Thus in the NiAs structure, the bonds must be largely covalent-metallic; each metal atom forms six fractional-order metal-metal bonds to its nearest neighbors in the same sheet and six bonds to the octahedrally disposed nonmetal atoms. The same factors that diminish the endothermicity of lattice defects lead also to a small energy gap, or even an overlap between valence band and conduction band. Although there is a regrettable lack of thermodynamic data and of studies of the electronic properties of these quasimetallic substances, their extreme tolerance for stoichiometric deviations can be qualitatively understood; both ζ and $\bar{n}$ are very large. Thus Ehrlich (1939, 1949) (*16*) has interpreted the densities and cell dimensions of the titanium chalcogenides as indicating that at least 5% of metal and nonmetal sites are vacant in the stoichiometric compounds TiS, TiSe, and TiTe. It is noteworthy that, outside the NiAs and similar structures favoring the formation of metal-metal bonds, grossly nonstoichiometric compounds (especially oxides) arise mostly from atoms or ions in oxidation states that confer the d^1, or d^2, or d^3 configuration, such as Ti(II) and V(II)—i.e., at the beginning of the transition series proper. Ternary compounds of the valence-controlled framework-structure type—e.g., tungsten bronzes—are also formed by the elements at the beginning of the transition series, but from higher oxidation states—e.g., Ti(IV — III), W(VI — V), Mn(IV — III). This correlation of nonstoichiometric behavior with electron configuration of the metals will fall into place when the constitution of nonstoichiometric compounds is better established.

Problem 2. *Are Grossly Nonstoichiometric Compounds Thermodynamically Stable?*

This question must be asked on two grounds. First, because the high concentrations of lattice defects found in some cases (the TiO phase is an extreme example) must raise doubt about the relation of the nonstoichiometric phase to the type structure in terms of which it is described. Secondly, successions of ordered intermediate phases have been discovered during the last few years, in phase diagrams where, previously, nonstoichiometric compounds of broad range had been reported.

Theoretically, the discussion must turn on the relative energies of complex ordered structures and of defective, random structures. Bertaut (5) (1953) attempted to compute the electrostatic lattice energy of the pyrrhotite phase $FeS_{1.14}$ ($Fe^{+2}_{0.625}$, $Fe^{+3}_{0.250}|\square^+$) ($S^{-2}|\square_-$) or ($Fe^{+2}_5$, Fe^{+3}_2, $\square$) (S^{-2}_8), for several alternative cases: a completely disordered structure with higher-valent cations and vacancies randomly distributed over all cation sites; and structures with the vacancies ordered into alternate cation sheets, with various hypotheses about the disposition of the higher valent cations. It emerged that while additional stabilization energy comes from the optimum ordered arrangement of the Fe^{+3} ions, the energy liberated by ordering the vacancies alone is very large. Bertaut's calculation gave around 320 kcal. per mole, or 500 to 1000 times the energy of the usual order-disorder transformation—so large that the entropy contribution to the free energy would be negligible and the equilibrium constant for vacancy disorder physically meaningless. If this is so, it can plausibly be argued that a nonstoichiometric phase, with irrational composition and inherently random distribution of vacancies or interstitials, should be highly endothermic with respect to ordered phases of rational and fixed composition. The unit of ordering is unlikely to be very large, in view of the low probability (high negative entropy) of achieving too complex an ordering pattern, although the unit cells of some ordered intermediate phases in both intermetallic and ionic structures are astonishingly large and pose some awkward questions. It might be expected, therefore, that the true equilibrium diagrams of oxide and sulfide systems should display a succession of well defined phases of such fixed compositions as lend themselves to the appropriate ordering processes. True equilibrium cannot always be attained in real systems because of the interplay between kinetic and equilibrium considerations; point defects can only be ordered or eliminated at temperatures where there is sufficient diffusional mobility. Vacancies and interstitials are trapping sites for altervalent ions; these can migrate and attain order by a series of electron switches, as long as all cation sites are tenanted by the same kind of atom, but if impurity atoms are present they can lock a measure of randomness into the cation arrangement by blocking electron transfer processes. Metastable, random, nonstoichiometric phases may then persist. It is worth speculating how far the wealth of detailed information now being obtained about the cerium, praseodymium, and terbium oxide systems is the direct consequence of the purer rare earth preparation now available, as compared with pre-ion-exchange days.

This argument needs close examination on both structural and thermodynamic grounds. Structurally, the requirements of ordering seem to be met in two distinct ways. In the first, vacant lattice sites (or interstitial atoms) undergo a superstructure ordering within the crystal lattice of the idealized composition. The superstructure may impose a change of symmetry; there may be small consequential shifts of position and changes of dimensions. In general, the ordered intermediate phase retains, for its pseudocell, a clear relation to that of the corresponding, if hypothetical, random, defective phase.

This type of ordered intermediate phase appears to arise within two of the type structures that appear especially prone to the formation of grossly nonstoichiometric compounds: the NiAs and CaF_2 structures. The former is exemplified by Jellinek's (24) work on the chromium sulfides (1957), CrS_{1+x}. In prewar work, Haraldsen (1937, 1938) (22) reported wide stoichiometric ranges: $CrS_{1.00}$ to $CrS_{1.18}$, $CrS_{1.22}$ to $CrS_{1.40}$, and $CrS_{1.45}$ to $CrS_{1.50}$. It now appears that after sufficiently prolonged annealing, there are six phases of rather closely defined composition: Cr_2S_3 (two forms, one of which may be deficient in sulfur), Cr_3S_4, Cr_5S_6, Cr_7S_8, and CrS (possibly not ideal in composition). The compositions of the intermediate sulfides correspond to rational ways of ordering vacant chromium sites in alternate sheets of the structure.

Bevan (1955) (6), Brauer and Holtschmidt (1951), and Brauer and Gradinger (1954) (14, 15) for the cerium oxides, and Eyring and others (1954, 1961) (18) for the praseodymium and terbium oxides, have found essentially analogous sequences of intermediate phases: $MO_{1.5}$, $MO_{1.65}$, $MO_{1.72}$ $(= M_7O_{12})$,

$MO_{1.78}$ (= M_9O_{16} or $M_{32}O_{57}$), $MO_{1.81}$ (= $M_{16}O_{29}$). These phases also almost certainly arise from the ordering of vacant oxygen sites in the defective fluorite structure.

Immediately adjacent to an anion or cation vacancy the electrostatic lattice energy is considerably reduced. An alternative way of changing the cation-anion ratio of a structure without a radical change in the coordination environment of any atom (though at the cost of increasing the repulsive terms in the lattice energy sum) is found in the remarkable series of homologous oxides of molybdenum, titanium, and vanadium, discovered by Magnéli and his collaborators (*2, 27, 28*): Mo_nO_{3n-1}, Ti_nO_{2n-1} (n = 4,5...9), and V_nO_{2n-1} (Magneli 1953, 1960; Andersson, 1954). In these oxides the octahedral coordination about the metal atoms is preserved but, at regular spacings, edge sharing is added to corner sharing in the molybdenum oxides, or face sharing to edge sharing in the rutile structure.

Both types of ordering leave little scope for nonstoichiometry without interfering with the complex long-range order of the large unit cells. There is, accordingly, some tendency for crystallographers to hold the view that grossly nonstoichiometric compounds are illusory.

Examination of Bevan's careful work on the CeO_{2-x} system shows that the cell dimensions of the intermediate phases differ significantly in the adjoining two-phase ranges. This implies a significant, if small, composition range at the temperatures at which equilibrium was frozen into the crystal lattice (Table I).

Table I.   Nonstoichiometry of Intermediate Phases in Cerium Oxide Systems

Nominal Formula	*Upper and Lower Limits*	*Dimensions of Equivalent Hexagonal Cell, A. (Rhombohedral)*		*Dimensions of Cubic Cell, a_c, A.*
		a	*c*	
CeO_2	$CeO_{2.000}$?	(3.825) (3.826)	(9.368) (9.372)	5.409 5.411
$Ce_{16}O_{29}$	$CeO_{1.812}$ $CeO_{1.804}$	3.890 3.900	9.531 9.538	
Ce_9O_{16}	$CeO_{1.785}$ No detectable range	3.910	9.502	
Ce_7O_{12}	$CeO_{1.722}$ $CeO_{1.710}$	3.912 3.921	9.657 9.637	
Ce_8O_{13}	$CeO_{1.650}$ $CeO_{1.681}$	(2 × 3.934) (2 × 3.929)	(2 × 9.365) (2 × 9.625)	11.126 11.114

From the thermodynamic standpoint, the conclusion that ΔG is dominated by a very large positive ΔH term turns entirely on whether the calculation of the endothermicity of random, defective crystals is valid. In so far as direct thermodynamic measurements or phase equilibrium studies are available for oxide systems (and these, as the most truly ionic of allegedly nonstoichiometric compounds, should be the ones for which the Bertaut type of calculation should be least unreliable), it seems clear that the endothermicity of the random, compared with the ordered, structure has been grossly overestimated.

Thus, for the phases derived from the fluorite structure, Bevan's room temperature observations can be supplemented by the high temperature x-ray work and tensiometric measurements of Brauer and Gingerich (1960) (*12*). Above 600° C. the composition ranges of the $CeO_{1.82}$ and $CeO_{2.00}$ oxides broaden, so that they merge into a single cubic phase. Although the phase boundaries have not been traced, the lower intermediate oxides also transform or merge into the same single cubic phase at high temperatures (10), extending from $CeO_{2.00}$ to at least $CeO_{1.65}$. In the corresponding praseodymium oxide series, Eyring's equilibrium pressure measurements not only show the intermediate phases, but also that the univariant ranges between them narrow and disappear at higher temperatures. Another related system, with interstitial atoms in a fluorite-type structure, is that of the uranium oxides UO_{2+x}, covered by the very detailed free energy and phase equilibrium studies of Roberts and Walter (1961) (36), Blackburn (1958) (8), Aronson and Belle (1958) (4), etc.

Since Roberts has discussed nonstoichiometric fluorite-type oxides in several papers, the thermodynamics need be only briefly summarized. Below 1123° C., the distinct nature of the nonstoichiometric $\overline{UO_2}$ and $\overline{U_4O_9}$ phases, and the more highly ordered nature of the latter, are shown by the differences in partial molar enthalpy of oxygen in the two phases, and by the considerable decrease in entropy accompanying the $UO_{2+x} \longrightarrow U_4O_{9-y}$ phase reaction (Table II).

Table II.   U-O System at 1300° K.

		ΔG, Kcal.	$\Delta H/Mole$ O_2, Kcal.	$\Delta S/Mole$ O_2, E.U.
UO_{2+x} phase	$UO_2 + 0.0995\ O_2 \to UO_{2.199}$	−4.09	−60	−14.6
	$UO_{2.199} + 0.0185\ O_2 \to UO_{2.236}$	−0.619	−118	−61
U_4O_{9-x} phase	$UO_{2.236} + 0.007\ O_2 \to UO_{2.250}$	−0.216	−86	−46

Above 1123° C. the UO_{2+x}—which is not unsatisfactorily interpreted directly in terms of a simple statistical thermodynamic model—replaces the partially ordered U_4O_{9-y} phase over the whole composition range up to about $UO_{2.26}$ at 1400° C. It does not appear that a very large heat effect can be ascribed to the partial order $\rightleftharpoons$ complete disorder process relating to these two phases.

Similarly, the phase equilibria are known with certainty, and free energy measurements are available (although not as closely spaced as one might wish) to define the ferrous oxide phase as having continuity over a wide stoichiometric range at 1000° K. The evidence is incompatible with the idea that these and other compounds owe their existence to ordering processes or are metastable with respect to discrete intermediate phases.

Other classes of compounds, such as the nonstoichiometric hydrides, fall within the same argument. Thus, for the classical example of palladium hydride, it is possible to describe the constitution more precisely than by the former designation as an interstitial hydride. If the α phase is described in terms of the NaCl structure (cf. the neutron diffraction work), it is a defective one, with the hydrogen sublattice only partly filled. Aston's low temperature specific heat work [Nace and Aston, 1957 (31)] suggests that the hydrogen atoms become ordered to impose an idealized formula, Pd_4H. But this is at low temperature; the diffusion coefficient of hydrogen in palladium and the bivariant range of the equilibrium diagram show that at, or a little above, room temperature the structure is disordered.

Problem 3.   The Interaction of Lattice Defects

This problem is fundamental to an understanding of the real structure of nonstoichiometric and intermediate phases. Superstructures and shear structures, nucleation and reconstructive transformations, the quantitative details of the equilibrium of a compound with its components: all these hinge upon the interactions between point defects and valence defects.

The Virtual Charge Approximation. Lattice defects are necessarily created in complementary pairs. In the stoichiometric crystal, this means a pair of point defects; in stoichiometric unbalance, a point defect plus an electronic defect. These are not independent entities. Relative to the normal lattice constituents, cations of higher or lower valence bear a charge of $+e$ or $-e$, respectively; an interstitial cation represents a charge of $+ze$ at a position which would normally bear no charge; a vacant site bears a virtual charge of opposite sign to that of the ion properly located on it. Thus a cation vacancy is an interruption in the regular periodicity of the crystal lattice. Electrostatically, the results of removing a cation of charge $+ze$ or of superimposing a charge of $-ze$ on the occupied site are the same, and the latter can be regarded as an equivalent description. Hence, complementary point defects bear opposite virtual charges and attract each other; valence defects are attracted by (and in the state of lowest energy will be trapped at) their complementary point defects. Association of defects in this sense has been fairly fully discussed in relation to F-centers and defects in alkali halides. It has been less thoroughly pursued in a more general context.

A useful analogy, which has not yet been fully exploited, can be drawn between complementary defect pairs and electrolytes in solution. The Schottky-Wagner approximation (valid for highly dilute defects) corresponds to the Arrhenius strong electrolyte. Thus Wagner represents the nonstoichiometric equilibrium of cuprous oxide as

$$Cu_2O + O_2 \rightleftharpoons Cu_2O + 4e^+ + 4\,\square_+ + 2O^{-2}$$

for which, in so far as vacancies and positive holes are independent entities,

$$K.p_{O_2} = [e^+]^4[\square_+]^4$$

and since $e^+ = \square_+$, the conductivity and stoichiometric excess of oxygen should be proportional to $p_{O_2}^{1/8}$. The experimentally observed relation between oxygen pressure and stoichiometric defect (x in $Cu_2O_{1+x} \propto p_{O_2}^{1/5}$) indicates some fairly strong association between positive holes and copper vacancies.

In other nonstoichiometric systems—and in this context, as in others, there is a serious lack of quantitative data—Debye-Hückel effects and incomplete dissociation are much more pronounced. In some as yet unpublished work in my laboratory, Barraclough made extensive measurements on the nicely reversible $CaUO_{4-x}$ system and some relevant information can be extracted from his $(p,X)_T$ data. The equilibrium here involves

$$2UO_2^{+2} + O^{-2} \rightleftharpoons 2UO_2^+ + \square_- + \tfrac{1}{2}O_2$$

Trapped electrons and virtual charge on the oxygen vacancy together constitute the analog of a 2 to 1 electrolyte. At $700°$ C. the oxygen deficit varies as $P_{O_2}^{-1/4}$, implying that one electron—i.e., one UO_2^+ altervalent ion—is firmly bound to the vacancy. From the behavior at higher temperatures, the further dissociation can be followed and the interaction energy found to be about 17 kcal. per mole of defect pairs.

Association effects clearly vary widely in magnitude from one substance to another. As with electrolytes in solution, the nonionic terms in the potential function for interaction may be critically important. Bloem's detailed analysis of equilibria in the $Pb_{1\pm x}S$ system shows that although the total stoichiometric defect is very small, trapping of electrons at sulfur vacancies, and of positive holes at lead vacancies, dominates the behavior.

This way of looking at defect interaction could profitably be developed further. There is a useful parallel to be drawn between solvated ions or ion-pair complexes in solution, and defects or defect complexes in their crystal lattice environment. The idea is worth using when considering the growing hints of short range order and defect association in nonstoichiometric phases.

Clustering of Defects. In a crystal of almost ideal composition, vacant sites or interstitial ions are relatively widely separated: A random distribution implies that they are as far apart as possible. It might be adjudged, at first sight, that the interaction between defects—due to their real or virtual charges, or to the strain induced in the surrounding crystal lattice—was inherently repulsive.

This is, however, not the whole of the matter. The superstructure ordering of point defects; the collection of interstitial ions along certain lines or sheets, as in Magneli's model for the precursor of his shear structures; the temperature-dependent adjustment of composition of a nonstoichiometric phase at the boundary of the bivariant range; the nucleation of a new phase of different stoichiometry—these depend on accumulating vacancies or interstitials in some regions of the crystal lattice at the expense of others.

Thus the behavior of lattice defects bears some analogy to phase separation in fluids, or to the treatment of adsorption on localized sites. At low relative temperatures, the defects adopt a random distribution if they are sufficiently dilute; if their concentration exceeds a certain value they segregate into defect-poor and defect-rich regions which can coexist. The concentration at which this occurs, and the relative temperature scale, depend on what can be represented as a nearest-neighbor attraction in the interaction potentials. The magnitude of the attractive interaction energy defines a critical temperature above which no segregation of defects occurs.

On this view, interaction between defects determines the concentration at which a phase becomes saturated with defects, and also the manner in which defects aggregate or order. It can be foreseen that stoichiometrically defined intermediate phases are likely to undergo an order-disorder transition at higher temperatures and that, in general, some detectable stoichiometric range is likely before the disordering temperature is reached.

There is evidence that attainment of superstructure ordering, or the segregation of lattice defects, can be a fast process. Reference has been made to the conversion of the ordered intermediate phases in CeO_{2-x} system into a broad-range cubic defective fluorite phase at moderately high temperatures. In Bevan's and Brauer's work it was impossible to freeze the high temperature equilibrium by quenching. In some recent work on cuprous oxide, Stone and O'Keeffe (1962) (43) found that when homogeneous $Cu_2O_{1.0034}$ was quenched from 1000° with the utmost rapidity, the cuprous oxide retained only 4% of the copper vacancies and positive holes, as shown by measurements of the paramagnetism. Most of the cation vacancies, with their associated positive holes, segregated rapidly to build up nuclei of the higher oxide, CuO.

Defect Complexes. The argument this far has reached the following stage. The state of minimum energy of any system at very low temperatures corresponds, without question, to the attainment of order. Third law considerations imply that a nonstoichiometric phase, with its inherent randomness, should be metastable at 0° K. with respect to a mixture of ideal, stoichiometric compounds. The relative status of complex intermediate phases and of stoichiometrically simple compounds,

with small unit cells and derived from clearly defined valence states, is less clear—
e.g., of the series Ti_nO_{2n-1} as compared with TiO_2 and Ti_2O_3. It is also certain
that, wherever room temperature structural information has been supplemented
by high temperature equilibrium data, univariant two-phase regions of the phase
diagram are progressively invaded by bivariant equilibria. Simple lattice energy
calculations indicating that disordered nonstoichiometric states are very highly
endothermic are quantitatively incompatible with the experimental evidence.

Ordered intermediate phases, based either on superlattice ordering of defects
or on shear structures, etc., necessarily have rather large unit cells. Ordering
forces have to operate over distances that are large compared with nearest neighbor
distances. Thus in Magneli's shear structures, based on the ReO_3 or the rutile
type, the essential features are one- or two-dimensional arrays of lattice misfit,
configurations in which the distinction between normal lattice site and interstitial
site loses and changes its meaning. The arrays can be regarded as built up by the
logical packing of a particular kind of defect cluster. That a given stoichiometry
results in a fully ordered structure, rather than in a statistical distribution of stacking sequences, depends on a more subtle long range factor. In any case, to
establish order of this kind implies a substantial decrease of configurational entropy
per unit cell, which partly offsets, in the free energy, the exothermicity of the
ordered state.

Because there is a disparity between the predicted endothermicity of random
structures and the observed ΔH and ΔG for the breakup of intermediate phases,
there is merit in an alternative hypothesis—that it is not long-range ordering but
short-range interactions of defects, with each other and with the immediately surrounding crystal lattice, that stabilize significant deviations from stoichiometry.
Reverting to the analogy of electrolytes in solution, it may be noted that calculations ignoring the role of the solvent would show the energy of charge separation
to be so great that ionic compounds could not be dissolved, nor their ions be dis-
persed. In fact, most of the lattice energy is recovered by ion-solvent interaction
(dipole orientation and coordinate bond formation) in the first coordination shell;
more can be regained if complex ion formation occurs. Analogy suggests that
relaxation of the crystal lattice must equally be brought into the picture.

This suggests the need to look critically at what is really known about the
nature of lattice defects. Here Roth's paper on ferrous oxide (1960) (37),
$Fe_{0.87}O$, marks an important stage. Methods of diagnosing how nonstoichiometry
arises—e.g., that ferrous oxide is cation-deficient, $Fe_{1-x}O$—strictly go no further
than an enumeration of the number of atoms of each kind per unit cell. That the
changes in unit cell contents signify a corresponding number of simple vacancies
or interstitials is purely inferential and, as now appears, questionable.

Roth's neutron diffraction work indicates that it is wrong to infer from the
over-all nonstoichiometric reaction

$$2Fe^{+2} + \frac{1}{2} O_2 \rightleftharpoons O^{-2}|\square_- + 2\,Fe^{+3} + \square_+$$

two positive holes on normal cation sites and one additional cation vacancy arise
from each atom of oxygen in stoichiometric excess; the products are one positive
hole in the cation lattice, together with a defect complex of a type not hitherto
postulated. The expected positive hole-vacancy pair $(Fe^{+3}|\square_+)(\square_+)$ trans-
forms itself by movement of the Fe^{+3} ion to the interstitial site adjacent to the
vacancy—i.e., to a site tetrahedrally coordinated with oxygen:

$$(Fe^{+3}|\square_+)(\square_+) + \Delta \rightleftharpoons (Fe^{+3}|\Delta)(\square_+)_2$$

This defect complex is important in three respects: It maximizes the energy of interaction between real and virtual charges on the defects, and so contributes stabilization; surrounded, as it is, by iron cations on octahedrally coordinated sites in a close-packed oxygen lattice, the defect complex and its immediate environment are like a microdomain out of the spinel structure of Fe_3O_4, the next higher oxide; and the iron atom in a tetrahedral position between two octahedral vacancies corresponds to the transition state for a normal cation diffusion step. Apart from the (probable) trapping of the positive holes at these positions, this configuration of atoms will be represented by a certain steady-state population in the crystal lattice at temperatures where diffusion and equilibration can occur. There is a sense in which the germ of the next higher phase is already latent in the ideal stoichiometric structure.

The very recent work of Wallace and Craig (1961) on tantalum hydride is relevant here. Above 53° C. the system is stoichiometrically indeterminate (α phase) and completely random in structure; at low temperatures Ta_2H, of more or less definite composition (β phase), exists in equilibrium with metallic tantalum. It appears to be established that, for material of this ideal composition, the long-range order in the crystal lattice disappears at a temperature well below that at which the main energy absorption and entropy increase occur, associated with the $\beta \rightarrow \alpha$ transition. The interpretation placed on the combination of neutron diffraction and thermodynamic work is that, below the $\alpha \rightleftharpoons \beta$ transition point, hydrogen atoms in tetrahedral sites associate in clusters of four, in a definite configuration, and that most of the energy of the order-disorder transformation is gained in establishing this short-range order. Transitions and energy changes below the $\alpha \rightleftharpoons \beta$ transition point correspond to the mutual arrangement of the clusters or complexes, so as to achieve long-range order, but this is associated with only a small further decrease in entropy.

This situation may well be more general than has been hitherto realized. If the essential condition for gross stoichiometric deviations is that energy is gained by transforming simple point defects plus valence anomalies into some new configuration, the interaction of this configuration with the surrounding crystal lattice (its "solvation") may be energetically important. An atomic arrangement which, infinitely repeated, constitutes the stable structure of the next phase in a succession may, in isolation, provide the favored pattern for defect complexing.

It is postulated that defect complexes of this kind, independent and randomly distributed at medium or high temperatures, are the entities that undergo ordering to yield superstructures, shear structures, etc., as intermediate compounds of complex formula. In their turn, depending on the free energy of formation of the complexes, they must be dissociable at high enough temperatures or in high dilutions. The Schottky-Wagner model for random point defects and electronic defects should therefore be applicable at high temperatures. There is not much experimental evidence about the properties of well defined systems close to stoichiometry, where defects would be very dilute. In the number of cases—e.g., the beginning of the stoichiometric range of UO_{2+x} at high temperatures, or the approach of oxygen-deficient $CaUO_{4-x}$ to the ideal composition—the free energy and partial molar entropy vary very steeply with composition. This might be a range in which the dissociation equilibrium between free and complexed defects is subject to sensible displacement. The situation over the whole temperature range can be summarized as in Table III.

Table III.   Relation between Nonstoichiometric Compounds and Ordered Intermediate Phases

High Temperatures				*Low Temperatures*
Isolated, random point defects and valence defects	Defect pair associa- tion	Rearrangement of coordination environment in isolated defect clusters or "microdomains"	1- or 2-dimen- sional assays of ordered defects or reorganized defect complexes	Fully defined superstruc- tures or shear structures
Essentially disordered		Stabilization by short-range ordering effects	Partial order; random stack- ing sequences, etc.	Complete order- ing; long- range inter- actions
Random structures			Ordered structures	
Nonstoichiometric phases			Stoichiometric phases	

Russian workers have advanced some apparently related ideas.   Ariya and his colleagues (1958, 1961) (*3, 17*) have pointed out that the standard heat of formation of a compound across its stoichiometric range frequently falls rather smoothly on the curve joining the value for the stoichiometric compound and that of the next phase in the equilibrium diagram (Figure 2).   Furthermore, there is

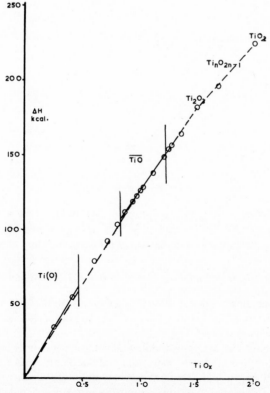

Figure 2.   Integral formation of oxides in nonstoichiometric Ti-O system

some evidence that in VO, with its remarkable stoichiometric range, there is a difference between the nature of lattice defects in oxygen-deficient and in vanadium-deficient material. The environment-sensitive properties, such as the magnetic moment, suggest that the altervalent ions—e.g., V^{+3} in VO_{1+x}—have the same environment as in the next definite structure of the phase succession (V_2O_3). They have described these findings in terms of the "microheterogeneity" of non-stoichiometric phases, without (at least in journals easily accessible to the author) precisely defining the structural import of that term. If the microdomain of new structural pattern can be identified with the environment of a single defect complex plus its surrounding and perturbed crystal lattice, the Russian concept is essentially the same as is put forward here. There are few nonstoichiometric systems for which a critical appraisal of thermochemical data can be made. The integral values for free energy and enthalpy across the UO_2 to U_4O_9 range (36) illustrate Ariya's contention well (Figure 3).

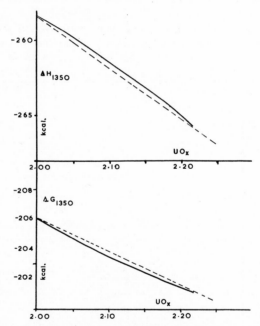

Figure 3. Integral heats of formation and free energy of order in nonstoichiometric UO_{2+x} range

Data from Roberts and Walter (36)

Problem 4. The Existence Range of Nonstoichiometric Compounds

It is evident that different binary compounds differ enormously in their tolerance for variations in composition. What factor or factors determine the limiting formulas in any case?

At one extreme are compounds such as MgO, for which it is doubtful whether any stoichiometric variability is detectable; although, in principle, a potential *n*-type semiconductor at high temperatures, it is doubtful whether observed effects exceed what is attributable to residual impurities or intrinsic conduction. For lead sulfide at about 1000° the measured existence limits are from $Pb_{1.0004}S$ to $PbS_{1.0001}$.

At the other extreme are the broad-range nonstoichiometric compounds. Attention has been drawn to the exceptional breadth of the TiO and VO phases, to the temperature-dependent phase breadth of FeO—from zero below 560° to $Fe_{0.95}O$ — $Fe_{0.85}O$ at 1100°; and the extension of the pseudo-fluoride CeO_{2-x} phase from sharply defined intermediate compounds to $CeO_{1.49}$ to $_{2.00}$ at moderately high temperatures. It is also apparent from various equilibrium diagrams— e.g., those of Biltz and Muller (1927) (7) on the uranium oxides, Eyring on PrO_{2-x} and TbO_{2-x}, and Rees, Martin, and Hall (1945) (35) on ZrH_{2+x}—that equilibrium pressure isotherms not infrequently rise so steeply near the uppermost ideal composition that the highest compound in a phase succession becomes increasingly defective in attainable composition as the temperature is raised.

Furthermore, a narrow existence range or an apparently immutable composition need not connote a rational stoichiometry or one compatible with interpretation in terms of a superstructure or shear structure. Nor does the change from one narrow range phase to another necessarily imply any radical change of structure, and especially of short-range order. These points are exemplified by the succession of phases in the Nb-N system [Schönberg 1954; Brauer 1961 (*11, 40*)], all involving somewhat incomplete filling of lattice sites with very similar local coordination.

Nominal Formula	*Composition Range*
Nb_2N	$NbN_{0.40}$–$NbN_{0.50}$
NbN–I	$NbN_{0.75}$–$NbN_{0.79}$
NbN–II (high temp.)	$NbN_{0.88}$–$NbN_{0.98}$
NbN-II (low temp.)	$NbN_{0.97}$–$NbN_{0.98}$
NbN-III	$NbN_{1.00}$–$NbN_{1.01}$

In general terms the relations between possible compound phases in any system are determined by the usual tangent relation between their free energy surfaces. The free energy of any phase is a function of the temperature, activity of the components, number of lattice sites and relative numbers of atoms of each kind in the crystal, concentrations of vacancies, interstitials and substitutions of each kind, concentrations of associated defects, energies of lattice disorder, of defect interactions, of valence change, of ionization, etc.:

$$G = f(T, \lambda_A, \lambda_B, N, N_A, N_B, N_A^h, N_B^h, \ldots . . E_A^h, E_A^i, \ldots . . \text{etc.})$$

If, at a given temperature and for optimized values of all other independent variables than λ_A, for example, we consider the projection of the free energy surfaces on the G,X plane, we could, in principle, calculate the $(G,X)_T$, etc., curve for each phase and so derive the boundary compositions of coexisting phases.

The question then arises whether the free energy curve of a nonstoichiometric phase is to be considered in isolation, unrelated to those of adjacent phases in the equilibrium diagram, or whether the free energy is a continuous function of composition over the entire range. In the former case, for compositions outside the stable existence range, the compound is metastable with respect to a two-phase mixture, but its metastability is contingent on the presence of the second phase; there is no inherent restriction to the possible deviation from ideal stoichiometry. The second alternative contains a built-in condition of absolute instability above a certain degree of defectiveness.

The latter has seemed promising enough to pursue. It has been seen that account must be taken of interactions which lead to association or clustering of defects and a tendency for longer range ordering. It is a short step to consider that, beyond a certain point, the tendency for defects to segregate is the driving force behind nucleation of a new phase, and the instability of the old. The rapidity with which so many systems adjust themselves from homogeneity at high temperatures to two-phase equilibria suggests that nucleation of a new structure is closely related to pre-existing microfeatures, such as an appropriate constellation or cluster of point defects. The breadth of two-phase ranges between nonstoichiometric phases in phase diagrams not infrequently diminishes with rise of temperature, leading in some cases to "critical miscibility" effects. Finally, many transformations involve a minimum of reconstruction—such as the succession of phases in the nickel arsenide and fluorite structural types—and unquestionably arise from the rearrangement of vacancies or interstitials.

It is not certain that all examples of nonstoichiometric compounds can be regarded from a single standpoint or represented by a single model. In principle, and depending on the relative importance of essentially metallic or essentially heteropolar properties, the basis of phase limits might be sought in electronic or in structural factors.

The former approach has been rather successful as applied to intermetallic nonstoichiometric phases—e.g., the concept of electron-atom ratio to interpret phase limits and effects of substitution in the Hume-Rothery type compounds. Mott and Jones (1936) (30, 46) identified the upper composition limit of the β phase of palladium hydride (around $PdH_{0.6}$) with the filling of the 4d band of palladium (about 0.55 hole per atom) by electrons of the hydrogen. Among the nonstoichiometric sulfides and similar compounds of transition metals (especially the arsenides, antimonides, borides, and silicides, which have been too little studied from the standpoint of nonstoichiometry) there are numerous compounds that are intrinsic semiconductors or poor metals; in the suboxide phases of titanium and vanadium, etc., and in ternary compounds such as the tungsten bronzes, there appear to be free delocalized metallic electrons [compare Sienko, 1961 (42)]. In all such cases it might be considered that changes in the stoichiometry of the crystal lattice as a whole, or valence control effects due to a third component, as in the tungsten bronzes, etc., affect the free energy by changing the population of electronic states in a way that could be treated by Brillouin zone theory. Frueh (1954) (19) went some way in applying these ideas to the binary and ternary phases in the Cu-Fe-S system. Digenite, $Cu_{1.8}S$ (electron-atom ratio 2.8), bornite, Cu_5FeS_4 (ratio 3.2), and chalcopyrite, $CuFeS_2$ (ratio 4) are based on the same structural pattern. They differ in electron-atom ratio, but that ratio, as calculated by Frueh, is just right to fill the Brillouin zone defined by the strongest diffraction lines. Between these ideal compositions the composition in the ternary system can change—by substitution of copper for iron, or by creating metal vacancies whereby the Cu+Fe:S ratio is changed—without impairing the filling of the principal Brillouin zone.

At the present stage of theoretical development it is hardly possible to go far enough, in terms of either band theory or the Pauling valence bond approximation, with a quantitative treatment of crystals involving free electrons and a relatively large electronegativity difference between the components. Nevertheless, the matter merits more attention.

The statistical thermodynamic approach, along lines already indicated, has been more tractable and suggestive. Models have been based on the Fowler-Guggenheim treatment of localized monolayers, in which account is taken of energy terms arising from interaction between point defects in nearest neighbor positions. They will need modifying as the more complex nature of lattice defects gets better understood.

Lacher's treatment of interstitial hydrogen in the palladium lattice (1937) (*26*) provides the pattern. By introducing a nearest-neighbor interaction energy, E^{ii}, it is found that below a critical temperature, T_c (defined by $E^{ii} = 2kT_c$), the concentration of interstitial atoms is not a single-valued function of the hydrogen activity over the whole range. The function shows two turning points, and its physical meaning is that concentrations of interstitial hydrogen between these turning points are unstable in the absolute sense; they break up into hydrogen-richer and hydrogen-poorer regions, of limiting compositions defined by the "equal areas" rule. Thus the concentration of hydrogen in monophasic material rises with increasing hydrogen pressure up to the point where interaction between neighboring interstitial hydrogen atoms results in ordered clusters. Further uptake of hydrogen enlarges the hydrogen-rich regions at the expense of the hydrogen-poor regions, at constant hydrogen pressure. The model reproduces the essential features of the α-phase–β-phase conversion, including the disappearance of the intervening univariant equilibria above a certain temperature.

At that date, palladium hydride was regarded as a special case. Lacher's approach was subsequently developed by the author (1946) (*1*) and by Rees (1954) (*34*) into attempts to frame a general theory of the nature and existence of solid compounds. The one model starts with the idea of the crystal of a binary compound, of perfect stoichiometric composition, but with intrinsic lattice disorder —e.g., of Frenkel type. As the stoichiometry adjusts itself to higher or lower partial pressures of one or other component, by incorporating cation vacancies or interstitial cations, the relevant feature is the interaction of point defects located on adjacent sites. These interactions contribute to the partition function of the crystal and set a maximum attainable concentration of each type of defect. Conjugate with the maximum concentration of, for example, cation vacancies, N^{h*}, and fixed by the intrinsic lattice disorder, is a minimum concentration of interstitials, N^{i*}. The difference, $N^{h*} - N^{i*}$, measures the nonstoichiometry at the nonmetal-rich phase limit. The metal-rich limit is similarly determined by the maximum attainable concentration of interstitials. With the maximum concentrations of defects, so defined, may be compared the intrinsic disorder in the stoichiometric crystals, and from the several energies concerned there can be specified the conditions under which the stoichiometric crystal lies outside the stability limits.

Rees adopted a yet more general standpoint. He refers the whole system to the parent crystal lattice of one component—e.g., the metal—and supposes a succession of phases AB, AB_2,.....AB_n to be derived, in principle, by insertion of B atoms into interstitial sites in the crystal lattice of A. Quite apart from hydrides and other compounds formerly classified as "interstitial" in type, there are numerous chemical systems where this simplifying concept does no violence to facts. No far-reaching reconstructive changes in the A sublattice need be involved, as the A-B ratio alters, although there are changes in binding forces which result in changes in interatomic distances. These affect the energetics of the system rather than the principle. The underlying thought is that B atoms enter a proportion of interstitial sites (type I), associated with a reaction energy, E^i_I, and, by their presence, differentiate other interstitial positions adjacent to them (type II sites) from those (of type I) in the unpopulated A lattice. They thus create interstitial sites of type II and energy E^i_{II}, proportionate to the number of type I sites filled. B atoms entering the A lattice at random will not order themselves strictly into a phase based on the occupation of type I sites only, but distribute themselves between type I sites and the type II sites which exist only in virtue of the presence of atoms in type I sites; so also occupation of type II sites creates sites of type III, etc. On this basis, and allowing as in the previous treatment for nearest-neighbor interactions E_I^{ii}, E_{II}^{ii}, it is possible to set down the partition function of the crystal and, in theory, to build up the complete dissociation pressure-composition diagram for the system.

There is no fundamental difference in the import of these two attempts at a general theory. Both involve the simplifying, but strictly unjustified, assumptions that association or complexing between unlike defects can be neglected and that the energy of formation of a defect does not vary for gross departures from stoichiometry. Whereas, on the Schottky-Wagner model, partial molar enthalpies should be independent of stoichiometric defect, both these theories lead to the conclusion that the partial molar enthalpy of the components depends predictably on the concentration of defects and the nearest-neighbor interaction energy: $H(x) = \overline{H}(0) - x.H_{jj}$, where $\overline{H}(x)$ is the partial molar enthalpy of oxygen, for example, in an oxide MO_{1-x} and H_{jj} is the interaction energy which appears also in defining the phase limits. This consequence can be put to the test of experiment, although at present but few reliable sets of thermodynamic data are available. In general, $\overline{H}$ does tend to vary with stoichiometric defect, but it is clear that neither the simplified model, nor any one model, is likely to represent the facts adequately. The diversity of real behavior can be judged by comparing the $\overline{H} - X$ relations for a few oxide systems of related type (Figure 4).

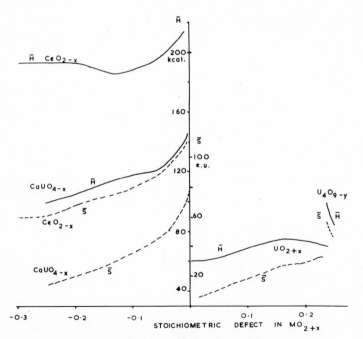

Figure 4.   Partial molar enthalpy and entropy of oxygen in nonstoichiometric phases based on fluorite structure

UO_{2+x}. *Oxygen-excess fluorite*
CeO_{2-x}. *Oxygen-deficient fluorite*
$CaUO_{4-x}$. *Oxygen-deficient, derived from fluorite*

Conclusions

The purpose of this paper has been to draw attention to a few fundamental problems. Where discrepancies arise between conclusions drawn from different modes of sound and self-consistent investigation, it is evident that the real trouble lies in incomplete knowledge. There are too few nonstoichiometric systems for which, as yet, reliable and sufficiently copious thermodynamic data are available, and too few for which equilibrium studies can be closely coupled with detailed structural work. On the structural side, the power of neutron diffraction to extract the maximum amount of evidence from suitable systems has been shown, and needs to be extended. There is also an urgent need for more high temperature x-ray diffraction work, carried out under conditions for which equilibrium studies give unambiguous thermodynamic evidence. It is not always safe to assume that quenching effectively preserves high temperature conditions; extrapolation is an inexhaustible source of fallacious reasoning. From developments along these lines there can be expected a much sounder basis for theory, and clearer insight into what remains one of the basic problems of chemistry.

Literature Cited

(1) Anderson, J. S., *Proc. Roy. Soc. (London)* A 185, 69 (1946).
(2) Andersson, G., *Acta Chem. Scand.* 8, 1599 (1954).
(3) Ariya, S. M., Morozowa, M. P., *Russ. J. Gen. Chem.* 28, 2647 (1958).
(4) Aronson, S., Belle, J., *J. Chem. Phys.* 29, 151 (1958).
(5) Bertaut, E. F., *Acta Cryst.* 6, 557 (1953).
(6) Bevan, D. J. M., *J. Inorg. Nucl. Chem.* 1, 49 (1955).
(7) Biltz, W., Müller, H., *Z. anorg. Chem.* 163, 257 (1927).
(8) Blackburn, P. E., *J. Phys. Chem.* 62, 897 (1958).
(9) Bloem, J., Kröger, F. A., *Z. physik. Chem.* 7, 1 (1956).
(10) Brauer, G., private communication.
(11) Brauer, G., *Z. anorg. Chem.* 309, 151 (1961).
(12) Brauer, G., Gingerich, K., *J. Inorg. Nucl. Chem.* 16, 87 (1960).
(13) Brauer, G., Gradinger, H., *Z. anorg. Chem.* 277, 89 (1954).
(14) Brauer, G., Holtschmidt, U., *Ibid.*, 265, 105 (1951).
(15) Brouwer, G., *Phillips Res. Repts.* 9, 366 (1954).
(16) Ehrlich, P., *Z. Elektrochem.* 45, 362 (1939); *Z. anorg. Chem.* 260, 19 (1949).
(17) Erofeeva, M. S., Lukinykh, N. L., Ariya, S. M., *Russ. J. Phys. Chem.* 35, 375 (1961).
(18) Eyring, L., *et al.*, *J. Am. Chem. Soc.* 76, 3890, 5239, 5242 (1954); 83, 2219 (1961).
(19) Frueh, A. J., *Geochim. Cosmochim. Acta* 6, 79 (1954).
(20) Hägg, G., Sücksdorf, I., *Z. physik. Chem.* B22, 444 (1933).
(21) Haraldsen, H., *Z. anorg. Chem.* 234, 337, 372 (1937).
(22) *Ibid.*, p. 353; 239, 369 (1938).
(23) Jette, E. R., Foote, F., *J. Chem. Phys.* 1, 29 (1932).
(24) Jellinek, F., thesis, Utrecht, 1957.
(25) Kurnakov, N. S., *Z. anorg. Chem.* 88, 109 (1914).
(26) Lacher, J. R., *Proc. Roy. Soc. (London)* A161, 525 (1937).
(27) Magneli, A., *Acta Cryst.* 6, 495 (1953).
(28) Magneli, A., *et al.*, U. S. At. Energy Comm., NP 8054 (1960).
(29) Mitoff, S. P., *J. Chem. Phys.* 31, 1261 (1959).
(30) Mott, N. F., Jones, H., "Theory of the Properties of Metals and Alloys," p. 200, Oxford Univ. Press, Oxford, 1936.
(31) Nace, D. M., Aston, J. G., *J. Am. Chem. Soc.* 79, 3619, 3627 (1957).
(32) Ormont, B. F., *Russ. J. Inorg. Chem.* 4, 1047 (1959).
(33) Rees, A. L. G., "Chemistry of the Defect Solid State," Methuen, London, 1954.
(34) Rees, A. L. G., *Trans. Faraday Soc.* 50, 335, 343 (1954).
(35) Rees, A. L. G., Hall, M. N. A., Martin, L. H., *Ibid.*, 41, 306 (1945).
(36) Roberts, L. E. J., Walter, A. J., *J. Inorg. Nucl. Chem.* 16, 87 (1960).
(37) Roth, W. L., *Acta Cryst.* 13, 140 (1960).
(38) Sawyer, J., *Nature* 185, 916 (1960); private communication.
(39) Schenck, R., Dingmann, T., *Z. anorg. Chem.* 166, 133 (1927).
(40) Schönberg, N., *Acta Chem. Scand.* 8, 208 (1954).
(41) Schottky, W., Wagner, C. Z. *physik. Chem.* B11, 163 (1930).
(42) Sienko, M. J., *J. Am. Chem. Soc.* 83, 3939, 4149 (1961).

(43) Stone, F. S., O'Keeffe, M., *Proc. Roy. Soc.* (*London*), **A267**, 501 (1962).
(44) Tengner, S., *Z. anorg. Chem.* **239**, 126 (1938).
(45) Thorne, R. J., Ackermann, R. J., IUPAC High Temperature Symposium, Montreal, 1961.
(46) Ubbelohde, A. R., *Proc. Roy. Soc.* **A159**, 295 (1937).
(47) Wagner, C., *Z. physik, Chem.* **B21**, 25 (1933); **B32**, 447 (1936); **B34**, 309 (1936).

RECEIVED September 6, 1962.

Nonstoichiometric Metal Oxides

Order and Disorder

A. D. WADSLEY

Division of Mineral Chemistry, Commonwealth Scientific and
Industrial Research Organization, Melbourne, Australia

Many examples exist in the oxide literature of compounds related to each other in structure as well as in composition. Their possible significance in the study of nonstoichiometric compounds is considered.

A nonstoichiometric metal oxide exists as a single phase over a range of chemical composition. "Berthollides," as compounds of this kind are sometimes called, form a significant part of the oxide literature which we can summarize here only in the most general way; a more detailed account is being published (*40*).

In one sense, a range of composition can be defined as a solid solution where one or more kinds of atom are gained or lost, and a binary oxide $\widetilde{BO}_x$ is nonstoichiometric when x is variable. This can be achieved either when B is a transition metal capable of existing in two valency states with similar ionic radii, or when B is partly replaced by another metal, A, of different valency, so that the ratio $(A + B)$ to O is also variable. Likewise, a ternary nonstoichiometric oxide, where the two metals A and B do not occupy equivalent positions, is one where one or more of the three elements are not present in constant proportions.

The evidence reported in the literature has been largely derived from phase equilibria studies coupled with x-ray diffraction examination, and in straightforward cases the composition, plotted against the volume of the unit cell, enables the phase boundaries to be defined (Figure 1). In most cases, some picture of the over-all change in composition can be given by comparing the measured densities with the values calculated on the assumption of one or more of the three possible structural models.

Subtraction. Ions of either sort, or both simultaneously in unequal and variable amounts, may be absent from the structure.

Interpolation. Additional atoms of either sort may occupy sites in the structure which are otherwise vacant.

Substitution. An excess of a metal component may be situated on sites vacated by oxygen.

These three mechanisms are widely used in studies of transient phenomena, but pose problems to the solid state chemist which must be answered in terms of the effects upon the atoms remaining, their positions, and their bonds to other atoms.

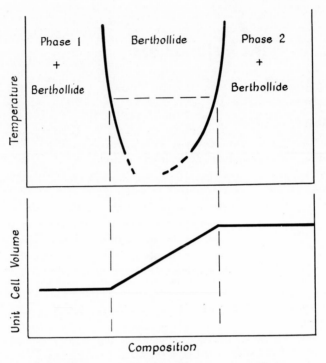

Figure 1.   Composition range of a berthollide

Above.   Range varies with temperature
*Below.   Phase boundaries determined from measurements of
unit cell volume*

In assessing nonstoichiometric solids, we are at once confronted by two kinds of evidence.   First, there is the case where equilibrium diagrams are compiled by the classical methods of phase analysis, by quenching from high temperatures, or by plotting vapor pressure data.   Under these circumstances the homogeneity range varies with temperature, as in the upper half of Figure 1.   At lower temperatures, however, the oxide is unstable and may break down into other phases with complex formulas, having little or no ranges of homogeneity.   This is the second kind of evidence, and these complex phases give diffraction data the crystallographer recognizes as *superlattices*, derived from the simpler structure of the berthollide by an order-disorder transition due to the resolution of the structural defects.   The transition may be an extremely slow process, and as prolonged heat treatment or annealing is often needed to form the ordered superstructures, the equilibrium diagram may be supplemented by reactions in the solid state in order to fill in the subsolidus regions, where a good deal of attention is now being directed.

Much of the early work was done before the need for high resolution diffraction equipment was generally recognized, and the Debye-Scherrer techniques available at that time may well have failed to reveal the fine detail at present being recorded.   The very ease with which powder patterns can be recorded, and indexed for phases of high symmetry in terms of a particular unit cell, does not in itself mean that a structure is satisfactorily determined by analogy with others of similar composition and crystallographic constants.   It is of equal importance to calculate structure factors for a particular arrangement of atoms and to compare them with the observed data, even in the simplest case.

The compounds of the heavier metals dominate the literature of the berthollides, and while more refined x-ray procedures enable the metal atoms to be located with relative ease, the lighter ones are often difficult, or even impossible, to find with direct methods. In simple cases this difficulty can be avoided, but not really solved, by fitting the light atoms into available spaces in the most likely way. But as problems in increasing complexity are tackled by the newer methods of structure determination, it is often possible only to guess the likeliest arrangement, and indeed the number of them present in the structure. Since the metals in their various valency states may have more than one kind of coordination, these atoms assume a position of considerable importance in describing a structure with some assurance. If a heavy-metal berthollide is examined at a number of composition intervals, it is more than likely that x-ray data, particularly those obtained with the powder camera, will fail to disclose nonmetal anomalies, and a composition region may be dismissed as homogeneous simply because the metal lattice appears to undergo little or no change. In these circumstances the systematic use of single crystal techniques is not merely an advantage but is essential, provided crystals can be prepared. Supplementary neutron diffraction studies, where the relative scattering of elements is not a function of atomic number, can be expected to assume increasing importance in straightforward problems of structure determination.

The dual evidence of a berthollide, together with ordered and related phases, has also been reported for the oxides of the lighter transition elements, and it is difficult to discuss this except in terms of order and disorder. This problem has been studied for simple cases where, for example, a stoichiometric phase, ABO_2, with the NaCl structure can exist in two forms, depending upon whether A and B are randomized in one set of sites or resolved into positions of their own.

The occupant of a lattice position can be expected to influence the selection of its immediate neighbors, provided attractive forces exist between them, complete or long-range order being achieved at low temperatures when the system has the lowest possible free energy of formation. At higher temperatures the increased energies of the atoms, together with their associated thermal motions, make it easier for them to adopt alternative empty positions or to interchange with other atoms, either of the same or of different kinds. The local ordering eventually leads to the state where two or more adjacent ordered regions are out of step, and these antiphase domains are separated by boundaries where disorder reaches a maximum, and from which they will propagate still further when the temperature is raised. The combination of these factors leads to a rapid decrease in order near a critical temperature where long-range order ceases altogether. All these events can take place in a single crystal and the domains, which should not be confused with individual crystallites in a polycrystal, are regions where order is limited to a few unit cells.

If the structure can be established in the ordered compounds, there is reason to believe that it will persist as microstructure in the nonstoichiometric phase. This affords a method of classification considered below.

Interpolation

Interpolation may be defined as the presence of an ion, metal or nonmetal, in positions formed by a host structure of fixed composition which may otherwise be empty. The kind of position itself may lead to a further subclassification, given in Table I.

Table I. Interpolation of Ions in Host Lattices of Fixed Composition

Type of Position Formed by Host	Guest Ion	System	Approximate Composition Range	Super-structures
Cage	Oxygen	Oxygen dissolved in hexagonal metals	BO_x, $0 < x < 0.5$ $B = Ti, Zr, Hf$	Known
		Compounds intermediate in structure between fluorite and BiF_3	BO_{2+x}, $0 < x < 0.4$ $B = U, (U, R^{+3})$	Known in uranium-oxygen system
	Metal ion A of different kind	Cubic (or pseudo-cubic) tungsten bronze type (intermediate between ReO_3 and perovskite)	A_xBO_3, $0 < x < 1$ $B = W, Nb, Ta, Ti$	At composition $Na_{0.75}WO_3$
		Sodium-titanium bronze	Na_xTiO_2, $0 < x < 0.2$	Unknown
		Platinum and palladium bronzes	$Na_xB_3O_4$, $0 < x < 1$ $B = Pt, Pd$	Unknown
Tunnel	Metal ion A of different kind	Hollandite-type structure	A_xBO_2, $0 < x < 0.12$ $B = Ti, Mn$	Unknown
		β-Vanadium bronze	$A_xV_2O_5$, $0.1 < x < 0.3$	Unknown
		Tetragonal tungsten bronze structure	A_xBO_3, $0.2 < x < 0.6$ $B = W, Nb, Ta$	Known
		Hexagonal tungsten bronze structure	A_xWO_3, $0 < x < 0.3$	Known
		Psilomelane-type structure	$A_xMn_5O_{10}(2-x)H_2O$, $0.5 < x < 0.75$	Unknown
Interlayer	Metal ion A of different kind	γ-Vanadium bronze	$A_xV_3O_8$, $1.1 < x < 1.3$	Unknown

The hexagonal metals titanium, zirconium, and hafnium have long been known to form a solid solution with oxygen up to the approximate composition $BO_{0.5}$, but the recent work has established that the oxygen atoms can enter particular positions in an ordered way, leading to the formation of at least three closely related phases (4), the ordered $Cd(OH)_2$ structure being the limiting case.

The interpolation of additional anions in the fluorite structure, found in many fluorides, oxyfluorides, and oxides, represents a partial transition to the BiF_3 structure, and while the complete interval is spanned in the case of the mixed fluoride PbF_2-BiF_3 (21), the composition range generally falls within the limits BX_x, $2.0 < x < 2.4$. The most extensively studied case is the oxidation of UO_2 to U_3O_7, where the appearance of several ordered tetragonal phases (1, 35), found on annealing and related to the high temperature phase U_4O_9, is now well authenticated (27). Although a structure for U_4O_9, based upon the ordered interpolation of additional oxygen atoms in the fluoride structure, has now appeared (*14*), some doubt must remain whether an x-ray analysis can be regarded as definitive, unpublished neutral diffraction experiments having suggested an entirely different oxygen structure (*10*).

The cubic tungsten bronzes are a classical example of a nonstoichiometric oxide. Here the ReO_3-type structure is continuously transformed into that of perovskite by the interpolation of univalent ions into cubic positions. But this simple and satisfying picture, illustrated by Figure 2, can no longer be accepted as a final one, as Ingold and DeVries (*29*) could not confirm the cubic diffraction symmetry in a recent optical study. At the composition $Na_{0.75}WO_3$, Atoji and Rundle (*11*) proved by neutral diffraction that sodium was ordered in the cubic sites, and while the tungsten lattice was regular, the oxygens were not in the ideal positions that had long been assumed for them. No satisfactory answer could in fact be found from the diffraction experiments. It is conceivable that several different oxygen structures exist, each one at some characteristic composition.

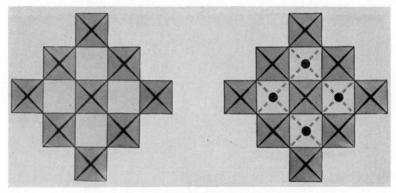

Figure 2.   Idealized octahedra

Left. ReO_3 type
Right.   Perovskite

Overgrowth of one of these upon another could then occur at intermediate points in the composition range, difficult to detect except as domains under the polarizing microscope (*29*). A recently reported titanium bronze, Na_xTiO_2, contained deformed structural elements of the Na_xWO_3 type, but the metal-oxygen octahedra were condensed upon each other, giving a host lattice of formula BO_2, not BO_3 (*8*) (Figure 3). This suggests that many bronzelike compounds intermediate in structure as well as in composition between the two might exist.

The ions interpolated in tunnel structures, listed in Table I, are situated in continuous cavities enclosed by the fixed framework of the host (*39*). Although there is no diffraction evidence that the guest ions are ordered, dielectric absorption in the phase $Ba_xTi_{8-x}Mg_xO_{16}$ favors a model with sequential ordering of barium ions and vacant positions in any one tunnel, but with no relationship to the sequence in any other tunnel (*22*). This seems to be true in some, at least, of the other nonstoichiometric phases falling into this group, and the application of newer techniques can be expected to amplify the rather limited knowledge of these substances.

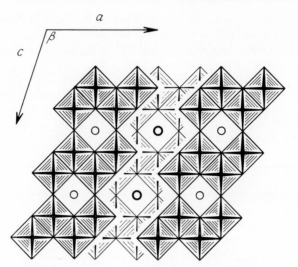

Figure 3. Na_xTiO_2 projected as idealized octahedra

○ *Na*

A good deal of work is still required to clarify the tetragonal and hexagonal tungsten bronze structures for which only the metal positions are known (*32, 34*). Superstructures of both have been observed, but little is known about them except in the case of the hexagonal phase at the composition BO_3, where they are due to the ordering of molybdenum, an impurity substituent for tungsten (*26*).

Subtraction

The loss of metal ions will not greatly affect a close-packed structure if the charge distribution is satisfied, but the removal of an oxygen atom, resulting in an anion vacancy, can lead only to a highly unsymmetrical environment for the metal atoms adjacent to it.

Ehrlich (*23*) was first to point out that metal and nonmetal absences occur simultaneously in $\widetilde{TiO_x}$, $0.7 < x < 1.2$, the stoichiometry depending upon the relative numbers of metal and oxygen atoms present at any one point, and one or other of these sublattices is filled only at the composition limits. For TiO one titanium as well as one oxygen is absent in every seven, randomized when quenched from high temperatures, or ordered into a superstructure when annealed (*5*). Attempts to determine this in terms of regular NaCl-type grouping, modified by periodic vacancies, have been unsuccessful (*3*). The closely allied vanadium-oxygen system also contains a berthollide, $\widetilde{VO_x}$, $9.0 < x < 1.2$, but ordering occurs at the composition $VO_{1.27}$, where the oxygen positions are all filled and the vacant metal sites grouped together as a centered hexagonal disk (*41*). This may perhaps be the only point at which this phase can order, and at other parts of the composition range the clusters, still present, may be randomized with respect to the other clusters. The resemblance to the NaCl structure then becomes only a statistical one. In the case of NbO, which is often given the formula $Nb_{3/4}O_{3/4}$ (one missing atom of each kind in four) the metals are in fourfold coordination with oxygen (*17*), and there is no resemblance, except a formal one, to the NaCl-type.

Table II.   Subtraction of Ions from Oxide Structures

Ion Removed	Structure of Host	Approximate Composition Range	Superstructures
Metal and nonmetal together	NaCl-type	$\overbrace{BO_x}$, $0.8 < x < 1.2$	Known for TiO, $VO_{1.27}$, and NbO
Metal	Spinel-type	$\overbrace{(A,B)_xO_4}$	Known for "γ-Fe_2O_3"
Oxygen	Intermediate between fluorite and C-type rare earth oxide	$\overbrace{BO_x}$, $2.0 > x > 1.5$	Known when B = Ce, Pr, Tb, (Zr, R^{+3})
	Hexagonal UO_3	$\overbrace{UO_{3-x}}$, $0 < x < 0.5$	Known
	Perovskite-type	$\overbrace{ABO_{3-x}}$, $0 < x < 0.5$	Known when $x = 0.5$
	Hexagonal $BaTiO_3$-type	$\overbrace{ABO_{3-x}}$, $0 < x < ?$	Known for $BaNiO_{3-x}$
Ordered removal of metal	Hexagonal $BaTiO_3$-type	Unknown	Known

The loss of oxygen alone from transition metal oxides has been widely reported (Table II). Those with the fluorite structure can lose oxygen as well as gain it, and the over-all similarity to the C-type rare-earth oxide structure led to the belief that a wide range of homogeneity was possible, $\overbrace{BO_x}$, $2>x>1.5$. Bevan, as well as Erying and his coworkers, reported several ordered intermediate phases virtually of fixed composition in the systems CeO_2-Ce_2O_3 (*16*), PrO_2-Pr_2O_3 (*24*), and TbO_2-Tb_2O_3 (*13*), all with lower symmetry, but details of the atomic arrangements are still unknown. If one phase in each system has the pyrochlore structure, itself a berthollide of approximate formula B_4O_7 which has been identified in mixed metal oxides of related composition (*18, 20*), the oxygen atoms still present

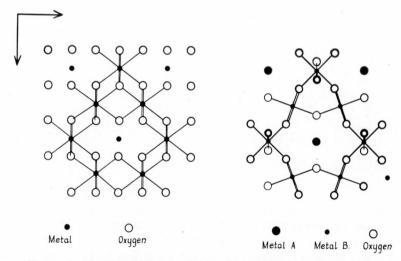

Figure 4.   Sections of fluorite (left) and pyrochlore (right) structures
Note different arrangements of oxygen

will have been reshuffled to change the metal coordination number from eight to six. Oxygen "vacancies," as such, will not exist (Figure 4). Whether or not the other intermediates, one having the formula B_7O_{12} (*19*), contain zones of both kinds remains to be worked out.

Although hexagonal uranium trioxide has a reported homogeneity range $\widetilde{UO_x}$, $3.0{>}x{>}2.67$, neutron diffraction has established that U_3O_8, the oxygen-deficient end, has a different oxygen structure from UO_3(*9*) (Figure 5). The many phases intermediate between the two, summarized recently by Hoekstra and Siegel (*28*), may also prove to have structures containing fragments of both end members, where the metal atoms can adopt different kinds of coordination.

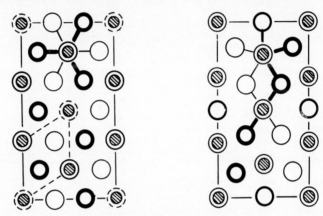

Figure 5. U_3O_8 structure

Left. αUO_3, uranium shaded. A structure for U_3O_8 has been suggested where oxygens, dashed circles, are omitted
Right. Actual structure determined by neutron diffraction (9)

Oxygen-deficient perovskites are also known. The transition over the composition limits $\widetilde{ABO_x}$, $3{>}x{>}2.5$ has not been examined as closely as in the case of the hexagonal $BaTiO_3$ structure [for the case A = Ba and B = Ni (*31*)], but two structure analyses corresponding to the lower limit $ABO_{2.5}$ have recently been reported. In the first of these, $Ca_2Fe_2O_5$, complete rows of oxygens are regularly missing and the accompanying movements of atoms remaining in those planes impose a tetrahedral, instead of octahedral, group of oxygens around the iron atom (Figure 6). This leads to a reduction in the number of oxygens around the calcium atom (*15*) as well. The titanium atoms in $K_2Ti_2O_5$ have five oxygen ligands, not six, and potassium also is located in an unsymmetrical environment (*6*). Gorter (*25*) pointed out that disorder can readily occur in systems of this kind. As a consequence changes of coordination become difficult to observe, as the diffraction data would appear to be derived from a simpler lattice type.

The subtraction of metals from oxide structures is not particularly common. Iron atoms, removed from normal positions in FeO, may be interpolated into tetrahedral positions (*36*) to form spinel-like regions, grouped more or less at random. Spinels, AB_2O_4, may be nonstoichiometric at high temperatures, but disproportionate on annealing. The literature on the classic berthollide γFe_2O_3-Fe_3O_4, is still conflicting, but superstructures of different kinds have nevertheless been reported.

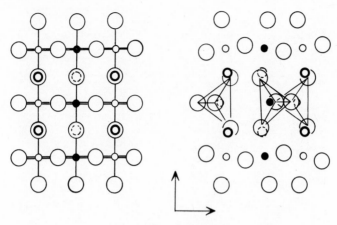

Figure 6.   Structures

Left.   *Perovskite structure [projected onto (110)].   Largest circles*
oxygen, intermediate A ions, and smallest B ions
Right.   *In $Ca_2Fe_2O_5$ oxygens missing from central row of octahedra,*
remainder regrouped into tetrahedra, outlined

Shear

The loss of oxygen from transition metal oxides need not necessarily lead to vacancies accompanied by the redistribution of bonds. It can also lead to the compression of the structure along certain crystallographic planes by what may be called shear, where the polyhedra (octahedra in the well-documented cases) are condensed upon each other, so that the metal atoms close to these planes have more bridging oxygens in common.

The known systems where these shear structures have been found are given in Table III, and a family, or homologous series of compounds, which can be grouped under a common formula is recognizable in each case. The shear planes simply represent discontinuities repeated on the unit cell level at regular intervals. In any one series the same discontinuity is present in all members, where it separates identical blocks of the host structure which vary in size from one member to the next.

Table III.   Removal of Oxygen Accompanied by
Crystallographic Shear:

Structural Homologs

Host Structure	Reported Composition Range(s)	General Formula	Known Members
WO_3 (modified ReO_3 type)	WO_x, $2.83 < x < 2.90$	$(Mo, W)_nO_{3n-1}$	$n = 8, 9, 10, 11, 12,$ 14
TiO_2 (rutile type)	TiO_x, $1.9 < x < 2.0$ $1.7 < x < 1.8$	Ti_nO_{2n-1}	$n = 4$ to 10 inclusive
B_3O_8 ($B = Ti + Nb$), postulated	BO_x, $2.3 < x < 2.4$	$B_{3n}O_{8n-3}$	$n = 3$ and 4
U_3O_8	. . . .	$U_3O_{8-\delta}$	. . . . . .

Six homologs in the mixed tungsten-molybdenum oxide series B_nO_{3n-1} have been isolated (33). The basic structure is the ReO_3-type with octahedra sharing

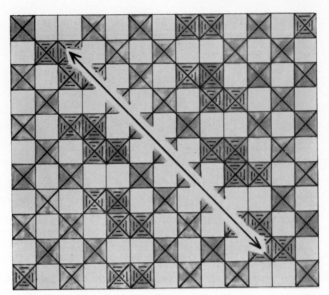

Figure 7.   Structure of B_9O_{26}, homolog $n = 9$ of series
B_nO_{3n-1}

Arrow shows extension characteristic of this particular member.
Hatched octahedra form "shear planes"

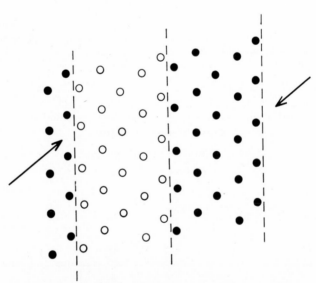

Figure 8.   Metal atoms of Ti_5O_9 projected in a direction
equivalent to $\bar{1}01$ for TiO_2

Vertical dashed lines separate TiO_2 blocks, five atoms thick
(direction marked by arrows).   Atoms of adjacent blocks
drawn as filled and open circles

corners, but at the discontinuity they share edges. Figure 7 illustrates a typical member, $n = 9$, with the formula B_9O_{26} ($=BO_{2.89}$). The next member, $n = 10$, has the formula $B_{10}O_{29}$ ($=BO_{2.90}$). It is closely related to B_9O_{26}; the shear planes are identical but the ReO_3 blocks are slightly larger.

The seven homologs Ti_nO_{2n-1}, $n = 4$ to 10 inclusive, have all been prepared, each phase being strictly stoichiometric (5). The structure of Ti_5O_9 which has been determined (Figure 8) contains rutile blocks of uniform size, five octahedra thick, joined by shear planes of a characteristic type (2). The metal atoms at the edge of one block are in empty spaces of the adjacent one, and the octahedra associated with them share faces (three oxygens), rather than edges (two) and corners (one). Again the other members of this series differ only in the size of the blocks. Two members of the series $B_{3n}O_{8n-3}$ have been found in the mixed oxide system TiO_2-Nb_2O_5 (38), where the same general pattern is also recognizable, despite the fact that a host compound B_3O_8 of predictable structure has not yet been isolated.

In all three cases, including perhaps the series $U_3O_{8-\delta}$ found recently in an electron diffraction study (37) and not yet known except in outline, the variation in the size of the blocks present in a single specimen will lead to disorder. This could be achieved experimentally either by quenching or by the formation of "mixed crystals" at eutectic points.

Intergrowth

Since there is an exact correspondence of atoms at the boundaries of the blocks, the shear structures can be represented as the ordered overgrowth of a particular phase upon itself. There are certain cases where this is also true for oxides and oxyhydroxides of different structure and composition, which may rise to a nonstoichiometric compound if disorder exists, or to a series of phases related by a general formula if there is order.

Several examples are reported in Table IV. The bismuth compounds consist of single sheets of BiO square pyramids separated regularly by one or more perovskite sheets (Figure 9) (12). Elements of the pervoskite structure may also intergrow with NaCl-type sheets in the phases $(ATiO_3).AO$, and ordered phases are now known in a composition region once thought to contain a berthollide.

Table IV.   Ordered Intergrowth of Two Different Structural Types

General Formula	Approx. Composition of Fragments of Two Kinds	Ordered Members	Disorder
$(Bi_2O_2)(A_{n-1}B_nO_{3n+1})$ A = Ca, Sr, Pb, K, Na or Bi B = Ti, Nb, Ta	Bi_2O_2 and ABO_3 (perovskite)	$n = 1, 2, 3, 4,$ and 5	Not reported
$(ATiO_3)_n.AO$ A = Ca, Sr	AO (NaCl) type and $ATiO_3$ (perovskite)	$n = 1, 2,$ and 3	Reported in early literatur̲
$A_nTi_6O_{10+n}{}^a$ A = Na, K	$A_2Ti_6O_{13}$ and $A_2Ti_3O_7$	$n = 0, 3,$ and 4	Known
Hexagonal Ba-substituted spinels[b]		Six ordered phases	Unknown

^{a} In this case A is number of sites, and not necessarily number of alkali metal ions present in them.

^{b} Ba- spinels have complex sequences of fragments, and are not readily represented by a single generalized formula.

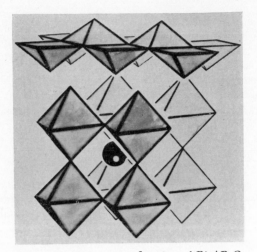

Figure 9.   Perspective drawing of $Bi_2AB_2O_9$

Perovskite layers of octahedra, A ion drawn as
black sphere, alternating with $(Bi_2O_2)^{+2}$ sheets of
square pyramids

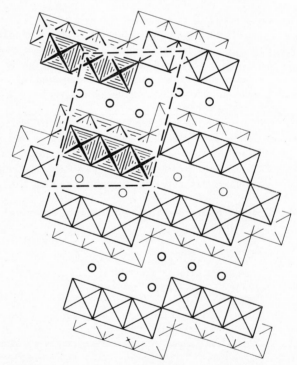

Figure 10.   Sheet of $Na_2Ti_6O_{13}$ structure sand-
wiched between two sheets of $Na_2Ti_3O_7$

TiO_6 octahedra drawn as squares, hatched groups of six
being common to both.   Na ions circles.   Broken line
outlines half unit cell of "$Na_{10}Ti_{18}O_{41}$"

The well-known hexagonal barium-substituted spinels contain spinel-type blocks separated by layers where a barium replaces an oxygen atom, and different stacking sequences of these two units, which may also be of different sizes, result in six ordered phases (30). It was reported in the early experiments that an apparent single crystal proved to contain several of these compounds. Disorder might perhaps have existed at high temperatures, the various phases unmixing during cooling.

Intergrowth has also been noted in a recent study of the alkali titanates $Na_2Ti_3O_7$ and $Na_2Ti_6O_{13}$, both of which have structural features of the same kind (7). A complete solid solution between these two members is entirely possible, and ordering is likely to occur only at points where the ratio between the two kinds of unit is a simple whole number. Figure 10 shows single units of tri- and hexatitanate alternating with each other, and the formula of this substance, $Na_{10}Ti_{18}O_{41}$, which can be reduced to $Na_{2.2}Ti_4O_{9.1}$, suggests that it may be a tetra-titanate, a berthollide where both sodium and oxygen are variables.

Conclusions

While it is to some extent arbitrary, a classification of this kind provides a means of discussing some of the general features now emerging from studies of metallic oxides. We have stressed the evidence that a nonstoichiometric phase is disordered, but may be related to chemically similar phases of fixed composition where an "anomaly" of structure is ordered and identifiable by x-ray diffraction methods. Where such ordered phases are found, it is possible that features of them are retained as blocks or domains with short range order in the related berthollide. Efforts should be directed towards order-disorder effects, with a view to reconsidering the status of the nonstoichiometric compound with a very wide composition range.

Literature Cited

(1) Anderson, J. S., *Bull soc. chim. France*, 1953, 781.
(2) Andersson, S., *Acta Chem. Scand.* 14, 1161 (1960).
(3) Andersson, S., private communication.
(4) Andersson S., Åsbrink, S., Holmberg, B., Magnéli, A., *Bull. Natl. Inst. Sci. India* 14, 136 (1959).
(5) Andersson, S., Collén, B., Kuylenstierna, U., Magnéli, A., *Acta Chem. Scand.* 11, 1641 (1957).
(6) Andersson, S., Wadsley, A. D., *Ibid.*, 15, 663 (1961).
(7) Andersson, S., Wadsley, A. D., *Acta Cryst.* 15, 194 (1962).
(8) Andersson, S., Wadsley, A. D., *Nature (London)* 192, 551 (1961).
(9) Andresen, A., *Acta Cryst.* 11, 612 (1958).
(10) Aronson, S., Belle, J., *J. Chem. Phys.* 29, 151 (1958).
(11) Atoji, M., Rundle, R. E., *Ibid.*, 32, 627 (1960).
(12) Aurivillius, B., *Arkiv Kemi* 1, 463, 499 (1949); 2, 519 (1950); 5, 39 (1952).
(13) Baenziger, N. C., Eick, H. A., Schuldt, H. S., Eyring, L., *J. Am. Chem. Soc.* 83, 2219 (1961).
(14) Belbeoch, B., Piekarski, C., Perio, P., *Bull. Soc. Franc. Minéral. Crist.* 83, 206 (1960).
(15) Bertaut, F., Blum, P., Sagnières, A., *Acta Cryst.* 12, 149 (1959).
(16) Bevan, D. J. M., *J. Inorg. Nucl. Chem.* 1, 49 (1955).
(17) Brauer, G., *Z. anorg. u. allgem. Chem.* 248, 1 (1941).
(18) Casey, J. J., Katz, L., Orr, W. C., *J. Am. Chem. Soc.* 77, 2187 (1955).
(19) Chase, G. A., *Acta Cryst.* 15, 91 (1962).
(20) Collongues, R., Perez y Jorba, M., Lefèvre, J., *Bull. Soc. Chim. France*, 1961, 70.
(21) Croatto, U., *Gazz. Chim. Ital.* 74, 20 (1944).
(22) Dryden, J. S., Wadsley, A. D., *Trans. Faraday Soc.* 54, 1574 (1958).
(23) Ehrlich, P., *Z. Elektrochem.* 45, 362 (1939).

(24) Ferguson, R. E., Guth, E. D., Eyring, L., *J. Am. Chem. Soc.* **76**, 3890 (1954).
(25) Gorter, E. W., *Intern. Congr. Pure Appl. Chem. XVII Congr.* **1**, 303 (1959).
(26) Graham, J., Wadsley, A. D., *Acta Cryst.* **14**, (1961).
(27) Hoekstra, H. R., Santoro, A., Siegel, S., *J. Inorg. Nuclear Chem.* **18**, 166 (1961).
(28) Hoekstra, H. R., Siegel, S., *Ibid.*, **18**, 154 (1961).
(29) Ingold, J. H., De Vries, R. C., *Acta Met.* **6**, 736 (1958).
(30) Jonker, G. H., *Intern. Congr. Pure Appl. Chem. XVI Congr. Sect. Chim. Min.* **1958**, 117.
(31) Lander, J. J., *Acta Cryst.* **4**, 148 (1951).
(32) Magnéli, A., *Acta Chem. Scand.* **7**, 315 (1953).
(33) Magnéli, A., *Acta Cryst.* **6**, 495 (1953).
(34) Magnéli, A., *Arkiv Kemi* **1**, 213 (1949).
(35) Perio, P., *Bull. Soc. Chim. France*, **1953**, 776.
(36) Roth, W. L., *Acta Cryst.* **13**, 140 (1960).
(37) Sato, L., Doi, H., Ishii, D., Uchikoshi, H., *Ibid.*, **14**, 736 (1961).
(38) Wadsley, A. D., *Acta Cryst.* **14**, 660, 664 (1961).
(39) Wadsley, A. D., *Intern. Congr. Pure Appl. Chem. XVI Congr. Sec. Chem. Min.* **1958**, 139.
(40) Wadsley, A. D., "Non-Stoichiometric Compounds," L. Mandelcorn, ed., Academic Press, New York, 1963.
(41) Westman, S., Swed. Dept. of Army Contr. No. DA-91-591-EUC-1319, Final Tech. Rept. 1, 8 (1960).

RECEIVED September 6, 1962.

The Crystal Chemistry of Molybdenum Oxides

LARS KIHLBORG

Institute of Chemistry, University of Uppsala, Uppsala, Sweden

The existence of at least nine phases in the molybdenum-oxygen system is well established. Their crystal structures are briefly described and it is shown that they can be classified into four main families dependent on whether they possess a basic structure of rutile type, ReO_3 type, or MoO_3 type, or have complex structures where polygonal networks can be distinguished. The known tungsten and mixed molybdenum tungsten oxides fit into this scheme. Because of their complicated formulas many of these compounds may be termed "nonstoichiometric," but variance in composition has not been observed for any of them.

The phase relationships in the molybdenum-oxygen system have been the subject of several investigations in recent years. Hägg and Magnéli carried out the first phase analysis by means of x-ray diffraction methods, and found three compounds which formed in the temperature range 650° to 750° C. with compositions between MoO_2 and MoO_3 (5)—Mo_4O_{11} (o-rh.), Mo_8O_{23}, and Mo_9O_{26} (mon.). Subsequently, the stoichiometric formulas of these compounds were established by Magnéli from structure determination (13, 14). During an investigation into the decomposition of MoO_3 in vacuo two more phases were observed (12); later a somewhat detailed phase analysis covering temperatures between 500° and 800° C. made it possible to indicate the temperature ranges in which seven intermediate oxides were formed (8) (Table I). The results of a recent study by Plante are in good agreement with this (25).

Three compounds with a lower oxygen content than MoO_2 have been reported—Mo_2O_3 (29), $\sim MoO$ (6), and Mo_3O (26)—but they were not obtained in a pure state and are poorly described. Attempts by the present author to prepare the metallic oxide Mo_3O using the method reported did not yield anything but the starting materials (10). The existence of these oxides as distinct phases cannot be considered certain until they have been investigated in more detail, and they are not discussed here.

The true stability ranges of the various oxides will be very difficult to establish because of the slow reaction and transformation rates, especially those occurring below about 600° C. There is a pronounced tendency for some of the phases to form and remain for long periods in a metastable state. Moreover, in samples of MoO_3 reduced in various ways crystals have occasionally been found which may

Table I. Composition and Formation Temperatures for Molybdenum Oxides

Composition, O/Mo	Formula	Temperature Range of Formation, ° $C.$[a]
2.00	MoO_2	
2.75	Mo_4O_{11} monoclinic	<615
	Mo_4O_{11} orthorhombic	$615-\sim800$
2.765	$Mo_{17}O_{47}$	$<\sim560$
2.80	Mo_5O_{14}	$<\sim530$, probably metastable
2.875	Mo_8O_{23}	$650-780$
2.889	$Mo_{18}O_{52}$ triclinic	$600-750$
	Mo_9O_{26} monoclinic	$750-780$
3.0	MoO_3	

[a] By reducing MoO_3 with Mo or MoO_2 in evacuated silica tubes.

represent further molybdenum oxides, probably of low stability, and not listed in Table I.

There are no indications that the molybdenum oxides considered exhibit variations of lattice dimensions which would indicate extended homogeneity ranges. They form well developed crystals which give excellent x-ray photographs and they are stable in air up to about 200° C. The crystal structures of all of them have now been studied. They often possess a basic structure, which provides a basis for classification. Such a classification is illustrated in Table II; here the known tungsten and mixed molybdenum-tungsten oxides have also been listed, since they fit naturally into such a scheme.

All the oxide structures may profitably be visualized as built up of one or more types of the following polyhedra: MoO_6 octahedra, MoO_4 tetrahedra, and MoO_7 pentagonal bipyramids, joined by sharing corners or edges. However, the co-ordination is mostly irregular within the polyhedra, sometimes to a considerable extent.

Table II. Structure

Basic Structure	Extension of Basic structure	Types of Polyhedra
Rutile	Infinite in 3 dimensions	Octahedra
ReO₃	Infinite in 3 dimensions	Octahedra
	Infinite in 2 dimensions forming slabs of finite thickness	Octahedra
		Octahedra and tetrahedra
MoO₃	Layers infinite in 2 dimensions	Octahedra
	Layers infinite in 1 dimension, forming strips of finite width	Octahedra and tetrahedra
	No basic structure	Octahedra (and pentagonal bipyramids)

Several of these structures have been thoroughly described and discussed, especially by Magnéli (*22*), and only three families, containing structures not yet published, are briefly discussed below. Full details of these structure investigations will appear elsewhere.

The ReO₃ Family

The simplest representative of the ReO_3 family among the oxides considered is WO_3 in its different polymorphic forms, where the basic ReO_3 structure, although distorted, extends infinitely in three dimensions.

Where the basic structure extends infinitely in two dimensions only, forming slabs of a finite width, two alternative ways of connecting these slabs to form a three-dimensional structure have been observed. In the first case the slabs are connected across the boundaries by mutual edge sharing between the octahedra, thus forming "shear structures" (*28*). Oxides with this type of structure are Mo_8O_{23} and Mo_9O_{26} (mon.), compounds which are members of a homologous series of phases $M_nO_{3n-1}(ReO_3)$, where n determines the characteristic thickness of the ReO_3-type slabs and the type of basic structure indicated within the brackets (*16*). Mixed molybdenum-tungsten oxides have been prepared which represent higher members of this series (*23*). $W_{20}O_{58}$ is the only representative of a similar series, $M_nO_{3n-2}(ReO_3)$, hitherto known.

In the other observed configuration, the slabs are connected by tetrahedra, an arrangement represented by the two forms of Mo_4O_{11}. The slabs have the same thickness in both these structures, and the main difference is in the orientation of the rows of octahedra in adjacent slabs; the rows are parallel in Mo_4O_{11} (mon.) and reversed in Mo_4O_{11} (o-rh.). This is seen in Figure 1, A and B. It is also theoretically possible to form a homologous series with this type of structure by varying the thickness of the slabs, but phases of such an arrangement have not been observed so far.

Types of Molybdenum and Tungsten Oxides

General Arrangement	*Phases*	*Ref.*
Distortions from ideal atomic positions	MoO_2	(*17*)
	WO_2	(*17*)
Distortions from ideal atomic positions	WO_3	(*1, 3, 7*)
Slabs connected by octahedra sharing edges in border regions. Shear structures	Mo_8O_{23}	(*13*)
	Mo_9O_{26} (mon.) and higher members of series (Mo, $W)_nO_{3n-1}(ReO_3)$	(*13*) (*23*)
	$W_{20}O_{58}$	(*21*)
Slabs connected by tetrahedra	Mo_4O_{11} (mon.)	(*11*)
	Mo_4O_{11} (o-rh.)	(*14*)
Octahedra connected within one layer in one direction by shared edges, in other direction by shared corners	MoO_3	(*2*) (*3*) (*30*)
MoO_3-type strips connected by tetrahedra and increased edge sharing at boundaries	$Mo_{18}O_{52}$ (tricl.)	(*11*)
Complicated linking pattern in 2 dimensions involving 3-, 4-, 5-, and 6-membered rings; simple coupling by apical corners in third dimension	$Mo_{17}O_{47}$	(*9*)
	Mo_5O_{14}	(*11*)
	$MoW_{11}O_{36}$	(*4*)
	$MoW_{14}O_{45}$	(*4*)
	$W_{18}O_{49}$	(*19*)

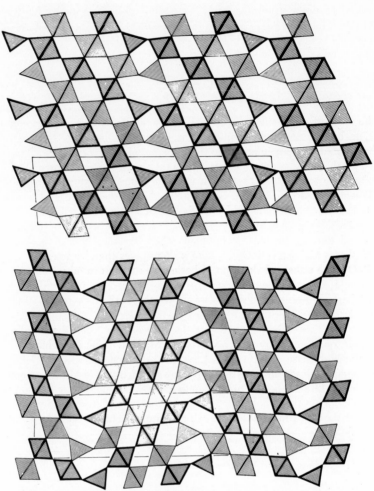

Figure 1.   Arrangement of polyhedra in Mo_4O_{11}

A. *Monoclinic*
B. *Orthorhombic*

Lightly and heavily outlined polyhedra situated at different levels, sepa-rated by about half repeat distance perpendicular to plane of paper. ReO_3 type slabs connected by tetrahedra across planes lying vertically. Limits of unit cells indicated

The structure of the monoclinic form has been refined by the least squares method. The Mo-O distances are therefore known with an accuracy that allows a detailed discussion of the distortions from regular coordination around the molybdenum atoms. The tetrahedral coordination is very regular, while the octahedral coordination is rather irregular, especially in octahedra joined to tetrahedra.

The MoO_3 Family

MoO_3 has a layer structure, each layer consisting of zigzag rows of octahedra which share edges, while the rows are mutually connected by shared corners.

This is illustrated by the central part of Figure 2. Successive layers are stacked so that the lowest octahedral corner of one layer lies above the hole formed between four octahedra in the layer below.

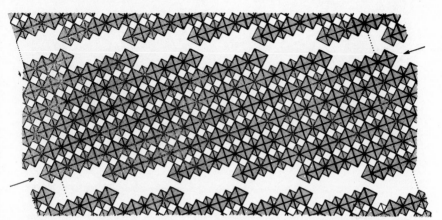

Figure 2.   MoO$_3$ layer (idealized by regular octahedra) divided into strips of type occurring in Mo$_{18}$O$_{52}$

One zigzag row formed by octahedra at two levels, sharing edges, indicated by arrows

The structure of Mo$_{18}$O$_{52}$, for which a least squares refinement has almost been completed, may be derived from that of MoO$_3$ by dividing each layer into infinite, step-edged strips by stepped lines as in Figure 2 and then allowing the parts to slip mutually along octahedral edges inclined to the layer plane.

In this way six octahedra at each end of every zigzag row share edges with six octahedra of a row in the neighboring strip; in this instance, a total of 11 octahedral edges are shared between two rows. Edge sharing brings the cations rather close together and this is counteracted by electrostatic repulsion. Any rearrangement of the atoms which tends to reduce the number of shared edges is therefore favored. In the present case, such a rearrangement can easily be accomplished by moving the Mo atom in the next outermost octahedron at the end of each row across one of the octahedral faces and into a tetrahedral site. In this way there is a reduction of 10 in the number of edges shared between the 12 polyhedra joining the rows of different strips. This is the structure of Mo$_{18}$O$_{52}$ actually arrived at in the refinement mentioned above, and Figure 3 illustrates the arrangement in the part of the structure considered, idealized in the form of regular octahedra and tetrahedra. As a result, there is a net increase by only one shared edge per 36 Mo atoms (one zigzag row) when going from MoO$_3$ to Mo$_{18}$O$_{52}$.

The layers in Mo$_{18}$O$_{52}$ are no longer smooth but regularly stepped and forming a "step lattice"—a term introduced by Sillén and Edstrand (27).

The deficiency of oxygen by comparison with MoO$_3$ is thus primarily brought about by increased edge sharing along lines occurring at regular intervals, an arrangement identical to that of the shear structures based on ReO$_3$ discussed above. Similarly in the present case various homologous series may be proposed. These can be assigned the general formula M$_n$O$_{3n-m+1}$(MoO$_3$), where $2n$ is the number of octahedra in a zigzag row within one MoO$_3$-type strip, and

Figure 3.   Connection in $Mo_{18}O_{52}$ between MoO_3-type strips of Figure 3

A. *Line of sight perpendicular to layer, orientation same as in Figure 2.   Polyhedra at three levels*
B. *Line of sight parallel to layer and perpendicular to zigzag rows of octahedra. Ends of three rows shown*

thus a measure of the width of these strips, and $2m$ is the number of octahedra at the end of each zigzag row that are engaged in increased edge sharing.

In the case illustrated by Figure 2 m is equal to 3, giving the hypothetical homologous series Mo_nO_{3n-2} (MoO_3), in which the phase $Mo_{18}O_{52}$ is the only member hitherto observed.   The double formula is preferred to the simple Mo_9O_{26}, because it points out the characteristic width of the basic structure by analogy with the case of $W_{20}O_{58}$ (*21*).

Although $Mo_{18}O_{52}$ is the only reduced phase of this family that has been prepared pure in appreciable amounts, single crystals have been studied which should be members of the series with $m = 2$ and $m = 4$.   In particular, several crystals have been investigated whose diffraction patterns are in agreement with the data required by the member $Mo_{25}O_{72}$ of the series M_nO_{3n-3} (MoO_3) ($m = 4$).

By increasing the value given to n, the MoO_3 structure is ultimately obtained in all these series.   It is evident that, at least in theory, topochemical reduction of MoO_3 should be made possible by such a shear mechanism initially appearing along very widely separated dislocation lines; this may be the clue to the structure of the discolored "molybdenum trioxide" crystals which are the main product when MoO_3 is heated strongly in vacuo (*12*).

The $W_{18}O_{49}$-Type Family

The last family in Table II is, for lack of a better name, designated $W_{18}O_{49}$

after the first member described. However, this is not a basic structure, as are
the other cases. The family includes a number of rather odd structures; those of
$Mo_{17}O_{47}$ and Mo_5O_{14} are shown in Figure 4. A common feature of this family
is the complicated connection of polyhedra in two dimensions, forming polygonal
networks of at least three- and six-membered rings, and a simple piling up of the
polyhedra by shared corners in the third dimension perpendicular to the rings. In

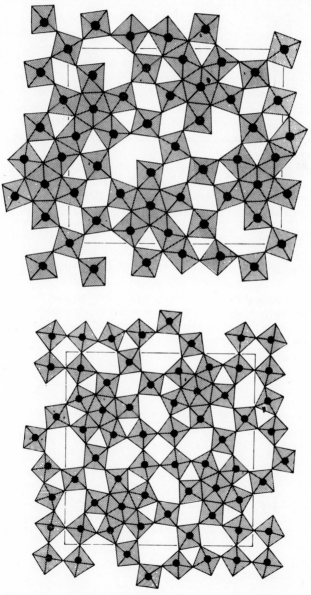

Figure 4.   Crystal structures of $Mo_{17}O_{47}$ (A) and Mo_5O_{14}
                                   (B)

In line of sight identical networks joined by common apexes

$Mo_{17}O_{47}$, Mo_5O_{14}, and $W_{18}O_{49}$ there are also four- or/and five-membered rings and these structures have an additional feature in common, in the seven-coordination of some metal atoms, surrounded by oxygens at the corners of pentagonal bipyramids which share the pentagonal edges with five octahedra. However, the short distances between some pairs of metal atoms occurring in $Mo_{17}O_{47}$ and $W_{18}O_{49}$, reminiscent of the conditions in MoO_2 and several other transition metal dioxides (24), have no counterpart in Mo_5O_{14}.

All the phases in this family except $Mo_{17}O_{47}$ may be described as "tunnel compounds" according to Wadsley (28), since they contain wide empty tunnels lined by rings of five or six octahedra which run straight through the structures. In the six-membered rings of $Mo_{17}O_{47}$ the coupling leaves one single bonded oxygen in the middle of the rings, thus blocking the tunnels (Figure 4, A).

In respect to the tunnel formation these compounds are closely related to the tetragonal and hexagonal tungsten bronzes (15, 18, 20), where the alkali metal atoms are situated in tunnels formed by the tungsten-oxygen framework. The substructure of the compounds $MoW_{11}O_{36}$ and $MoW_{14}O_{45}$ studied by Graham and Wadsley (4) are, moreover, completely consistent with the framework of the hexagonal bronzes.

The x-ray data clearly indicate that no scattering material is present within the tunnels of the oxides. This does not exclude the possibility that traces of impurities may play an important role in the nucleation of these needle-shaped crystals by initiating tunnel formation along the needles.

Remarks on Stoichiometry

The compounds discussed above are not nonstoichiometric in the strict sense of the word, since they form well defined, ordered phases which can be assigned precise stoichiometric formulas. Accordingly, they are not berthollides. They may, however, be regarded as nonstoichiometric in the wider sense of the term which has become current, since fractional valence numbers must be assigned to the metal atoms and the ordered structures which they exhibit constitute a preferred alternative to the formation of disordered phases of variable composition.

Acknowledgment

The author thanks G. Hägg and A. Magnéli for their continued and encouraging interest in these investigations.

Literature Cited

(1) Andersson, G., *Acta Chem. Scand.* 7, 154 (1953).
(2) Andersson, G., Magnéli, A., *Ibid.*, 4, 793 (1950).
(3) Bräkken, H., *Z. Krist.* 78, 484 (1931).
(4) Graham, J., Wadsley, A. D., *Acta Cryst.* 14, 379 (1961).
(5) Hägg, G., Magnéli, A., *Arkiv Kemi Mineral. Geol.* 19 A, No. 2 (1944).
(6) Hatterer, A., Herold, A., Rerat, C., *Compt. Rend.* 241, 750 (1955).
(7) Kehl, W. L., Hay, R. G., Wahl, D., *J. Appl. Phys.* 23, 212 (1952).
(8) Kihlborg, L., *Acta Chem. Scand.* 13, 954 (1959).
(9) *Ibid.*, 14, 1612 (1960).
(10) *Ibid.*, in press.
(11) Kihlborg, L., unpublished manuscript.
(12) Kihlborg, L., Magnéli, A., *Acta Chem. Scand.* 9, 471 (1955).
(13) Magnéli, A., *Ibid.*, 2, 501 (1948).
(14) *Ibid.*, p. 861.
(15) *Ibid.*, 7, 315 (1953).

(16) Magnéli, A., *Acta Cryst.* **6**, 495 (1953).
(17) Magnéli, A., *Arkiv Kemi, Mineral. Geol.* **24 A**, No. 2 (1946).
(18) Magnéli, A., *Arkiv Kemi* **1**, 213 (1949).
(19) *Ibid.*, p. 223.
(20) *Ibid.*, p. 269.
(21) *Ibid.*, p. 513.
(22) Magnéli, A., *Nova Acta Regiae Soc. Sci. Upsaliensis* (IV) **14**, No. 8 (1950).
(23) Magnéli, A., Blomberg-Hansson, B., Kihlborg, L., Sundkvist, G., *Acta Chem. Scand.* **9**, 1382 (1955).
(24) Marinder, B.-O., Magnéli, A., *Ibid.*, **11**, 1635 (1957).
(25) Plante, E. R., Dissertation, University of Kansas, 1960.
(26) Schönberg, N., *Acta Chem. Scand.* **8**, 617 (1954).
(27) Sillén, L. G., Edstrand, M., *Z. Krist.* **104**, 178 (1942).
(28) Wadsley, A. D., *Revs. Pure Appl. Chem. (Australia)* **5**, 165 (1955).
(29) Watt, G. W., Davies, D. D., *J. Am. Chem. Soc.* **70**, 3751 (1948).
(30) Wooster, N., *Z. Krist.* **80**, 504 (1931).

RECEIVED September 6, 1962. Part of a research program financially supported by the Swedish Natural Science Research Council and by the Office of Chief of Research and Development, U. S. Department of the Army, through its European office.

4

Ordered Phases and Nonstoichiometry in the Rare Earth Oxide System

LeROY EYRING and BO HOLMBERG

Department of Chemistry, Arizona State University, Tempe, Ariz.

Stable phases in the rare earth oxide systems are tabulated and discussed. New data on the structure of sesquioxides quenched from the melt are reported. The structural interrelations between the A, B, and C type sesquioxides and the fluorite dioxides are pointed out. The sequences of several intermediate oxides in the CeO_x, PrO_x, and TbO_x systems are observed to be related to the fluorite structure and the C form sesquioxide with respect to the metal atom positions. A hypothetical homologous series of the general formula M_nO_{2n-1}, related to the fluorite structure and the A form sesquioxide with a more or less fixed oxygen lattice, is suggested.

The rare earth oxides constitute a richly intricate sequence of phases with many subtle variations. A thorough and accurate description of these materials will provide an exacting test for any theory having predictive value.

Table I tabulates stable phases of limited composition range which have been observed. The description of the precise phase diagram in each system showing the ranges of composition of each phase and the extent of its nonstoichiometry is for some future time, although the general outline is emerging in some cases. Only the most painstaking efforts will provide useful data which will clarify rather than confuse the phase relationships.

A thermodynamically complete and satisfying picture of the higher oxides will be difficult to obtain, since the ordering process which accompanies equilibration at lower temperatures may be very slow. In fact, slow reactions, metastable states, and hysteresis are observed more or less generally in these oxide systems. The apparent equilibrium oxygen pressure at some given composition and temperature depends upon whether one is oxidizing or reducing. This phenomenon, termed hysteresis, is not fully understood and is probably complex. The observed phenomenon could involve such factors as the slow ordering of the oxygen in the crystal. Under the conditions of preparation of most of the phases tabulated here the oxygen was extremely mobile but the metal atoms were probably immobile. Oxygen uptake is rapid, achieving nearly constant composition in a matter of minutes at 400° C. Mobility in the cation lattice is not great enough to be practically useful for reactions requiring transport below about 1200° C., which is approximately the Tamman temperature for these materials. However, electronic interchange between the cation would be rapid and would obviate the need of ion transport in certain cases.

In view of this difference in mobility, transitions involving metal movement through the lattice would be expected to be slow and transitions involving only oxygen movement to be rapid above about 400° C. All the structural data reported here were obtained from quenched samples.

Table I. Some Properties of Stable Phases in Rare Earth Oxide Systems

Oxide	Cation Radius, A. (1)	Color	Lattice[a] Type	Lattice[a] Parameter, A.	Ref.
$LaO_{1.500}$	1.14	White	Hex (A)	$a = 3.93$ $c = 6.12$	(18)
$CeO_{1.522}$	1.07	Mustard	Hex (A)	$a = 3.889 \pm 0.002$ $c = 6.054 \pm 0.002$	(3)
$CeO_{1.651}$		Black	b.c.c.	$a = 11.126 \pm 0.001$	(3)
$CeO_{1.688}$		Black	b.c.c.	$a = 11.107 \pm 0.001$	(3)
$CeO_{1.717}$		Blue black	Rhomb.	$a_h = 3.921 \pm 0.002$ $c_h = 9.637 \pm 0.002$	(3)
$CeO_{1.775}$		Dark blue	Rhomb.	$a_h = 3.910 \pm 0.002$ $c_h = 9.502 \pm 0.002$	(3)
$CeO_{1.812}$		Dark blue	Rhomb.	$a_h = 3.890 \pm 0.002$ $c_h = 9.538 \pm 0.002$	(3)
$CeO_{2.000}$		Pale yellow	f.c.c.(F)	$a = 5.409 \pm 0.001$	(3)
$PrO_{1.500}$	1.06	Yellow	b.c.c.(C)	$a = 11.152 \pm 0.002$	
$PrO_{1.500}$		Light green	Hex (A)	$a = 3.859 \pm 0.003$ $c = 6.008 \pm 0.003$	(10)
$PrO_{1.65}$		Black	b.c.c.	$a = 11.070$	(10)
$PrO_{1.714}$		Black	Rhomb.	$a = 6.750$ $\alpha = 99°23''$	(10)
			Pseudo cell	$a = 5.516$ $\alpha = 89°42'$	(10)
$PrO_{1.78}$		Black	Rhomb.	$a = 5.487 \pm 0.002$ $\alpha = 90°17'$	(10)
$PrO_{1.80}$		Black	(f.c.c.)	$a = 5.482 \pm 0.003$	(10)
$PrO_{1.81}$		Black	(f.c.c.)	$a = 5.478 \pm 0.004$	(10)
$PrO_{1.83}$		Black	(f.c.c.)	$a = 5.469 \pm 0.001$	(10)
$PrO_{2.00}$		Black	(f.c.c.)(F)	$a = 5.393 \pm 0.001$	(10)
$NdO_{1.500}$	1.04	Light blue	Hex (A)	$a = 3.82$ $c = 5.98$	(18)
$NdO_{1.500}$			b.c.c.(C)	$a = 11.080$	(18)
$SmO_{0.5}$		Black	Zincblende	$a = 5.376 \pm 0.001$	(9)
SmO_{1}			Rock salt	$a = 4.9883 \pm 0.0003$	(9)
$SmO_{1.500}$	1.00	Pale yellow	Monoclinic(B)	$a = 14.177$ $b = 3.633$ $c = 8.847$ $\beta = 99.96°$	(8)
$SmO_{1.500}$			b.c.c.(C)	$a = 10.934$	(18)
EuO_{1}		Dark red	Rock salt	$a = 5.1439 \pm 0.0005$	(9)
$EuO_{1.500}$	0.98	White	Monoclinic(B)	$a = 14.123 \pm 0.005$ $b = 3.605 \pm 0.001$ $c = 8.813 \pm 0.003$ $\beta = 100.13° \pm 0.02°$	(17)
$EuO_{1.500}$			b.c.c.(C)	$a = 10.860$	(18)
$GdO_{1.500}$	0.97	White	b.c.c.(C)	$a = 10.8122$	(18)
$GdO_{1.500}$		White	Monoclinic(B)	$a = 14.06$ $b = 3.572$ $c = 8.75$ $\beta = 100.10°$	(18)

(Continued)

Table 1. Continued

Oxide	Cation Radius, A. (1)	Color	Lattice[a] Type		Lattice[a] Parameter, A.	Ref.
$TbO_{1.500}$	0.93	White	b.c.c.(C)	a =	10.7281 ± 0.0005	(2)
$TbO_{1.500}$		White	Monoclinic(B)	a =	13.92	
				b =	3.536	
				c =	8.646	
				β =	$100.2°$	
$TbO_{1.65}$		Brown				
$TbO_{1.715}$		Brown	Rhomb.	a =	6.509 ± 0.002	(2)
				α =	$99°21' \pm 0.5'$	
			Pseudo cell	a =	5.319 ± 0.001	
				α =	$89°41'$	
$TbO_{1.81}$		Dark brown	Triclinic	a = $b = c$ =	5.286 ± 0.001	(2)
				α = β =	$89°25'$	
				γ =	$90°$	
$TbO_{1.95}$		Dark brown	f.c.c.(F)	a =	5.220 ± 0.001	(2)
$DyO_{1.500}$	0.92	White	b.c.c.(C)	a =	10.6647	(18)
$DyO_{1.509}$		White	Monoclinic(B)	a =	13.87	
				b =	3.518	
				c =	8.589	
				β =	$100.2°$	
$HoO_{1.500}$	0.91	White	b.c.c.(C)	a =	10.6065	(18)
$YO_{1.500}$	0.91	White	b.c.c.(C)	a =	10.6021	(18)
$ErO_{1.500}$	0.89	White	b.c.c.(C)	a =	10.5473	(18)
$TmO_{1.500}$	0.87	White	b.c.c.(C)	a =	10.4866	(18)
$YbO_{1.500}$	0.86	White	b.c.c.(C)	a =	10.4334	(18)
$LuO_{1.500}$	0.85	White	b.c.c.(C)	a =	10.3907	(18)

[a] A, B, and C refer to the three known forms of the sesquioxide. F designates the fluorite structure.

Oxide Systems

Dioxides. Table I indicates that cerium, praseodymium, and terbium form dioxides which crystallize in the fluorite lattice. The thermal decomposition pressure of oxygen is vastly different for each oxide at a given temperature. For example, in air at 1000° C. their compositions would be approximately $CeO_{2.00}$, $PrO_{1.70}$, and $TbO_{1.54}$. PrO_2 has a decomposition pressure of 1 atm. at about 310° C., while TbO_2 has been prepared only by the action of atomic oxygen on TbO_x.

The fluorite structure has been described in terms of a face-centered-cubic unit cell containing four units of MO_2. Table I lists the lattice parameters for these substances.

The over-all arrangement of atoms is shown abstractly in Figure 1. The cross-hatched squares represent metal atoms coordinated with eight oxygen atoms at the corners of a regular cube. The layers above and below are shifted in such a way that the metal-filled cubes fill the positions that are vacant in the plane shown in the diagram. In this arrangement the MO_8 coordination cubes are stacked so that each edge is shared with a neighboring MO_8 coordination group.

An alternative representation is to show the stacking order of the layers of atoms normal to the body diagonal (a threefold axis) of these cubes (Figure 2) (4). In this figure the metal atom layers are designated by a capital letter and the oxygen layers by a lower case. In any layer all the atoms are the same and are in a closest packed arangement but not at closest packed distances. The hexagons at the left of the figure show the relative position of the atoms in the A, B, and C layers.

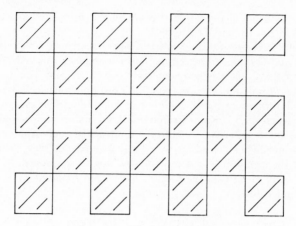

Figure 1. Fluorite type MO_2

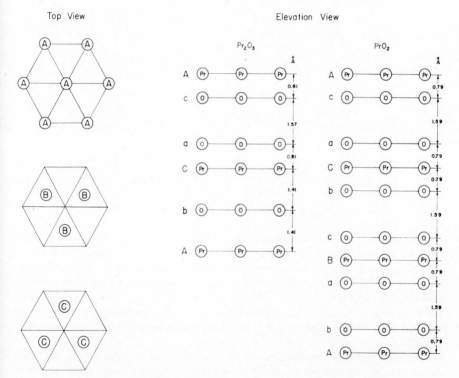

Figure 2. Structure of PrO_2 viewed as a series of atom layers along C_{hex} axis

CeO$_2$ is pale yellow, PrO$_2$ is black, and TbO$_2$ is dark brown. A light-colored PrO$_2$ has not been observed, even when treated with molecular oxygen at 600 atm. The dark colors of the PrO$_2$ and TbO$_2$ crystals suggest a deviation from stoichiometry, although, at least in the case of PrO$_2$, the deviation has not been detected by weighing.

All the sesquioxides of the rare earths are very light colored and all the intermediate oxides of Ce, Pr, and Tb are dark.

Sesquioxides. The sesquioxides exist in one or more of the three forms designated as A, B, and C types. The A type has a hexagonal unit cell, the B type is monoclinic, and the C form is body-centered cubic. Figure 3 indicates roughly the fields of stability of the various types. Transformations from the C form to either the A or B form occur for all oxides up to holmium. The accepted transition temperatures (when the C form is heated) will, no doubt, be lowered when very long annealing times are used. Figure 3 is idealized and extended from one given by Roth and Schneider (*18*), who have pointed out that the temperature and the size of the ions suffice to determine the type of sesquioxide. Transformations from the A or B form to the C form have been reported by Warshaw and Roy (*19*) in some cases.

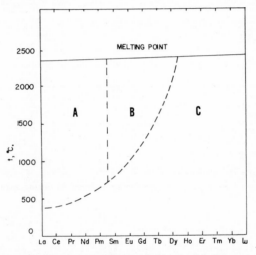

Figure 3. Fields of stability for M$_2$O$_3$

In experiments recently performed by the authors quenched sesquioxides were prepared by sprinkling a fine powder through an argon plasma jet. Material of appropriate mesh size forms perfect transparent spheres about 0.01 to 0.02 mm. in diameter. Powder diagrams were taken of the material so treated and it was observed that Nd$_2$O$_3$ was A form; Sm$_2$O$_3$, Tb$_2$O$_3$, and Dy$_2$O$_3$ were B form; Ho$_2$O$_3$ and Y$_2$O$_3$ were C form. These observations fix the intersections of the curves in Figure 3 with the liquidus line, if it is assumed that no transition occurs during cooling.

Lower Oxides. The question of the incorporation of oxygen into the rare earth metal lattice and the extent of oxide formation between the metal and the sesquioxide has not been systematically studied. The lower oxides reported in Table I were prepared by distilling the rare earth metals in a system of low oxygen partial pressure (*9*). This is one of the great unexplored regions of the rare earth oxide systems.

Ordered Intermediate Phases. Between the dioxides of Ce, Pr, and Tb and the sesquioxides discussed above is a sequence of oxides of intermediate composition. The best established of these are listed in Table I and shown diagrammatically in Figure 4. The existence of these stable intermediate oxides is indicated by their x-ray diffraction patterns (2–5, 10), kinetics of oxygen transport (16), $(P,X)_T$ isotherms (12, 13), electrical measurements (10), and weight change isotherms (7, 11).

Each measurement, sensitive to the existence of ordering, agrees on the main features of the phase relationships suggested below for each system. Table I should be consulted for the lattice parameters for each sequence.

$MO_{1.65}$. The dashed line in Figure 4 at this composition should be interpreted to indicate C-type oxides between the composition $MO_{1.5}$ and $MO_{1.70}$ which have been reported in each system or are implied by the isotherms. The real nature of these phases and the range of their composition are not known.

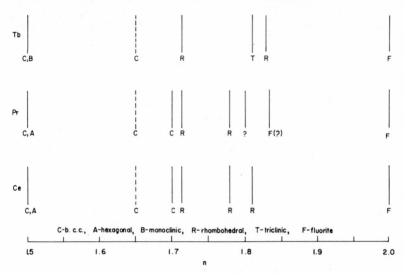

Figure 4.   Lattice-composition representation of most stable MO_n phases

$MO_{1.70}$. An upper limit to a C-type phase is indicated at this composition in x-ray diagrams in both the PrO_x and CeO_x systems and is shown graphically in the isotherms in the PrO_x system (12).

$MO_{1.714}$. A phase of narrow composition limits and with ideal composition M_7O_{12} is stable over a wide range of temperature and oxygen pressure for each system.

The strong lines in powder diagrams of this phase are characteristic of the fluorite phase. However, some of them are split into several components and, in addition, there are many weak lines. The splitting of the strong lines and all the weak lines are explained on the basis of a rhombohedral cell containing seven M atoms and twelve O atoms with $a = 6.750$ A. and $\alpha = 99°33'$ (for Pr_7O_{12}). The contents of the cell, if it were fully oxidized, would be M_7O_{14}. The removal of the two oxygen atoms along the threefold axis would give the correct stoichiometry, destroy the cubic symmetry, and allow the rhombohedral distortion to occur.

It is believed that this phase is the same in all three systems.

The proposed structure (2, 10) has the interesting feature of sequences of MO_6 octahedra, one above the other along the threefold axis to give chains running the full length of the crystal. This feature also occurs in the C-type M_2O_3 and is discussed later. Surrounding these MO_6 threads are sheaths of MO_7 polyhedra similar to those groups in the A and B structure of the sesquioxides.

$MO_{1.78}$. A distinct phase of relatively narrow composition range occurs as $PrO_{1.78}$. The splitting of the strong lines in the powder pattern can be accounted for in terms of a face-centered rhombohedral unit cell. The true unit cell for this phase is not known. Bevan (3) reports a rhomobohedral phase of narrow composition range at this stoichiometry (γ phase). It was indexed with a hexagonal unit cell.

$PrO_{1.80}$. Between $PrO_{1.79}$ and $PrO_{1.83}$ the phase diagram has not been resolved. Tensiometric measurements suggest a stable phase at $PrO_{1.80}$ at low temperature. X-ray diffraction patterns usually show broad lines which are definitely complex. It is believed that there may be some stable phases in this region which have not yet been isolated.

$MO_{1.81}$. In the TbO_x and CeO_x systems this phase is of striking stability. The powder patterns have been differently indexed, as may be seen from Table I. A miscibility gap exists in the CeO_x system between $x = 1.81$ and 2.00.

$TbO_{1.83}$. A phase in the TbO_x system of composition greater than $TbO_{1.81}$ has been observed in samples treated at 600-atm. pressure of molecular oxygen.

$PrO_{1.833}$. One of the most dramatic features of the entire praseodymium oxide system is the phase Pr_6O_{11}, which has a narrow range of composition over wide variation of temperature and pressure. This fact accounts for the observance of this phase when samples of heated oxides are cooled slowly in air.

The structure of this phase is generally credited in the literature as being fluorite, with $a = 5.468$ A. However, recent diffractometer traces of some samples of this composition show about a dozen extra very weak lines. A unit cell which would also account for these lines has not been discovered.

Since there is a miscibility gap between the composition $PrO_{1.83}$ and $PrO_{2.00}$, it would not be surprising to find that they have different structures.

Discussion

Coordination in M_2O_3 and MO_2 Phases. In the several rare earth oxides the configuration of oxygen atoms around the metal atom is found to be one of several different types.

In the fluorite structure each metal atom is surrounded by eight oxygen atoms at the corners of a cube; all the metal-oxygen distances are the same (Table II).

If the same symbolic representation were made for the C-type oxide as in Figure 1 for the dioxide, it would look much the same. The metal positions remain almost unchanged, while the MO_8 cubes become MO_6 coordination groups with oxygen atoms missing in one of two ways, across the face diagonal (an unusual arrangement) or along the body diagonal. The cubes with oxygen missing along the body diagonal lie in straight lines along a line through that body diagonal. Looked at from the point of view of atom layers, the stacking arrangement is the same as in MO_2. However, one fourth of the oxygen positions are vacant in each plane and these vacancies are in groups of four arranged in the form of a Y with threefold symmetry.

If the A form is reduced to the same representation as for the C form and fluorite lattice, Figure 5 results. Some of the cations have moved into interstitial positions. One may view the pattern as consisting of repeated strips of the dioxide, two cubes thick, remaining after the structure collapses on itself in such a way that the cubes share faces along a line of shear. In the layer above, each cube simply shifts down a space and the shear line becomes a shear plane. Of course, the metal atoms and the oxygen atoms have shifted slightly from their ideal position, as indicated below.

Table II.   Metal-Oxygen Distances in Coordination Polyhedra

Oxide	MO_6, A.	MO_7, A.	MO_8, A.
PrO_2			8–2.335
A Pr_2O_3		3–2.66	
		3–2.32	
		1–2.40	
		(1–3.60)	
C Pr_2O_3	6–2.40		
	and		
	2–1.96		
	2–2.50		
	2–2.76		
B Sm_2O_3	2–2.28	2–2.32	
	2–2.37	2–2.49	
	1–2.31	1–2.38	
	1–2.26	1–2.29	
	(1–3.12)	1–2.76	
	(1–3.60)	(1–3.80)	
		and	
		2–2.29	
		2–2.56	
		1–2.49	
		1–2.25	
		1–2.71	
		(1–3.60)	
C Sm_2O_3	6–2.36		
	and		
	2–1.92		
	2–2.45		
	2–2.71		

Metal-oxygen distances are presented by or calculated from Koehler and Wollan (*15*), Koehler (*14*), or Cromer (*6*).

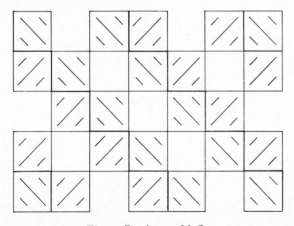

Figure 5.   A type M_2O_3

Seeing this relationship between the A form and the dioxide structure, one can imagine a homologous series where the MO_2 slabs simply vary in thickness, but are joined together in the same way as in the A form, by sharing faces.   The next member of such a series, having the general formula M_nO_{2n-1}, is shown in Figure 6.   The only two members of the series known at present are the A form, M_2O_3, and fluorite, MO_2.

In the sesquioxides the hexagonal A form has a seven coordination about the metal atoms.   The coordination group MO_7 can be described as an octahedron

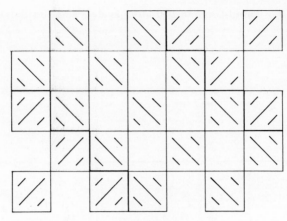

Figure 6.   Hypothetical MnO_{2n-1}
$(n = 3)$

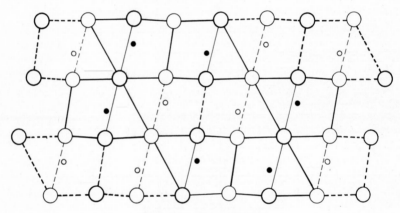

Figure 7.   A type M_2O_3

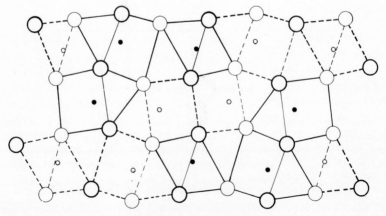

Figure 8.   B type Sm_2O_3

with an additional oxygen atom above the center of one of the faces. Actually there is also an oxygen atom below the opposite face but at a much greater distance from the metal atom. This last oxygen atom, together with the seven in the co-ordination group, forms a distorted cube. These distorted cubes form the basis of the representation given above for the A type lattice.

The monoclinic B form has a structure closely related to that of the A form. By choosing a monoclinic unit cell for the A form (taking as the new axis $a = a_h - b_h + 2c_h$, $b = -a_h - b_h$ and $c = a_h - b_h - c_h$) the relationship between them is easily seen. Figures 7 and 8 show these similar structures projected along the b axis. The metal in the B form is both six and seven coordinated. The MO_7 group is similar to that in the A form and has a distant oxygen neighbor in the same way as the MO_7 group in the A form. The MO_6 group is an octahedron with two distant oxygen neighbors at opposite faces. The metal-oxygen distances in A Pr_2O_3 and B Sm_2O_3 are shown in Table II. Figures 9, 10, and 11 illustrate the similarities and differences in coordination between the two forms. The oxygen atom arrangement in the A and B forms is almost the same as in the dioxide. However, the metal atom arrangement is very different. The coordination cubes in the dioxides are joined by sharing edges, but in the A form the distorted cubes of oxygen atoms are joined by sharing edges and faces.

Nonstoichiometry in Rare Earth Oxide Systems. As more work is done on the intermediate oxides at low temperatures, regions earlier thought to be non-stoichiometric are resolved into phases of narrow composition limit. It is possible that for carefully annealed specimens the entire range of composition will be re-solved into definite compounds of narrow composition limits separated by two-phase regions. This, of course, presumes that equilibrium can be achieved.

One small single crystal fragment, black in color, whose composition was about $PrO_{1.53}$ gave a very interesting diffraction pattern (*10*). It is a superposition of the pattern for $PrO_{1.5}$ (A type) and the single crystal pattern observed for $PrO_{1.71}$. The reflections which would be common to the $PrO_{1.5}$ (A type) and $PrO_{1.71}$ in the zero layer ($hk0$) precession diagram were enhanced and in the shape of X's. The same reflections in the upper levels were separated into multiple reflections. A precession diagram taken with the precession axis normal to the hexagonal axis showed the superposition of patterns from unit cells with c axes of 6.0 and 9.5 A. From the relationships shown in Figure 2, it is not surprising that a single crystal could consist of parts with the hexagonal A type and parts with the fluorite-type structure, both oriented with common threefold axes.

Some precession diagrams from single crystal preparations of compositions $PrO_{1.71}$ and $PrO_{1.79}$ are best explained in terms of multiple twinning in the C direction. Parts of the crystal have the ABCABCA . . . arrangement and other parts the ACBACBA . . . order. It is clear that many interesting nonequilibrium states consisting of stacking faults or jumbled arrangements of coordination poly-hedra may complicate the entire picture.

Above the critical temperature a single disordered phase seems to exist. Per-haps in these cases the coordination polyhedra are disordered to some extent. In these "cubic" systems where such a variety of coordination seems possible and where slip may occur in three directions, critical temperatures may be lower than would otherwise be observed.

In the bixbyite structure (C form) the six-coordinated oxygen atoms are of two arrangements and the oxygen positions are sufficiently irregular to suggest anion vacancies. In the intermediate oxides the structures may be considered to

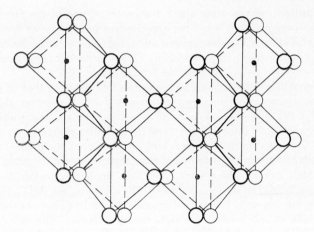

Figure 9.   A type M_2O_3

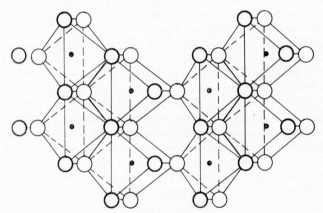

Figure 10.   B type Sm_2O_3

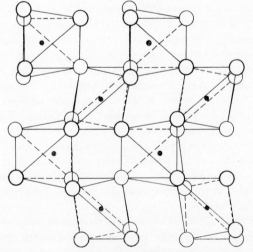

Figure 11.   C type M_2O_3

be related to or derived from the C type and the fluorite type, and the oxygen coordination polyhedra sufficiently irregular to justify speaking of anion vacancies.

However, a new series of oxides may be realized having the general composition M_nO_{2n-1}, which are related to the A, B, and fluorite type oxides in which the coordinated oxygen atoms are more regularly arranged, and may be considered to have metal interstitial atoms. Actually, in these systems, speaking either of anion vacancies or metal interstitials is probably imposing a nomenclature which has little relevance.

Acknowledgment

The authors express appreciation to Bruce Hyde and A. D. Wadsley for many stimulating discussions.

Literature Cited

(1) Ahrens, L. H., *Geochim. Cosmochim. Acta* 2, 155 (1952).
(2) Baenziger, N. C., Eick, H. A., Schuldt, H. S., Eyring, L., *J. Am. Chem. Soc.* 83, 2219 (1961).
(3) Bevan, D. J. M., *J. Inorg. Nucl. Chem.* 1, 49–55 (1955).
(4) Brauer, G., Gingerich, K. A., Holtschmidt, U., *Ibid.*, 16, 77 (1960).
(5) Brauer, G., Gradinger, H., *Z. anorg. allgem. Chem.* 276, 209 (1954).
(6) Cromer, D. T., *J. Phys. Chem.* 61, 753 (1957).
(7) Czanderna, A. W., Ph. D. thesis, Purdue University, 1957.
(8) Douglass, R. M., Staritsky, E., *Anal. Chem.* 28, 522 (1957).
(9) Eick, H. A., Baenziger, N. C., Eyring, L., *J. Am. Chem. Soc.* 78, 5147 (1957).
(10) Eyring, L., Baenziger, N. C., *J. Appl. Phys. Suppl.* 33, 428–33, (1952).
(11) Faeth, P. A., Ph. D. thesis, Purdue University, Lafayette, Ind., 1961.
(12) Ferguson, R. W., Guth, E. D., Eyring, L., *J. Am. Chem. Soc.* 76, 3890 (1954).
(13) Guth, E. Daniel, Eyring, L., *Ibid.*, 76, 5242 (1954).
(14) Koehler, W. C., *Phys. Rev.* 110, 37 (1958).
(15) Koehler, W. C., Wollan, E. O., *Acta Cryst.* 6, 741 (1953).
(16) Kuntz, U. E., Eyring, L., "Kinetics of High Temperature Processes," p. 50, Wiley, New York, 1959.
(17) Mozzi, R. L., Guentert, O. J., *J. Chem. Phys.* 36, 298 (1962).
(18) Roth, R. S., Schneider, S. J., *J. Res. Natl. Bur. Std.* 64A, 309 (1960).
(19) Warshaw, I., Roy, R., *J. Phys. Chem.* 65, 2048 (1961).

RECEIVED September 6, 1962. Work supported by the U. S. Atomic Energy Commission.

5

X-Ray and Density Study of Nonstoichiometry in Uranium Oxides

LAHMER LYNDS,[1] W. A. YOUNG,[1] J. S. MOHL,[1] and G. G. LIBOWITZ[2]

Research Division, Atomics International, Division of North American Aviation, Canoga Park, Calif.

The lattice parameters of nonstoichiometric uranium oxides, quenched from 1100° C., were determined within the composition range UO_2 to U_4O_9. Two separate linear relations for the lattice parameter as a function of oxygen content were obtained: one characteristic of UO_{2+x} and the other of U_4O_{9-y}. The two functions are: $a_0 = 5.4705 - 0.094\ x\ (0 \leq x \leq 0.125)$ and $a_0 = 5.4423 + 0.029\ y\ (0 \leq y \leq 0.31)$. Helium displacement densities were determined for some samples; the values obtained are consistent with an oxygen interstitial model for UO_{2+x} and an oxygen vacancy model for U_4O_{9-y}.

The nature of the defects causing nonstoichiometry in uranium dioxide has not been unequivocally established, although much previous work is consistent with an oxygen interstitial model. Possibly the most straightforward approach to the problem is the study of density variations as a function of composition. Such a study requires a determination of accurate and precise lattice constants and densities, and a knowledge of the phase relationships.

Phase relationships in the UO_2-U_4O_9 system have been studied by many authors using a variety of techniques. The results obtained by several investigators are given in Figure 1 (*14*). According to the results of Grønvold (*12*) and Schaner (*22*) there is essentially no deviation from stoichiometry in UO_2 at room temperature. Therefore, previous density determinations (*2, 8, 11, 12*) within this system, which were conducted at room temperature, are not meaningful in terms of nonstoichiometric uranium dioxide, since the observed increase in density with increasing oxygen content is due to the increased amount of the U_4O_{9-y} phase.

Schaner has demonstrated that the single phase at elevated temperatures can be frozen in by quenching. In the present investigation, limited to compositions between UO_2 and U_4O_9, samples were prepared by direct oxidation of stoichio-

[1] Present address, North American Aviation Science Center, Division of North American Aviation.
[2] Present address, Materials Sciences Laboratory, Aerospace Corp., El Segundo, Calif.

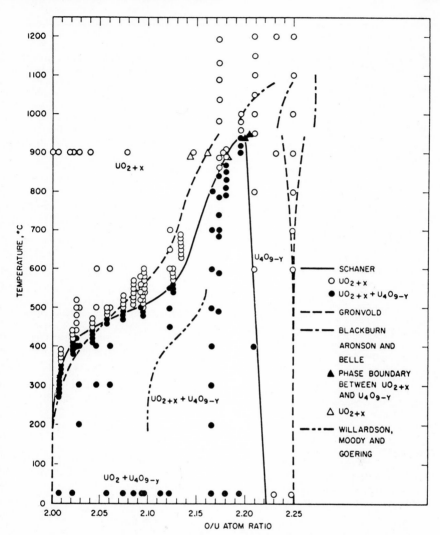

Figure 1.   UO₂–U₄O₉ phase diagram

metric UO_2, equilibrated in the high temperature monophasic region, and quenched. Schaner's phase diagram was used as a guide. Precise lattice constants and densities were determined for the single phase thus frozen in.

Experimental

Sample Preparation.   The samples were prepared by the direct oxidation of stoichiometric uranium dioxide obtained by the thermal decomposition of uranyl iodide (17).

Each sample was prepared in the same manner. A degassed quartz tube fitted with a Vycor standard taper joint was weighed on an analytical balance before and after loading with stoichiometric UO_2 (1 to 5 grams) and evacuated at 700° to 800° C. to 10^{-6} mm. Purified oxygen (99.5 mole %) was added to a pressure sufficient to attain the desired composition (50 to 600 mm.); pressures were measured to $\pm$ 0.5 mm. using a mercury manometer. The tube was then almost entirely immersed in a room temperature water bath and sealed off at a narrowed region just above the water level. From four to six tubes were arranged symmetrically in a resistance furnace so that each sample would receive equivalent thermal treatment, heated to 1100° to 1150° C., and maintained at temperature for 60 to 100 hours. Each tube and its contents were then quenched in a matter of seconds by a quick transfer into water. Application of a spark coil to each tube indicated that only a negligible amount of gas remained in the tube after this treatment. As an additional check a manometric measurement after oxidation of one sample yielded zero pressure. Each tube was carefully cut open, the sample removed, and the tube volume determined to $\pm$ 0.01 cc. by filling with distilled water and weighing. All samples were handled in an argon-filled glove box after quenching and during preparation for x-ray diffraction studies.

X-Ray Measurements. A Norelco Type 52058 symmetrical focusing back-reflection camera was used to obtain precise lattice constants. This camera has a radius of 60 mm. and provides excellent resolution between $\theta = 59°$ and $\theta = 88.74°$. A small portion of each sample was ground to a fine powder, mixed with a small quantity of Dow-Corning silicone grease, and applied to the camera target as a thin film. The diffraction patterns were obtained using 2- to 4-hour exposures with Ni-filtered Cu radiation ($K\alpha_1 = 1.54051$ A. and $K\alpha_2 = 1.54433$ A.) (16) at 34 kv. and 30 ma. Sample temperatures were monitored during exposure and the lattice constants adjusted to 25° C., using a correction factor of 0.00006 A. per degree (12). The films were developed on one side only, to minimize parallax errors. The positions of the lines were measured to $\pm$ 0.1 mm.; film shrinkage or expansion was considered in all calculations. The lattice constants were calculated by the method of Mueller, Heaton, and Miller (19), adapted for the IBM-709 by Korst, Tannenbaum, and Miller (15). This program assumes that systematic errors in $\Delta a_0/a_0$ are directly proportional to $\phi \tan \phi$, where $\phi = \pi/2 - \theta$, and also corrects for random errors by a least squares method. The maximum error in the lattice constants is estimated to be $\pm$ 0.0005 A.

Density Measurements. Densities were obtained using the helium displacement apparatus described by Schumb and Rittner (23) with minor modifications. Compressed nitrogen was used to raise the mercury level; a steel metric scale and cathetometer were used to measure the heights of the mercury levels in the manometer and telescopes were used to observe the levels defining the constant volume.

Sample Analysis. The composition of each sample was determined after oxidation by one or more of three methods: polarographic analysis, volumetric analysis, and gas law calculation. The polarographic method (9) provides a quantitative determination of U(VI) formed as a result of oxidation. It was assumed that only U(IV), U(VI), and O^{-2} were present and a value for the ratio of oxygen to uranium was then calculated. The error in the O/U ratio determined by this method is a function of the ratio and varies from $\pm$ 0.0005 in the vicinity of UO_2 to $\pm$ 0.005 near $UO_{2.25}$. Occasional difficulties with the polarograph necessitated the use of a ceric ammonium sulfate–ferric ammonium sulfate volumetric method (21) which is quantitative for U(IV); O/U ratios were then calculated to $\pm$ 0.005 using the assumption given above. The O/U ratios were also calculated by use of the ideal gas law from the volumes of the samples and tubes and the pressures and temperatures of the oxygen added. Suitable choice of sample and tube volumes yielded an uncertainty of ±0.0005.

Results

X-Ray Data. The x-ray data and the O/U ratios obtained by the different analytical methods are shown in Table I. For several samples, as a check for homogeneity, two random portions were chosen for x-ray examination. The maximum difference found was only 0.0007 A. Where differences occurred, the average lattice parameter was used. The high angle $\alpha_1 - \alpha_2$ doublets were fully resolved and very sharp lines were obtained for all compositions reported in Table I, the patterns obtained for O/U > 2.17 being somewhat sharper than those for O/U < 2.13. However, attempts to prepare usable samples in the O/U range 2.13 to 2.17 were unsuccessful; the diffraction lines were always extremely diffuse. Possible reasons for the diffuse nature of the patterns are discussed below.

Table I.   Lattice Constants in UO_2-U_4O_9

	Oxygen/Uranium Ratio			Lattice Constant at 25° C., A.	
From U(VI)	*From U(IV)*	*Gas law*	*Av.*	*Obsd.*	*Av.*
2.001			2.001	5.4706	5.4706
2.005	2.004		2.004	5.4701	5.4701
2.005		2.020	2.012	5.4694 5.4693	5.4694
2.034		2.034	2.034	5.4672 5.4671	5.4672
	2.074	2.071	2.072	5.4636 5.4635	5.4636
2.086		2.090	2.088	5.4622 5.4617	5.4620
	2.116	2.102	2.109	5.4606	5.4606
	2.124	2.115	2.120	5.4591	5.4591
2.126	2.130	2.114	2.123	5.4589 5.4589	5.4589
2.167		2.180	2.174	5.4515 5.4510	5.4512
		2.198	2.198	5.4485	5.4485
2.193		2.205	2.199	5.4486 5.4479	5.4482
2.210		2.218	2.214	5.4462 5.4462	5.4462
2.217			2.217	5.4466 5.4464	5.4465
	2.227	2.220	2.224	5.4453	5.4453

Density Data.   The density data are given in Table II and in Figure 2. Here the error is estimated to be 0.2%, based on determinations of the density of mercury which yielded results differing from the accepted value by no more than 0.16%. The standard deviations for seven to ten measurements on each sample varied from 0.02 to 0.10%. The first sample listed in Table II is "iodide" UO_2; the others were prepared from the same batch of this material with S6a and S9a being prepared by oxidation of S6 and S9, respectively.

Table II.   Helium Displacement Densities

Sample	O/U Ratio	Density at 25° C., ±0.02 G./Cc.
S	2.001	10.23
S6	2.109	10.62
S6a	2.120	10.70
S9	2.198	11.06
S9a	2.224	11.10

Discussion

Lattice Parameters.   Previous investigators (*1, 10, 13*) of lattice parameters as a function of O/U ratio have shown a continuous linear change in lattice

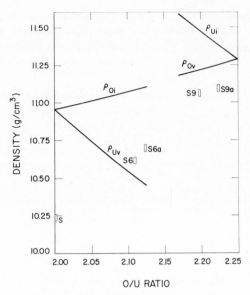

Figure 2.   Densities in UO_2–U_4O_9

parameter from UO_2 to U_4O_9. Therefore, it was generally assumed that the U_4O_9 structure was merely that of the fluorite UO_2 lattice with an additional oxygen in the $(1/2, 1/2, 1/2)$ position. The fact that the U_4O_9 structure is more complex has recently been demonstrated by Belbeoch, Piekarski, and Perio (7). As seen in Figure 3, the present data can best be represented by two straight lines, one characteristic of $\bar{U}O_{2+x}$ and the other probably characteristic of U_4O_{9-y}. Least squares treatment of the data yields the following relations, in Angstrom units:

$$a_0 = 5.4705 \pm 0.001 - (0.094 \pm 0.001)x, (0 \le x \le 0.125) \tag{1}$$

$$a_0 = 5.4423 \pm 0.003 + (0.029 \pm 0.002)y, (0 \le y \le 0.31) \tag{2}$$

The lattice constant found for stoichiometric UO_2, 5.4705 A., agrees with the results of Grønvold (12) and of Anderson and Sawyer (3). Extrapolating Equation 2 to $y = 0$ yields a value for stoichiometric U_4O_9 which is in excellent agreement with that of the pseudo-cell obtained by Belbeoch, Piekarski, and Perio (7), who found that U_4O_9 is a superlattice composed of a $4 \times 4 \times 4$ pseudo-network and has a cell constant of 21.77 A. This agreement indicates that Equation 2 does indeed represent the U_4O_{9-y} phase in this system. The fact that the two straight lines in Figure 3 do not have the same slopes can be taken as additional evidence that the U_4O_9 structure is not a simple extension of the UO_2 structure.

In comparing the lattice parameter *vs.* O/U ratio data with those of previous investigations, it should be pointed out that the curved plot shown by Schaner (22) can also be represented (within his experimental error) by two linear functions similar to those found in this work. The work of the other investigators (1, 10, 13) cannot properly be compared to the present study because their samples were not quenched from elevated temperatures or were, at best, slowly quenched.

The diffuse x-ray patterns obtained in the intermediate region (O/U = 2.13 to 2.17) are indicative of a strained structure such as might exist just above a miscibility gap. However, if this were the case, the two-phase UO_2-U_4O_9 region indicated by this work would be considerably to the left (lower O/U ratios) of the range shown by previous investigators (*14*) (Figure 1). Some additional observations are of interest in this respect. Using a solid-state galvanic cell with wüstite as a reference electrode, Aronson and Belle (*4*) determined the thermodynamic properties of UO_{2+x} as a function of x at temperatures from 877° to 1077° C. Recently, Roberts and Walter (*20*), in combining their equilibrium pressure measurements with an extrapolation of the data of Aronson and Belle, obtained a plot of the partial molal free energy of oxygen in UO_{2+x} as a function of composition at 1123° C. which they indicated could best be fitted by two straight lines intersecting at about $UO_{2.125}$. Using a more recent value for the free energy of formation of wüstite, Miller, Merton, and Porter (*18*) redetermined the partial molar free energy of oxygen in UO_{2+x} from Aronson's and Belle's data and found a definite break at $UO_{2.125}$. Thus there appears to be a transition of undetermined nature at O/U = 2.125 which is reflected in the present work by the diffuse x-ray patterns obtained at approximately the same composition. If it is assumed that the excess oxygen enters the UO_2 lattice at the cell center positions, the fact that one half of the unit cells would be so occupied at the composition $UO_{2.125}$ may be of significance. In any case there appears to be a need for further study, particularly by x-ray diffraction at high temperature, in order to understand more fully the phase relations within this system.

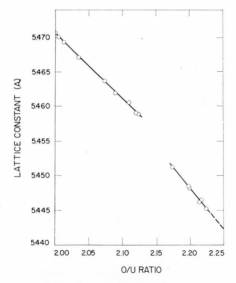

Figure 3.   Lattice constants in
$UO_2 - U_4O_9$

Densities.   The theoretical density of a binary stoichiometric compound, MX, containing n molecules per unit cell is given by

$$\rho_s = n(M + sX)/NV \tag{3}$$

where M and X are the atomic weights, s is the atomic ratio, N is Avogadro's number (6.0249 × 10^{23}), and V is the volume of the unit cell. For a non-stoichiometric compound, $MX_{s \pm \delta}$, two values for the density may be calculated, depending upon whether the deviation from stoichiometry is due to the presence of interstitial atoms of one element or to vacant lattice sites of the other. For the case of excess X the interstitial density is

$$\rho_{Xi} = n(M + sX + \delta X)/NV \tag{4}$$

On the other hand, for metal vacancies the formula for the nonstoichiometric compound, $MX_{s+\delta}$, should be written $M_{s/(s+\delta)}X_s$. Therefore the density for vacancies becomes

$$\rho_{Mv} = ns[M/(s + \delta) + X]/NV \tag{5}$$

For the case of M, the two values are

$$\rho_{Xv} = n(M + sX - \delta X)/NV \tag{6}$$

and

$$\rho_{Mi} = ns[M/(s - \delta) + X]/NV \tag{7}$$

Thus, experimental determination of the density and of the volume, V, from x-ray measurement of the lattice parameters, would yield an unequivocal determination of the nature of the defects causing nonstoichiometry.

Substitution of the values 238.07, 16, 4, and 2 for M, X, n, and s, respectively, in Equations 4 and 5, and using Equation 1 to determine V as a function of x ($V = a_0{}^3$), yields for UO_{2+x}

$$\rho_{Oi} = (1793.0 + 106.23x)/(5.4705 - 0.094x)^3 \text{ g./cc.} \tag{8}$$

and

$$\rho_{Uv} = (3586.1 + 212.45x)/(2 + x)(5.4705 - 0.094x)^3 \text{ g./cc.} \tag{9}$$

Using the same values for M, X, and n as above and Equation 2 for the calculation of V, we obtain for the theoretical densities of U_4O_{9-y}, expressed in terms of $UO_{2.25-\delta}$, the values

$$\rho_{Ov} = (1819.6 - 106.23\delta)/(5.4423 + 0.117\delta)^3 \text{ g./cc.} \tag{10}$$

and

$$\rho_{Ui} = (4094.1 - 239.01\delta)/(2.25 - \delta)(5.4423 + 0.117\delta)^3 \text{ g./cc.} \tag{11}$$

If adsorption is negligible, helium displacement techniques yield the maximum measurable density, the "real" density; this value is less than the theoretical density unless the material contains no closed pores—i.e., voids surrounded by material containing no cracks large enough to admit helium. Such voids are normally present unless the sample is composed of particles that are themselves void-free single crystals. Even in the presence of voids, however, a determination of the change in density upon varying the atomic ratio of a given sample will indicate the nature of the defects, provided the void space remains sensibly constant during the variation.

The sharp increase in the densities observed in this study (Figure 2 and Table II) may be due in part to a decrease in void space as a consequence of sintering. However, the greater density of sample S9 with respect to S6 cannot be attributed to sintering alone, since the two samples were made from the same batch of "iodide" UO_2 and simultaneously subjected to the same thermal treatment. Hence, it is reasonable to ascribe the difference to the increase in oxygen content. Moreover, the increases in density upon simultaneous oxidation of S6 and S9 to S6a and S9a are the same, within the estimated errors, as the corresponding increases in the theoretical densities assuming oxygen defects. These observations are consistent with the view that the deviation from stoichiometry in UO_{2+x} is due to oxygen interstitials rather than to uranium vacancies and that in U_4O_{9-y} the deviation is due to oxygen vacancies in the complex U_4O_9 structure. Such a view is supported by the magnetic susceptibility measurements of Arrott and Goldman (5), who concluded that the excess oxygen in UO_{2+x} occupies interstitial positions, and by the diffusion study of Auskern and Belle (6), who found that the diffusion of oxygen in uranium dioxide increases with increasing oxygen content.

Acknowledgment

The authors are grateful to W. L. Korst and G. M. Wolten for assistance with the diffraction work and for helpful criticism in the preparation of this paper, and to R. A. Osteryoung for assistance with the polarographic analyses.

Literature Cited

(1) Ackerman, R. J., Argonne National Laboratory, Ill., **ANL-5482** (1955).
(2) Anderson, J. S., Roberts, L. E. J., Harper, E. A., *J. Chem. Soc. (London)* **1955**, 3946.
(3) Anderson, J. S., Sawyer, J. O., *Proc. Chem. Soc. (London)* **1960**, 145.
(4) Aronson, S., Belle, J., *J. Chem. Phys.* **29**, 151 (1958).
(5) Arrott, A., Goldman, J. E., *Phys. Rev.* **108**, 948 (1957).
(6) Auskern, A. B., Belle, J., *J. Nucl. Materials* **3**, 267 (1961).
(7) Belbeoch, B., Piekarski, C., Perio, P., *Acta Cryst.* **14**, 837 (1961).
(8) Blackburn, P. E., Weissbart, J., Gulbransen, E. A., *J. Phys. Chem.* **62**, 902 (1958).
(9) Burd, R. M., Goward, G. W., Westinghouse Electric Corp., Bettis Plant, Pittsburgh, Pa., **WAPD-205** (1959).
(10) Burdese, A., *Gazz. Chim. Ital.* **89** (3), 718 (1959).
(11) Clayton, J. C., Aronson, S., Westinghouse Electric Corp., Bettis Plant, Pittsburgh, Pa., **WAPD-178** (1958); **WAPD-BT-10**, 96 (1958).
(12) Grønvold, F., *J. Inorg. Nucl. Chem.* **1**, 357 (1955).
(13) Herring, H. Perio, P., *Bull. Soc. Chim. France* **19**, 351 (1952).
(14) Hoekstra, H. R., ed., "Uranium Dioxide, Properties and Nuclear Applications, Phase Relationships in Uranium-Oxygen and Binary Oxide Systems," Chap. 6, p. 251, U. S. Atomic Energy Commission, 1961.
(15) Korst, W. L., Tannenbaum, I. R., Miller, K. T., Research Division, Atomics International, private communication.
(16) Lonsdale, K., *Acta Cryst.* **3**, 400 (1950).
(17) Lynds, L., *J. Inorg. Nucl. Chem.* (to be published).
(18) Miller, C. F., Merton, U., Porter, J. T., General Atomic Division, General Dynamic Corp., San Diego, Calif., **GA-1896** (1961).
(19) Mueller, M. H., Heaton, L., Miller, K. T., *Acta Cryst.* **13**, 828 (1960).
(20) Roberts, L. E. J., Walter, A. J., Atomic Energy Research Establishment, Harwell, Berkshire, England, **AERE-R 3345** (1960).
(21) Rodden, C. J., Warf, J. C., "Analytical Chemistry of the Manhattan Project," p. 67, McGraw-Hill, New York, 1950.
(22) Schaner, B. E., *J. Nucl. Materials* **2**, 110 (1960).
(23) Schumb, W. C., Rittner, E. S., *J. Am. Chem. Soc.* **65**, 1962 (1943).

RECEIVED September 6, 1962. Work sponsored by the U. S. Atomic Energy Commission.

6

Nonstoichiometry in Fluorite-Type Oxides

L. E. J. ROBERTS

Atomic Energy Research Establishment, Harwell, Berkshire, England

The ionic defects characteristic of the fluorite lattice are interstitial anions and anion vacancies, and the actinide dioxides provide examples. Thermodynamic data for the uranium oxides show wide ranges of nonstoichiometry at high temperatures and the formation of ordered compounds at low temperatures. Analogous ordered structures are found in the Pa-O system, but not in the Np-O or Pu-O systems. Nonstoichiometric compounds exist between PuO_2 and $PuO_{1.6}$ at high temperatures, but no intermediate compounds exist at room temperature. The interaction of defects with each other and with metallic ions in the lattice is discussed.

An "anomalous" solid solution, in which lattice points are occupied by ions of unusual charge, is closely analogous to a nonstoichiometric ionic solid, in which the same condition must hold as the crystal departs from the "ideal" formula associated with the structural type. Many studies of solid solutions of oxides, fluorides, and oxyfluorides having the fluorite (CaF_2) lattice have established that the defects characteristic of this structure are interstitial anions and anion vacancies. Some of the systems that have been studied are summarized in Table I; in most cases, the densities of the solid solutions have been measured and have agreed closely with values predicted on the assumption of a complete cation sublattice, sometimes containing cations of two types. It can be seen that the fluorite structure can tolerate large concentrations of anion defects; so long as the x-ray evidence establishes that the structure remains fluorite, the cations must be statistically distributed on the f.c.c. cation sublattice.

Table I. Anomalous Solid Solutions Having Fluorite Structure

Fluorite Phase	Lattice Const., A.	Dissolved Phase	Compn. of Limiting Solid Solution	Lattice Const., A.	Defect Type	Ref.
CaF_2	5.468	ThF_4	$MF_{2.48}$	5.588	Interstitial	(29)
$LaOF$	5.756	LaF_3	$LaO_{0.55}F_{1.88}$	5.816	Interstitial	(19)
ThO_2	5.586	ThF_4	$\sim ThO_{1.6}F_{0.8}$	5.663	Interstitial	(12)
$U_{0.5}Th_{0.5}O_2$	5.524	O_2	$MO_{2.32}$	5.510	Interstitial	(1)
ThO_2	5.586	Y_2O_3	$MO_{1.75}$	5.558	Vacancy	(18)
ThO_2	5.586	La_2O_3	$MO_{1.74}$	5.647	Vacancy	(17)
UO_2	5.457	Y_2O_3	$MO_{1.75}$	5.400	Vacancy	(13)

Uranium Oxides

All the elements of the actinide series from Th to Cm form fluorite-type dioxides, and the series affords an opportunity of studying the nonstoichiometry and ordered "defect" phases characteristic of the structure. To date, the most complete set of results refers to uranium dioxide, and these are discussed first.

Uranium dioxide can absorb additional oxygen at low temperatures, but the true solubility of oxygen in the lattice is low below 300° C. The phase diagram shown in Figure 1 is based upon a number of x-ray studies at room temperature (*3, 9, 15*), one extended to 970° (*14*), and three studies of the equilibrium pressures of oxygen over the oxides at high temperatures. At low temperatures, the stable phases are UO_2, the pseudocubic U_4O_9 phase, two (or more) tetragonal phases which can be represented as slight distortions of the fluorite phase, having c/a ratios of 1.016 and 1.030, and the orthorhombic U_3O_8 phase. The densities of U_4O_9 and of the two tetragonal phases are higher than that of UO_2; the additional oxygen is in interstitial positions, as would be expected. Above 300° C., there is a genuine solubility of oxygen in the UO_2 structure, the unit cell contracting linearly as the oxygen concentration increases. The contraction is undoubtedly due to the fact that the U(V) or U(VI) ion is smaller than the U(IV) ion. Lynds and Libowitz (*20*) give evidence that the nonstoichiometric UO_{2+x} phase also contains interstitial oxygen, a result expected from the behavior of solid solutions (*1*).

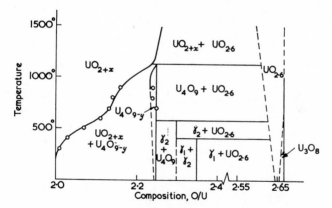

Figure 1. Uranium-oxygen phase diagram between UO_2 and U_3O_8

Reprinted by permission of the editor from *Quarterly Reviews,*
15, 442 (1961)

Thermodynamic Data for Uranium Oxides

Oxygen pressures have been measured from 950° to 1150° by an effusion method (*10*), from 500° to 1100° by a high-temperature e.m.f. method (*5, 22*), and from 1000° to 1450° by direct tensiometric means (*26*). The agreement between the results obtained by these very different methods is, in general, remarkably good. The tensiometric results used to construct the phase diagram from 1000° to 1200° are those shown in Figure 3 (*26*), which show the existence of two nonstoichiometric ranges of composition, UO_{2+x} and U_4O_{9-y}, and of two ranges where constancy of oxygen pressure with composition proves the coexistence of two solid phases—the $UO_{2+x} - U_4O_{9-y}$ region and the $U_4O_9 - UO_{2.6}$ region below 1123°, more properly described as the $UO_{2+x} - UO_{2.6}$ region at higher temperatures. The resulting phase diagram [Figure 1, and Figure 4 of (26)] can be plotted with considerable confidence; the phase boundaries deduced from our tensiometric results agree well with those deduced by Blackburn from effusion experiments with the exception of the O-rich limit of the U_4O_9 phase; we placed this at $UO_{2.25}$ (U_4O_9), since the equilibrium pressures for three independent compositions analyzed as $UO_{2.250}$, $UO_{2.257}$, and $UO_{2.262}$ all fell on the log p vs. $1/T$ plot for the $U_4O_9-UO_{2.6}$ two-phase region below 1200° C. (22, 26).

In a truly nonstoichiometric region, the activity of any component must be a continuous function of composition. This condition was shown to hold for the UO_{2+x} phase by a plot of the partial molal free energy of oxygen ($\overline{G}_{O_2} = RT \ln p$) against x; values of $\overline{C}_{O_2}$ were calculated both from tensiometric measurements (26) and from e.m.f. measurements (5), with excellent agreement between the two sets of results (22). The region between $UO_{2.01}$ and $UO_{2.00}$ has recently been investigated at Harwell and $\overline{G}_{O_2}$ shown to fall very rapidly as $x \to 0$, as would be expected from the low pressure of oxygen in equilibrium with UO_2 and uranium metal (10^{-32} atm. at 1396° K) (21). The equilibrium oxygen pressures were attained very rapidly above 1000° and the pressures measured were independent of the thermal history of the solid. There was no hysteresis; the same values were obtained on heating, on cooling, and on reheating, provided the composition of the sample did not change, as tended to occur at the highest temperatures because of loss of UO_3 gas.

Values of the partial molal enthalpies ($\overline{H}$) and entropies ($\overline{S}$) were calculated from the temperature coefficient of $\overline{G}_{(O_2)}$. The values of ($-\overline{S}$) consistently increased with x in UO_{2+x} and tended to 0 as $x \to 0$; much higher values of ($-\overline{S}$) were obtained for the U_4O_{9-y} phase, increasing as y increased. Values obtained for the entropy change, ΔS, for the reaction

$$UO_{2+x} + \frac{1}{2}(0.25 - 0.25\,y - x)O_2 = \frac{1}{4}\,U_4O_{9-y}$$

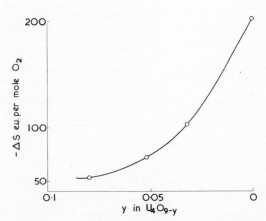

*Figure 2.   Entropy changes per mole of O_2
reacting in reaction*

$$UO_{2+x} + 1/2\,(0.25 - 0.25y - x)O_2 = 1/4\,U_4O_{9-y}$$

reveal that the U_4O_9 phase is highly ordered compared to the UO_{2+x} phase. Accurate values for the entropy change per mole of O_2 reacting (ΔS/mole O_2) can be obtained directly from a plot of ΔG against T, calculated from the measured equilibrium pressures over the UO_{2+x}–U_4O_{9-y} two-phase region. The values are shown plotted against y in Figure 2; very high values of $-\Delta S$ are obtained as $y \to 0$—i.e., as the composition of the product approaches U_4O_9. These values are far higher than the entropy changes characteristic of the formation of oxides (Table II), where 1 mole of O_2 is lost from the gas phase and an ordered crystalline solid oxide is formed from another or from a crystalline metal; such a process is characterized by an entropy change of 30 to 40 e.u. The additional loss of entropy as U_4O_9 is formed from UO_{2+x} can be explained only by a considerable ordering process taking place in the solid. The U_4O_9 phase is then related to the UO_{2+x} by an ordering of the interstitial oxygen ions and consequent ordering of the metal ions; the structure of U_4O_9 has not been reported in detail, but recent x-ray investigations agree that the true unit cell of U_4O_9 is very large (4, 8) which is consistent with the entropy results.

Table II. ΔS (1000° K.) per Mole of O_2 for Formation of Metal Oxides

			ΔS, E.U.
$U + O_2$	$=$	UO_2	-40
$3UO_2 + O_2$	$=$	U_3O_8	-38.5
$Ti + O_2$	$=$	TiO_2	-42
$Zr + O_2$	$=$	ZrO_2	-44
$1.894\ Fe + O_2$	$=$	$2Fe_{0.947}O$	-30.6
$1.5\ Fe + O_2$	$=$	$0.5\ Fe_3O_4$	-35.4
$7.64\ Fe_{0.947}O + O_2$	$=$	$2.41\ Fe_3O_4$	-37

The phase diagram (Figure 1) indicates that U_4O_9 disproportionates at $1123°$ to $UO_{2.6}$ and $UO_{2.244}$, and therefore the disordering reaction $^1/_4U_4O_9 \to UO_{2.25}$ cannot be directly observed. It is of interest to calculate the thermodynamic quantities for this hypothetical reaction, and this can be done most accurately by calculating ΔS and ΔH for the reaction

$$UO_{2+x} + \frac{1}{2}\,(0.25 - x)O_2 = \frac{1}{4}U_4O_9$$

as a function of x. The calculation consists of a direct calculation of ΔS and ΔH for the formation of U_4O_{9-y} from the results for the two-phase region, and then integrating the values of $\bar{S}$ and $\bar{H}$ for the U_4O_{9-y} region from ($^1/_4U_4O_{9-y}$) to ($^1/_4U_4O_9$). The results are shown in Figures 3 and 4; clearly extrapolation to $x = 0.25$ is justified and approximate values for the heat and entropy of "ordering" of $UO_{2.25}$ are -0.7 kcal. and -0.5 e.u. These are reasonable values for an ordering process in the solid phase and may be compared with values obtained for other crystallographic transitions, such as the transition $U\beta \to U\gamma$ which occurs at $1050°$ K., for which $\Delta H = 1.15$ kcal. and $\Delta S = 1.1$ e.u. It seems certain that the tetragonal γ_1 and γ_2 phases represent other modes of ordering of the interstitial oxygen in the fluorite lattice, but equilibrium measurements cannot be carried out at the low temperatures at which these phases are stable and their thermodynamic stability has not been proved.

Solid Solutions Containing UO_2

Fluorite solid solutions containing UO_2 all show the same property of dissolving interstitial oxygen, with a regular change in lattice constant dependent on

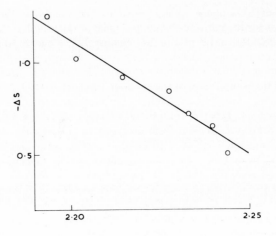

*Figure 3.　Entropy change per mole of UO_{2+x}
for reaction*

$$UO_{2+x} + 1/2\,(0.25 - x)O_2 = 1/4\,U_4O_9$$

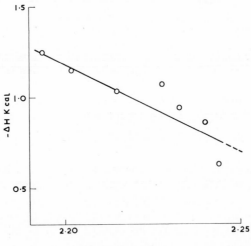

*Figure 4.　Enthalpy change per mole of UO_{2+x}
for reaction*

$$UO_{2+x} + 1/2\,(0.25 - x)O_2 = 1/4\,U_4O_9$$

the oxidation number reached by the uranium ions. The lattice constants of $U_xTh_{1-x}O_2$ solid solutions decrease until the uranium oxidation number is about 5.0, and increase as the uranium is oxidized further (*1*); the limit to the amount of interstitial oxygen which can be introduced has been shown to correspond to the composition $MO_{2.32}$, irrespective of the U/Th ratio. Thermodynamic data for these solid solutions have been obtained by e.m.f. (*6*) and tensiometric methods

(25); the system $U_xTh_{1-x}O_{2+y}$ behaves again like a true nonstoichiometric solid, and there are no signs of the formation of ordered phases like U_4O_9, at least when $x > 0.1$. This is not unexpected, for the complex ordering process involved in forming the huge $(U_4O_9)_n$ unit cell would be inhibited by the introduction of even a small proportion of Th^{+4} ions, of fixed valency, at random in the cation sublattice. Cation diffusion processes, which would be involved in ordering (unlike anion diffusion) are very slow below 1500° (7). Figures 5 and 6 show plots of the variation of $\overline{H}_{(O_2)}$ and $\overline{S}_{(O_2)}$ for the solid solutions $U_xTh_{1-x}O_{2+y}$ of composition such that the oxidation number of the uranium is 4.35—i.e., $y/x = 0.175$—plotted as a function of x. Neither $\overline{H}$ nor $\overline{S}$ values can be expected to be accurate to better than $\pm 10\%$, and it is remarkable that the values of $\overline{H}$ show only small variation until $x < 0.2$, and that the $(-\overline{S})$ values do not begin to decrease sharply until $x < 0.05$. These results, taken together with the variation of lattice constants, suggest that the interstitial oxygen is "trapped" near the uranium ions and reacts strongly with near uranium neighbors; no doubt the principle of local compensation of charge operates.

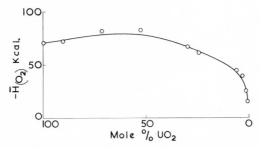

Figure 5. *Partial molal enthalpy change for solution of O_2 in $U_xTh_{1-x}O_{2+y}$*

When $y/x = 0.175$

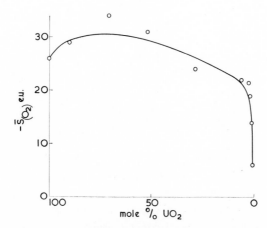

Figure 6. *Partial molal entropy change for solution of O_2 in $U_xTh_{1-x}O_{2+y}$*

When $y/x = 0.175$

Other Actinide Dioxides

The dioxides of the next elements in the actinide series, NpO_2 and PuO_2, do not show the same behavior as UO_2; such "nonstoichiometry" on the O-rich side as has been reported for these oxides has been shown to be due to surface processes of chemisorption (23). The relative instability of the higher oxidation state of Np and Pu, combined with the lattice contraction in going from UO_2 to NpO_2, would lead to the prediction that NpO_{2+x} or PuO_{2+x} phases would be less stable than the UO_{2+x} phase, but the total absence of any such phases is surprising. The Np_3O_8 phase is apparently the stable oxide of neptunium in air below 200°, and the lack of a NpO_{2+x} phase is not due to a simple lack of space in the lattice, for $Np(IV)$ is not easily oxidized even in fluorite solid solutions containing anionic vacancies, such as $NpO_2-Y_2O_3$ solid solutions (24). Further examination of this problem may shed some light on the type of bonding in these oxides.

The protoactinium oxide system, however, shows many similarities to the uranium oxide system. Three cubic, fluorite-type oxides and one tetragonal oxide with compositions between PaO_2 and Pa_2O_5 have been reported (28). Recent work at Harwell on the oxidation of PaO_2 has shown that PaO_2 can absorb oxygen at 200° to 300° with the formation of at least one cubic and three tetragonal oxides between PaO_2 and Pa_2O_5. The structures of all these oxides depend on a small distortion of the fluorite-type cell and the analogy with the tetragonal uranium oxides is very strong. A nonstoichiometric PaO_{2+x} range may exist, but confirmation of this must await a high-temperature study.

"Vacancy" Phases

Solid solutions of the actinide dioxides with the oxides of divalent and trivalent ions follow closely the behavior of similar solid solutions of CeO_2, PrO_2, and ZrO_2. Generally, a fluorite-type solid solution is obtained when samples containing less than 50 mole % of the foreign oxide are quenched from high temperatures, but at greater dilution of the fluorite-type oxide other structures such as rare earth type C or the Pr_7O_{12} structure have been reported, indicating segregation of the cations on to special sites (11).

Evidence of the selective interaction of vacancies with some departure from a purely random distribution is afforded by the nonlinear variation of cell constant with composition in such cases as the $UO_2-Y_2O_3$ solid solutions containing between 20 and 50 mole % of $YO_{1.5}$ (13). No x-ray lines except those due to a fluorite lattice could be discerned in this region, but it is clear that some approach to "ordering" is taking place. Once the anionic vacancies are filled with additional oxygen, making up the complete MO_2 structures, the cell edge varies linearly with composition from pure UO_2 to at least 50 mole % of $YO_{1.5}$ (a composition $U_{0.5}$-$Y_{0.5}O_2$) (2, 24). Hence the two cations must be distributed at random on the cation sublattice and it is the interaction of the vacancies which accounts for the behavior of the "reduced" solid solutions of UO_2 and Y_2O_3.

Yttria can dissolve some UO_2 while retaining the rare earth type C structure, up to a limiting composition of about $Y_{0.94}U_{0.06}O_{1.53}$. This structure, itself based on the fluorite structure, can then tolerate some degree of oxygen excess. The type C form of "plutonium sesquioxide" is in reality a separate oxide of composition about $PuO_{1.6}$, perhaps another example of the same general type. A range of ordered phases analogous to the rare earth oxide phases does not exist between $PuO_{1.6}$ and PuO_2; no intermediate phase is stable at room temperature (16). One more stable phase of composition about $PuO_{1.8}$ exists above $600°$ (27), and there are undoubtedly wide nonstoichiometric ranges of composition at higher temperatures (22). Thermodynamic studies of the $PuO_2-PuO_{1.6}$ system at high temperatures, which are in progress, may explain the lack of many ordered structures in this case, and provide an interesting comparison with the rare earth oxides.

Literature Cited

(1) Anderson, J. S., Edgington, D. N., Roberts, L. E. J., Wait, E., *J. Chem. Soc.* **1954**, 3324.
(2) Anderson, J. S., Ferguson, I. F., Roberts, L. E. J., *J. Inorg. Nucl. Chem.* **1**, 340 (1955).
(3) Anderson, J. S., Roberts, L. E. J., Harper, E. A., *J. Chem. Soc.* **1955**, 3946.
(4) Andresen, Enlarged Symposium on Reactor Materials, Stockholm, October 1959.
(5) Aronson, S., Belle, J., *J. Chem. Phys.* **29**, 151 (1958).
(6) Aronson, S., Clayton, J. C., *Ibid.*, **32**, 749 (1960).
(7) Auskern, A. B., Belle, J., *J. Nucl. Mater.* **3**, 267, 311 (1961).
(8) Belbeoch, B., Piekarski, C., Perio, P., *Acta Cryst.* **14**, 837 (1961).
(9) Belbeoch, B., Piekarski, C., Perio, P., *J. Nucl. Mater.* **3**, 60 (1961).
(10) Blackburn, P. E., *J. Phys. Chem.* **62**, 897 (1958).
(11) Chase, G. A., *Acta Cryst.* **15**, 91 (1962).
(12) D'Eye, R. W. M., *J. Chem. Soc.* **1958**, 196.
(13) Ferguson, I. F., Fogg, P. G. T., *Ibid.*, **1957**, 3679.
(14) Gronvold, F., *J. Inorg. Nucl. Chem.* **1**, 357 (1955).
(15) Hoekstra, H. R., Santoro, A., Siegel, S., *Ibid.*, **18**, 166 (1961).
(16) Holley, C. E., Mulford, R. N. R., Huber, E. J., Head, E. L., Ellinger, F. A., Bjorklund, C. W., Geneva Conference, 1958, paper P/701.
(17) Hunt, F., Dürrwachter, W., *Z. anorg. Chem.* **265**, 5 (1951).
(18) Hunt, F., Mezger, R., *Z. phys. Chem.* **201**, 268 (1952).
(19) Klemm, W., Klein, H. A., *Z. anorg. Chem.* **248**, 167 (1941).
(20) Lynds, L., Young, W. A., Mohls, J. S., Libowitz, G. G., ADVAN. CHEM. SER., No. 39, 58 (1963).
(21) Markin, T. L., personal communication.
(22) Markin, T. L., Roberts, L. E. J., Symposium on Thermodynamics of Nuclear Materials, p. 693, I.A.E.A., Vienna, 1962.
(23) Rand, M. H., Jackson, E. E., personal communication.
(24) Roberts, L. E. J., Adwick, A. G., Rand, M. H., Russell, L. E., Walter, A. J., Geneva Conference, 1958, paper P/26.
(25) Roberts, L. E. J., Edgington, D. N., Walter, A. J., unpublished results.
(26) Roberts, L. E. J., Walter, A. J., *J. Inorg. Nucl. Chem.*, **22**, 213 (1962).
(27) Russell, L. E., personal communication.
(28) Sellers, P. A., Fried, S., Elson, R. E., Zachariasen, W. H., *J. Am. Chem. Soc.* **76**, 5935 (1954).
(29) Zintl, E., Udgard, A., *Z. anorg. Chem.* **240**, 150 (1939).

RECEIVED September 6, 1962.

7

Nonstoichiometry in Metal Hydrides

G. G. LIBOWITZ

Materials Sciences Laboratory, Aerospace Corp., El Segundo, Calif.

The available information on nonstoichiometry in metal hydrides is reviewed. By considering the lattice defects associated with the nonstoichiometry, an equation relating the interaction energy between hydrogen vacancies, the hydrogen content, and the equilibrium hydrogen pressure above a hydride has been derived assuming random distribution of vacancies. Utilizing this relation, the vacancy interaction energies of zirconium and hafnium hydrides are calculated to be 1.5 and 1.0 kcal. per mole, respectively. By correlating these values with those of other hydrides, an inverse relationship between the magnitude of the vacancy interaction energy and the homogeneity range of a nonstoichiometric hydride is observed. The equation referred to is rederived, using the quasichemical approach rather than a random distribution assumption. Comparison with experimental data showed no significant improvement.

The metal hydrides can be divided into three arbitrary types: covalent hydrides, saline hydrides, and transition metal hydrides. The covalent hydrides do not exhibit significant deviations from stoichiometric compositions and are not of interest here. The saline hydrides are those of the alkali and alkaline earth metals, and have properties similar to those of the corresponding halides, since the hydrogen anion can be considered a halide ion. However, they deviate from stoichiometry somewhat more than the alkali and alkaline earth halides.

The transition metal hydrides exhibit such wide variations from stoichiometric compositions that they have often been considered interstitial solid solutions of hydrogen in the metal. This implies that the metal lattice has the same structure in the hydride phase as in the pure metal. That this is not the case can be seen in Table I, where of 28 hydrides formed by direct reaction of metal and hydrogen, only three (Ce, Ac, Pd) do not change structure on hydride formation. Even in these three cases, there is a large discontinuous increase in lattice parameter. The change in structure on addition of hydrogen plus the high heats of formation (20 to 50 kcal. per mole) (27) indicates that the transition metal hydrides should be considered definite chemical compounds rather than interstitial solid solutions.

The nonstoichiometry of the hydrides, therefore, must be attributed to lattice defects such as vacancies or interstitials. The reason for the large homogeneity ranges in these hydrides is the low interaction energy between defects.

Table I.   Structure of Metals and Corresponding Hydrides

Metal	Metal Structure $(38)^a$	Hydride	Hydride Structure $(15, 27, 39)$
Sc, Y, La	h.c.p.	ScH$_2$, YH$_2$, LaH$_2$	f.c.c.
Ce	f.c.c. (a = 5.16 A.)	CeH$_2$	f.c.c. (a = 5.58 A.)
Pr, Nd, Lu	h.c.p.	PrH$_2$, NdH$_2$	f.c.c.
Sm	Rhombohedral	SmH$_2$	f.c.c.
Eu	b.c.c.	EuH$_2$	Orthorhombic
Gd through Tm	h.c.p.	MH$_2$	f.c.c.
Yb	f.c.c.	YbH$_2$	Orthorhombic
Ac	f.c.c. (a = 5.31 A.)	AcH$_2$	f.c.c. (a = 5.67 A.)
Th	f.c.c.	ThH$_2$; Th$_4$H$_{15}$	f.c.t.; b.c.c.
Pa	b.c.t.	PaH$_3$	β-W (cubic)
U	Orthorhombic	UH$_3$	β-W (cubic)
Pu	Monoclinic	PuH$_2$	f.c.c.
Ti	h.c.p.	TiH$_2$	f.c.c.
Zr, Hf	h.c.p.	ZrH$_2$, HfH$_2$	f.c.t.
V	b.c.c.	VH	b.c.t.
Nb, Ta	b.c.c.	NbH, TaH	f.c. orthorhombic
Pd	f.c.c. (a = 3.89 A.)	PdH	f.c.c. (a_0 = 4.03 A.)

^{a} Structures shown are those of room temperature stable phase.

The properties of the nonstoichiometric hydrides are discussed in groups: the saline hydrides, the Group IVA hydrides, the rare earth hydrides, the actinide hydrides, the Group VA hydrides, and palladium hydride.

Saline Hydrides

The saline hydrides do not show appreciable deviations from stoichiometry at room temperature. Lithium hydride, which has been studied more extensively, exhibits a slight deficiency in hydrogen. Since the saline hydrides are predominantly ionic, variation from the stoichiometric composition must involve a valence change, which can manifest itself either as F-centers (42) or colloidal ($8, 42$) lithium.

At elevated temperatures, the variations from stoichiometric compositions become much larger, as indicated by the following homogeneity ranges for some saline hydrides which have been investigated: NaH$_{0.7}$–NaH at 500° C. (3), CaH$_{1.92}$–CaH$_2$ at 800° C. (40), and BaH$_{1.8}$–BaH$_2$ at 550° C. (41). Since these compounds do not consist of ions exhibiting variable valencies [one of the criteria necessary for a compound to be stable over an appreciable range of composition (1)], it is not clear exactly what type of defect would cause the large degree of nonstoichiometry in these ionic hydrides.

Group IVA Hydrides

The cubic phase in each of the Group IVA hydrides has the fluorite structure, so that the hydrides should have the stoichiometric formula, MH$_2$, when all the normal lattice positions are occupied. However, these structures become unstable before reaching the stoichiometric composition, and undergo a phase transition to a tetragonal structure. The room temperature homogeneity ranges of these hydrides are shown in Table II. Titanium hydride also forms a tetragonal phase

(55) at lower temperatures. The reason for the transition from cubic to tetragonal structure is not known. McQuillan and Pesall (31) have suggested that it is due to changes in the electronic bonding mechanism by which hydrogen is held in the hydride structure, and they point out that the onset of tetragonality is probably associated with a loss in mobility of the hydrogen atoms in the lattice. Another possible approach may be the application of order-disorder theory, as has been done for the tantalum-hydrogen system (24).

Table II.   Room Temperature Homogeneity Ranges of Group IV Metal Hydrides

Hydride	Homogeneity Range
Titanium hydride (cubic) (27)	$TiH_{0.9}$ to $TiH_{1.99}$
Zirconium hydride (cubic) (28)	$ZrH_{1.5}$ to $ZrH_{1.6}$
Zirconium hydride (tetrag.) (28)	$ZrH_{1.7}$ to $ZrH_{1.99}$
Hafnium hydride (cubic) (46)	$HfH_{1.65}$ to $HfH_{1.8}$
Hafnium hydride (tetrag.) (46)	$HfH_{1.86}$ to $HfH_{2.0}$

It is extremely difficult to prepare the stoichiometric hydrides. The maximum compositions reached were $ZrH_{1.98}$ (28) and $TiH_{1.99}$ (55). Sidhu (45) has reported on an Hf/H ratio of 2.10. However, this is probably due to an error in measurement of hydrogen uptake. By extrapolating curves of diffusional jump frequency (obtained from proton magnetic resonance studies) vs. the degree of nonstoichiometry in titanium hydride, Stalinski, Coogan, and Gutowsky (49) found an inherent deviation from stoichiometric composition of 0.025—i.e., the maximum hydrogen content corresponded to the formula $TiH_{1.975}$. They attributed this to inaccessible hydrogen vacancies due to either the presence of impurities or edge dislocations. At elevated temperatures, the maximum obtainable hydrogen-metal ratio decreases. In a theoretical study of the zirconium hydride system (discussed below) Martin and Rees (33) found that the maximum hydrogen content decreased with increasing temperature. They explained this by disorder in the parent metal lattice, the degree of disorder increasing with temperature.

The homogeneity ranges of the lower cubic hydrides also change appreciably with temperature. At 550° C., cubic zirconium hydride exists from $ZrH_{1.3}$ to $ZrH_{1.7}$, while cubic hafnium hydride extends down to $HfH_{0.4}$ at 800° C. (9).

Rare Earth Hydrides

From the standpoint of nonstoichiometry, the rare earth hydrides are probably the most interesting. They can be divided into three classes: La through Nd; Sm through Lu, excluding Eu and Yb; and Eu and Yb.

The hydrides of La through Nd all form dihydrides having the fluorite structure (39), with the metal atoms forming a face-centered cube, and the hydrogen atoms occupying the tetrahedral positions. However, they all take up additional hydrogen to approach the composition MH_3 with decreasing lattice parameters but no change in structure. It has been shown (18) by neutron diffraction, that the extra hydrogen atoms enter the lattice interstitially in the octahedral interstices of the f.c.c. metal lattice, so that at the stoichiometric composition, MH_3, all the tetrahedral and octahedral positions will be occupied to give the bismuth trifluoride structure. Korst (20) observed that the lattices of some of these hydrides began to contract at compositions corresponding to $MH_{1.85}$ rather than $MH_{2.0}$, indicating that octahedral interstices were being occupied before all the tetrahedral positions were filled. Additional evidence for this can be seen from electrical resistivity measurements on these hydrides. The hydrogen-deficient dihydrides are metallic conductors. However, as additional hydrogen is added beyond $MH_{2.0}$, these hydrides become semiconductors (*47, 48, 52*), indicating that the hydrogen atoms occupying the octahedral interstices are bound differently than the hydrogen atoms occupying the tetrahedral positions.

Figure 1 shows the resistances of cerium hydride (*6*) and praseodymium hydride (*7*)as a function of hydrogen-metal ratio as obtained by Daou. R_0 is the resistance of the pure metal. After a slight initial increase in resistance, presumably due to the slight solubility of hydrogen in the metal phase, there is an almost linear decrease in resistance in the two-phase region consisting of metal and hydrogen-deficient dihydride. This indicates that the hydrogen-deficient dihydride has a lower electrical resistivity than the pure metal. However, there is a sharp rise in resistance before the stoichiometric composition, MH_2, is reached: at about $H/Ce = 1.90$ for cerium hydride and $H/Pr = 1.85$ for praseodymium hydride. Therefore, it appears that occupation of the octahedral interstices commences at these compositions.

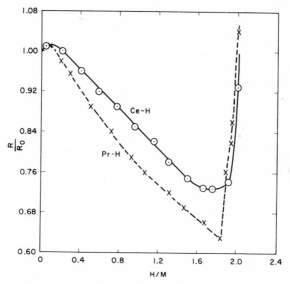

Figure 1.   Electrical resistance as a function of hydrogen content for cerium-hydrogen and praseodymium-hydrogen systems (6, 7)

Since the octahedral interstices become occupied before all the tetrahedral positions are filled, the stoichiometric composition, $MH_{2.00}$, is reached only because there are equal numbers of hydrogen vacancies and hydrogen interstitials (or Frenkel defects) in the lattice. Libowitz (*25*) calculated defect concentrations ranging from 2 to 5% in some of these rare earth hydrides. This is a rather high degree of intrinsic disorder for a stoichiometric compound. The energy necessary to form Frenkel defects (hydrogen interstitial plus hydrogen vacancy) in the rare earth hydrides was calculated (*25*) to be about 12.9 kcal. per mole. From an x-ray investigation of the change in lattice parameter of lanthanum hydride between LaH_2 and LaH_3, Goon (14) has calculated a value of 2.4 kcal. per mole for the energy of excess hydrogen interstitials. If the assumption is made that this energy remains reasonably constant with hydrogen interstitial concentration, the energy necessary to form a hydrogen vacancy is about 10.5 kcal. per mole. This is considerably lower than the 69 and 58 kcal. per mole necessary to form hydrogen vacancies in uranium hydride and palladium hydride, respectively (26).

The second class of hydrides mentioned above (Sm, Gd, Tb, Dy, Ho, Er, Tm, and Lu) also form dihydrides having a fluorite-type lattice and they also take up additional hydrogen beyond the stoichiometric composition, MH_2. However, they do not retain the same structure up to MH_3, but rather form a new phase, in which the metal atoms form a hexagonal close-packed structure (39). The positions of the hydrogen atoms in the hexagonal hydrides have not been reported. They have the stoichiometric formula, MH_3, but are usually deficient in hydrogen. Yttrium hydride, although it is not a rare earth hydride, also falls into this class. Scandium, which also is usually classed with the rare earth metals, also forms a fluorite-type dihydride, and has been observed to take up additional hydrogen to a composition $ScH_{2.027}$, but no hexagonal hydride could be prepared (30).

The homogeneity ranges of both the dihydrides and hexagonal hydrides, as given by Pebler and Wallace (39) and Sturdy and Mulford (51) for gadolinium hydride, are shown in Table III. Although the maximum hydrogen-metal ratio for the hexagonal phase is shown as 3, this stoichiometric composition has not been attained in most cases. The dihydride takes up a considerable amount of hydrogen before forming the hexagonal hydride. Since the lattice of the dihydride contracts with the addition of excess hydrogen, it can be assumed that the excess hydrogen enters the octahedral interstices as in the first class of rare earth hydrides.

Table III.   Homogeneity Ranges of Some Rare Earth Hydrides

Rare Earth	Dihydride (Fluorite Type)	Trihydride (Hexagonal)
Samarium	$SmH_{1.93}$–$SmH_{2.55}$	$SmH_{2.59}$–SmH_3
Gadolinium	–$GdH_{2.3}$	$GdH_{2.85}$–GdH_3
Terbium	$TbH_{1.90}$–$TbH_{2.15}$	$TbH_{2.81}$–TbH_3
Dysprosium	$DyH_{1.94}$–$DyH_{2.08}$	$DyH_{2.68}$–DyH_3
Holmium	$HoH_{1.95}$–$HoH_{2.24}$	$HoH_{2.64}$–HoH_3
Erbium	$ErH_{1.95}$–$ErH_{2.31}$	$ErH_{2.82}$–ErH_3
Thulium	$TmH_{1.99}$–$TmH_{2.41}$	$TmH_{2.76}$–TmH_3
Lutetium	$LuH_{1.85}$–$LuH_{2.23}$	$LuH_{2.78}$–LuH_3
Yttrium	$YH_{1.91}$–$YH_{2.23}$	$YH_{2.77}$–YH_3

The hydrides of europium and ytterbium do not have properties resembling the other rare earth hydrides and must be considered a separate class. Although they both form dihydrides, the structures are not fluorite-type as in the other rare earth dihydrides, but orthorhombic (21) isomorphous with the alkaline earth dihydrides. They are probably more like the saline hydrides in bonding characteristics. In their preparation by Korst and Warf, deuterium rather than hydrogen was used. Both deuterides were slightly deficient in deuterium, the maximum compositions being $EuD_{1.95}$ and $YbD_{1.98}$. The differences between these and the other rare earth hydrides are due to the electronic configuration of the metals. In ytterbium, the $4f$ shell is completely filled, while in europium the seven $4f$ orbitals contain one electron each (according to Hund's rule of maximum multiplicity), so that the electrons in the $4f$ orbitals in both these metals are more stable than in the other rare earths, and they are not as available for bonding. Recently, a higher hydride of ytterbium (53) was prepared under a hydrogen pressure of 20 atm.

It had the nonstoichiometric composition $YbH_{2.55}$ and a fluorite-type structure, and, therefore, appears to be analogous to the first class of rare earth hydrides.

As in other systems, the homogeneity ranges of the rare earth hydrides increase with temperature. The lower limit of composition of cerium dihydride decreases to $CeH_{1.76}$ at 800° C. (50), while the lower limits of the dihydrides of praseodymium, neodymium (35), and gadolinium (51) decrease to about $MH_{1.6}$ at 800° C. On the other hand, the lower limit of yttrium dihydride only goes down to $YH_{1.94}$ at 800° C. (15). The only hexagonal trihydrides which have been studied at elevated temperatures are those of gadolinium (51) and yttrium (15), and their lower composition limits do not appear to vary significantly with temperature.

Actinide Hydrides

Only three of the actinide hydrides have been studied to the point of providing sufficient information as to their deviations from stoichiometry: thorium, uranium, and plutonium.

Thorium forms two hydrides: a dihydride having a f.c. tetragonal structure (44) similar to the dihydrides of zirconium and hafnium, and a body-centered cubic hydride having the stoichiometric formula Th_4H_{15} (56). There is very little information on the homogeneity ranges of the thorium compounds, although it has been found difficult to prepare the higher hydride at compositions above $Th_4H_{14.5}$. From a pressure-composition-temperature study (37) of the thorium-hydrogen system at elevated temperatures, a homogeneity range of about $ThH_{1.7}$ to $ThH_{2.3}$ for the dihydride is indicated at 500° C. The mechanism by which the excess hydrogen enters the f.c. tetragonal dihydride lattice has not been determined, although it probably occupies octahedral interstices similar to the rare earth dihydrides. At 800° C., the lower composition limit of the hydride decreases to $ThH_{1.5}$, while the lower limit of the higher hydride decreases to Th_4H_{13} at 350° C.

Uranium forms a trihydride which does not deviate from stoichiometry to any measurable degree at room temperature, but does so to a significant degree at elevated temperatures (29). For example, at 650° C., the deviation is larger than 5% to give $UH_{2.84}$. The relation between lattice defects and nonstoichiometry in this compound is discussed below.

Plutonium's behavior towards hydrogen is exactly analogous to the second class of heavier rare earth metals. The lower composition limits of the dihydride range from $PuH_{1.88}$ at 500° C. to $PuH_{1.75}$ at 800° C. The dihydride accommodates excess hydrogen up to a composition $PuH_{2.74}$ before forming the hexagonal phase, which has the lower composition limit, $PuH_{2.9}$ (36).

Group VA Hydrides

The body-centered cubic Group VA metals dissolve a considerable amount of hydrogen before distorting to either a b.c. tetragonal or orthorhombic structure. These behave somewhat more like solid solutions of hydrogen in metal than do the more definite hydrides previously discussed. They appear to have the stoichiometric formula MH, but this has never been reported, the maximum being about $MH_{0.9}$.

Recently, higher hydrides of niobium and of vanadium have been prepared by special techniques (5, 32). They both have the cubic fluorite-type structure of the rare earth hydrides. These compounds are discussed in more detail by Gibb (11).

Palladium Hydride

Palladium forms a hydride which, if stoichiometric, would have the formula PdH, and a sodium chloride–type structure, since hydrogen atoms occupy the octahedral positions in a f.c.c. Pd lattice (54). However, the maximum hydrogen content obtained by direct combination of palladium and hydrogen has been about $PdH_{0.7}$. The homogeneity ranges of palladium hydride are $PdH_{0.58}$–$Pd_{0.7}$ at 0° C. (13) and $PdH_{0.34}$–$PdH_{0.61}$ at 290° C. (12). The defect energies in palladium hydride are discussed below.

Nonstoichiometry and Lattice Defects

It has been pointed out by Anderson (1) that deviations from stoichiometry in a compound must be accompanied by defects in the lattice of that compound. The metal hydrides are particularly suitable for studying such defects because of their unusually wide variations from stoichiometric compositions, and because of the ease of controlling the composition of the hydride and thereby the concentration of defects by simply varying the hydrogen pressure.

Assuming that hydrogen entered the metal lattice interstitially, and neglecting any change in structure on hydriding, Lacher (22) derived a relation between the hydrogen pressure above a hydride, and its hydrogen content. The assumption was also made that the interstitial hydrogen atoms attracted each other with some unspecified force. The equation obtained by Lacher can be put in the form:

$$\ln p = K(t) + 2 \ln \left(\frac{\theta}{1 - \theta} \right) + (E_{ii}/kT)(1 - 2\theta) \tag{1}$$

where p is the hydrogen pressure, θ is the fraction of interstitial sites occupied by hydrogen atoms, and E_{ii} is a parameter indicative of the attractive interaction energy between interstitial hydrogen atoms. Good agreement between Equation 1 and the experimental data on the palladium-hydrogen system was obtained.

Rees (43) extended Lacher's treatment, making an additional assumption that not all interstitial sites are crystallographically equivalent with respect to addition of hydrogen. The energies associated with each site differ, and the number of sites of any particular kind available for occupation depends upon the number of the previous kind already occupied. This additional assumption leads to a series of component pressure-composition isotherms representative of the number of hydride phases formed. Applying these equations to their data (17) on the zirconium-hydrogen system, Martin and Rees (33) calculated values of 66.6 kcal. per mole for the energy of absorption of hydrogen atoms in β-zirconium, and 70.4 kcal. per mole, in the cubic hydride phase. Using a value of 6 for the coordination number of the hydrogen sites, the hydrogen to hydrogen interaction energies obtained by Martin and Rees were 0.84 and 1.52 kcal. per mole for the tetragonal and cubic phases, respectively. These values are probably somewhat in error, since the experimental work upon which they are based is in very poor agreement with more recent studies (4, 23, 28) on the zirconium-hydrogen system (probably because of the high oxygen content of the samples used). Kant (19) applied Rees' equations to the titanium-hydrogen system and obtained 63.9 and 0.3 kcal. per mole for the absorption energy and interaction energy of hydrogen, respectively, in the β-phase of titanium, and 66.9 and 1.2 kcal. per mole for the corresponding energies in cubic titanium hydride.

Since the transition metal hydrides can be considered definite chemical compounds, it would be more illustrative to derive these expressions from the standpoint of the hydride phase deviating from stoichiometry, rather than the addition of interstitial hydrogen to the metallic phase. Thus, the deficiency in hydrogen in these hydrides can be attributed to either hydrogen vacancies or additional interstitial metal atoms in the hydride lattice. A third possibility, the substitution of metal atoms for hydrogen atoms in the lattice, can be neglected because of their great disparity in size. Using a modification of the statistical mechanical treatment of nonstoichiometric compounds by Anderson (2), Libowitz (26) derived relations between the hydrogen content of a nonstoichiometric hydride, the equilibrium hydrogen pressure above the hydride, and the temperature. In this treatment, the free energy of the hydrogen in the hydride phase, as computed from the partition function, is equated to the free energy of hydrogen in the gaseous phase. For the case of the deficiency in hydrogen being due to hydrogen vacancies in the lattice, the following expression was obtained:

$$\ln p = \ln p_0 + 2\ln\left(\frac{n}{s-n}\right) + (zE_{vv}/skT)(s-2n) \tag{2}$$

while for the case of additional metal interstitials:

$$\ln p = \ln p_0 + (2/s)\ln\left[(n+\alpha n - s)/(s-n)\right]$$
$$+ (2\alpha/s)\ln 2\left[(n+\alpha n - s)/\alpha n\right]$$
$$+ (z'E_{II}/4\alpha sn^2 kT)[4s^2 - n^2(\alpha+2)^2] \tag{3}$$

when n is the hydrogen content (expressed as H/M ratio) at hydrogen pressure, p, and temperature, T; p_0 is the hydrogen pressure over the two-phase region consisting of nonstoichiometric hydride and hydrogen saturated metal; s is the maximum obtainable hydrogen-metal ratio, presumably the stoichiometric value; E_{vv} and E_{II} are the attractive interaction energies between hydrogen vacancies and metal interstitials, respectively; z is the number of nearest neighbor sites around each hydrogen site, while z' is the number of nearest neighbor interstices around each interstitial position; and α is the number of interstices per metal atom site. Equation 2 is similar to Lacher's equation (Equation 1), except that an interaction energy between vacancies, rather than between interstitial hydrogen atoms, is being considered.

The form of Equation 2, shown graphically in Figure 2, is such that in a definite composition range, there are three values of n for each value of p for $zE_{vv} > 4\,kT$, and only a single value of n for $zE_{vv} < 4\,kT$. Therefore, a critical temperature, $T_c = zE_{vv}/4k$, can be defined, below which values of n between n_α and n_β become unstable. Experimentally, as hydrogen is removed from the hydride phase below T_c, the pressure decreases until a lower phase (usually the hydrogen-saturated metal phase) is formed. With further removal of hydrogen, the pressure remains constant, giving rise to a pressure plateau indicative of a two-phase region. The position of the plateau pressure, p_0, in a theoretical isotherm is determined such that the areas under the curve are equal above and below the plateau pressure, as shown in Fowler's (10) treatment of adsorption isotherms. The value of the plateau pressure corresponds to that of the metastable state at $n/s = 0.5$. n_β is the lower composition limit of the nonstoichiometric hydride. Equation 3 gives curves similar to the ones shown in Figure 3, except that the metastable state of the system occurs when one half the available interstices are occupied, rather than at $n/s = 2$.

In a thermodynamic treatment of nonstoichiometry in hydrides, assuming the solid solution of metal in the metal hydride, Messer (34) obtained theoretical pressure-composition isotherms using relations between the activity coefficients and mole fractions of the components of the solution. By extending Messer's

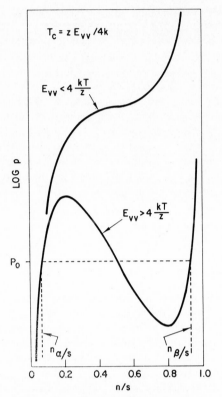

Figure 2. Theoretical pressure-composition isotherms

method to treat lattice defects as chemical species, Equations 2 and 3 were also derived from thermodynamic considerations (26).

These equations were compared to the experimental data on the uranium-hydrogen and palladium-hydrogen systems (26). Good agreement was obtained only if values less than the theoretical stoichiometric values were used for s in Equations 2 and 3. The value of s decreased with increasing temperature, as was found by Martin and Rees (33) for zirconium hydride. This indicates that there are always some vacancies unavailable for occupancy by hydrogen, as observed in the case of titanium hydride by Stalinski, Coogan, and Gutowsky (49). However, their explanation that this is due to the presence of impurities appears unlikely because of the increasing unavailability of vacancies with temperature in these cases.

Since s does not remain constant with temperature, there are two unknown parameters in each equation. An IBM-7090 computer was used to obtain the best value of s and E_{vv} (or E_{II}) at each temperature. Much better agreement was obtained with the assumption of hydrogen vacancies rather than metal interstitials for the case of uranium hydride. A comparison of the theoretically derived curves with the experimental points for uranium hydride is shown in Figure 3. For the case of palladium hydride, equally good agreement was obtained with both assumptions. However, on the basis of x-ray data, it was decided that the nonstoichiometry was due to hydrogen vacancies. The calculated vacancy interaction energies, E_{vv}, were 4.4 kcal. per mole for uranium hydride and 0.35 kcal. per mole for palladium hydride. Using these values for the interaction energy, the energies of vacancy formation could be calculated from heats of dissociation. They were found to be 69 and 58 kcal. per mole for uranium hydride and palladium hydride, respectively.

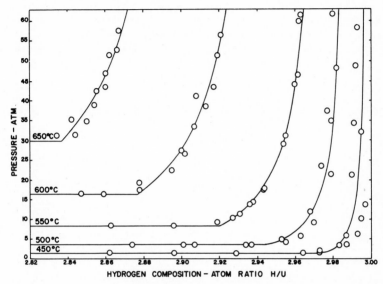

Figure 3.   Pressure-composition isotherms for uranium-hydrogen system

From Equation 2 and some recent pressure-composition-temperature data (9, 28), the interaction energies of hydrogen vacancies in tetragonal zirconium hydride and tetragonal hafnium hydride have now been computed. The assumption was made that the coordination number of hydrogen sites about each hydrogen site was 6, although the structure was not quite cubic (Table IV). The F-sum value is simply a measure of the scatter of the experimental points from the theoretical curve, to be used as a basis for comparison. The agreement between Equation 2 and the data is not as good for these two cases as for uranium hydride and palladium hydride.

Table IV.   Vacancy Interaction Energies

Temp., ° C.	Max. H/Zr Ratio	E_{vv}, Kcal./Mole	F-Sum
	Tetragonal Zirconium Hydride		
600	1.921	1.6	3.8
550	1.942	1.4	6.7
500	1.898	1.4	2.0
	Tetragonal Hafnium Hydride		
	Max. H/M Ratio		
251	1.992	0.9	6.3
272	1.965	0.9	4.0
298	1.961	1.1	1.6
322	1.907	1.1	0.6

Although the assumption was made, in deriving Equation 2, that the vacancies were randomly distributed, the interaction energy, E_{vv}, can qualitatively be considered a measure of the degree to which a compound can deviate from stoichiometry. If E_{vv} is large, there is a greater tendency for vacancies to cluster, and cause a phase transformation. On the other hand, if E_{vv} is small, clustering is correspondingly less, and the lattice can accommodate a large number of vacancies before it undergoes a phase transformation, thus leading to a large homogeneity range. The homogeneity ranges have been calculated over the temperature ranges studied for the four hydrides for which E_{vv} values have been computed. The results are shown in Table V, where it can be seen that on a rough qualitative basis, there is a definite increase in the maximum permissible vacancy concentration with decreasing E_{vv}.

Table V. Interaction Energies and Homogeneity Ranges of Hydrides

Hydride	E_{vv}, Kcal./Mole	Max. % of Vacant Sites, $100 \, (s - n_\beta)/s$
Uranium hydride	4.3	0.8 at 450° C.
		3.1 at 650° C.
Zirconium hydride (Tetrag.)	1.5	9 at 500–600° C.
Hafnium hydride (Tetrag.)	1.0	15 at 250° C. to
		8 at 320° C.
Palladium hydride	0.35	30 at 160° C. to
		50 at 290° C.

Attempts to fit these equations to other metal-hydrogen systems such as cubic zirconium hydride were unsuccessful. This is probably due to the assumption of random distribution of vacancies, which is essentially the Bragg-Williams approach—i.e., the average number of vacancy pairs was assumed to be independent of the interaction energy. Utilizing the quasi-chemical approach of Guggenheim (16) in which the number of vacancy pairs is proportional to the exponential of the vacancy interaction energy, a relation analogous to Equation 2 can be derived in the following manner:

The formation of hydrogen vacancies, $\square_H$, in a metal hydride can be represented by the reaction:

$$H(\text{site}) \quad \rightarrow \quad \square_H + (1/2) \, H_2$$

and the equilibrium constant for the reaction is:

$$K = a_\square p^{1/2}/a_H \qquad (4)$$

where $a_\square$ and a_H are the chemical activities of vacancies and hydrogen atoms, respectively. By regarding the hydride lattice as a solid solution of vacancies and hydrogen atoms, and using the quasi-chemical treatment (16), the activities can be expressed as follows:

$$a_\square = X_\square \left[\frac{\beta + 1 - 2X_H}{X_\square(\beta + 1)} \right]^{z/2}$$

$$a_H = X_H \left[\frac{\beta - 1 + 2X_H}{X_H(\beta + 1)} \right]^{z/2}$$

where $\beta^2 = 1 + 4X_H X_\square \, [\exp \, (E_{vv}/kT) - 1]$, X_H and $X_\square$ are the mole fractions of hydrogen atoms and vacancies, respectively, and z is as defined in Equation 2.

Substituting these expressions in Equation 4 and taking the logarithm gives:

$$\ln p = 2 \ln K + (2 - z) \ln (X_H/X_\square) + z \ln \left[\frac{\beta - 1 + 2X_H}{\beta + 1 - 2X_H} \right] \qquad (5)$$

The mole fraction of hydrogen atoms is defined as:

$$X_H \equiv N_H/(N_H + N_v)$$

where N_H is the number of hydrogen atoms, and N_v, the number of vacancies. From the definitions of n and s as given in Equation 2, we can write

$$X_H = N_H/(sN_m) = n/s$$

and

$$X_\square \equiv 1 - X_H = (s - n)/s$$

Substituting these relations in Equation 5 gives

$$\ln p = 2 \ln K + (2 - z) \ln \left(\frac{n}{s - n} \right) + z \ln \left[\frac{s\beta - s + 2n}{s\beta + s - 2n} \right] \qquad (6)$$

This equation also has the form shown in Figure 2. Therefore, at $n = s/2$, $p = p_0$ and $\ln K = (1/2) \ln p_0$.

Equation 6 was applied to some metal-hydrogen systems which gave poor agreement with Equation 2, as well as to the systems which agreed well with the random distribution assumption. There was no significant improvement, as illustrated by the two cases shown in Table VI. For cubic zirconium hydride, where Equation 2 was in poor agreement with the experimental data, the F-sum values were actually worse for the quasi-chemical approach (Table VI). For uranium hydride, which agrees fairly well with the random distribution assumption, the F-sum values are approximately the same for the two approaches, but Equation 6 gives E_{vv} values which are not as constant and also slightly higher than those obtained from Equation 2. Obviously, a better method of treating the clustering of vacancies must be found. At present, attempts to apply cluster theory to this problem are under way at this laboratory.

Table VI.   Vacancy Interaction Energies

Temp., °C.	Assuming Random Distribution of Vacancies, Equation 2		Using Quasi-chemical Treatment, Equation 6	
	E_{vv}, kcal./mole	F-sum	E_{vv}, kcal./mole	F-sum
	For Cubic Zirconium Hydride			
850	1.91	1.0	2.21	1.1
800	1.68	2.5	1.92	3.2
700	1.13	16.2	1.24	19.3
600	1.03	16.2	1.15	19.1
550	0.86	13.7	0.94	15.7
500	0.82	15.1	0.90	17.5
	For Uranium Hydride			
650	4.4	0.9	5.7	0.9
600	4.2	1.1	5.3	1.3
550	4.3	0.9	5.1	0.8
500	4.4	5.6	5.1	3.7
450	4.3	9.1	4.6	10.0

Literature Cited

(1) Anderson, J. S., *Ann. Repts. Chem. Soc.* **43**, 104 (1946).
(2) Anderson, J. S., *Proc. Roy Soc. (London)* **A185**, 69 (1946).
(3) Banus, M. D., McSharry, J. J., Sullivan, E. A., *J. Am. Chem. Soc.* **77**, 2007 (1955).
(4) Beck, R. L., U. S. At. Energy Comm., Rept. **LAR-10** (1960).
(5) Brauer, G., Muller, H., *Angew. Chem.* **70**, 53 (1958).
(6) Daou, J. N., *Compt. Rend.* **247**, 1595 (1958).
(7) *Ibid.*, **250**, 3165 (1960).
(8) Doyle, W. T., Ingram, D. J. E., Smith, M. J. A., *Proc. Phys Soc.* **74**, 540 (1959).
(9) Edwards, R. K., Veleckis, E., *J. Phys. Chem.* **66**, 1657 (1962).
(10) Fowler, R. H., *Proc. Cambridge Phil. Soc.* **32**, 144 (1936).
(11) Gibb, T. R. P., Jr., ADVAN. CHEM. SER. No. **39**, 99 (1963).
(12) Gillespie, L. J., Galstaun, L. S., *J. Am. Chem. Soc.* **58**, 2565 (1936).
(13) Gillespie, L. J., Hall, F. P., *Ibid.*, **48**, 1207 (1926).
(14) Goon, E. J., *J. Phys. Chem.* **63**, 2018 (1959).
(15) Gschneider, K. A., "Rare Earth Alloys," Van Nostrand, Princeton, N. J., 1961.
(16) Guggenheim, E. A., "Mixtures," pp. 38–40, Oxford Univ. Press, London, 1952.
(17) Hall, M. N. A., Martin, S. L. H., Rees, A. L. G., *Trans. Faraday Soc.* **41**, 306 (1944).
(18) Holley, C. E., Jr., Mulford, R. N. R., Ellinger, F. H., Koehler, W. C., Zachariasen, W. H., *J. Phys. Chem.* **59**, 1226 (1955).
(19) Kant, A., Watertown Arsenal Rept. **WAL-TR-541/1** (May 1958).
(20) Korst, W. L., Ph.D. thesis, Univ. of Southern California, June 1956.
(21) Korst, W. L., Warf, J. C., *Acta Cryst.* **9**, 452 (1956).
(22) Lacher, J. R., *Proc. Roy Soc. (London)* **A161**, 525 (1937).
(23) La Grange, L. D., Dykstra, L. J., Dixon, J. M., Merten, U., *J. Phys. Chem.* **63**, 2035 (1959).
(24) Lehman, G. W., Gehman, W. G., *Bull. Am. Phys. Soc.* **7**, 27 (1962).
(25) Libowitz, G. G., *Ibid.*, **7**, 438 (1962).
(26) Libowitz, G. G., *J. Appl. Phys.* **33**, 399 (1962).
(27) Libowitz, G. G., *J. Nucl. Matls.* **2**, 1 (1960).
(28) *Ibid.*, **5**, 228 (1962).
(29) Libowitz, G. G., Gibb, T. R. P., Jr., *J. Phys. Chem.* **61**, 793 (1957).
(30) McGuire, J. C., Kempter, C. P., *J. Chem. Phys.* **33**, 1584 (1960).
(31) McQuillan, A. D., Pesall, N., *Acta Cryst.* **14**, 1287 (1961).
(32) Maeland, A. J., Gibb, T. R. P., Jr., Schumacher, D. P., *J. Am. Chem. Soc.* **83**, 3728 (1961).
(33) Martin, S. L. H., Rees, A. L. G., *Trans. Faraday Soc.* **50**, 343 (1954).
(34) Messer, C. E., U. S. At. Energy Comm., Rept. **NYO 3912** (1952); **NYO 3914** (1954).
(35) Mulford, R. N. R., Holley, C. E., Jr., *J. Phys. Chem.* **59**, 1222 (1955).
(36) Mulford, R. N. R., Sturdy, G. E., *J. Am. Chem. Soc.* **77**, 3449 (1956).
(37) Nottorf, R. W., U. S. At. Energy Comm., Rept. **AECD 2984** (1945).
(38) Pearson, W. B., "Handbook of Lattice Spacings and Structures of Metals and Alloys," Pergamon Press. London, 1958.
(39) Pebler, A., Wallace, W. E., *J. Phys. Chem.* **66**, 148 (1962).
(40) Peterson, D. T., Fattore, V. G., *Ibid.*, **65**, 2062 (1961).
(41) Peterson, D. T., Indig, M., *J. Am. Chem. Soc.* **82**, 5645 (1960).
(42) Pretzel, F. E., *et al.*, *J. Phys. Chem. Solids* **17**, 232 (1961); **19**, 139 (1961); **23**, 325 (1962); *J. Appl. Phys.* **33**, 510 (1962).
(43) Rees, A. L. G., *Trans. Faraday Soc.* **50**, 335 (1954).
(44) Rundle, R. E., Shull, C. G., Wollan, E. O., *Acta Cryst.* **5**, 22 (1952).
(45) Sidhu, S. S., *Ibid.*, **7**, 447 (1954).
(46) Sidhu, S. S., McGuire, J. C., *J. Appl. Phys.* **23**, 1257 (1952).
(47) Stalinski, B., *Bull. Acad. Polon. Sci.* Cl III, **5**, 1001 (1957).
(48) *Ibid.*, **7**, 269 (1959).
(49) Stalinski, B., Coogan, C. K., Gutowsky, H. S., *J. Chem. Phys.* **33**, 933 (1960); **34**, 1191 (1961).
(50) Streck, R., Dialer, K., *Z. anorg. u.allgem. Chem.* **306**, 141 (1960).
(51) Sturdy, G. E., Mulford, R. N. R., *J. Am. Chem. Soc.* **78**, 1083 (1956).
(52) Warf, J. C., Donohue, J., Hardcastle, K., Office of Naval Research, ONR Rept. **NP-6531** (1957).
(53) Warf, J. C., Hardcastle, K., *J. Am. Chem. Soc.* **83**, 2206 (1961).
(54) Worsham, J. E., Wilkinson, M. K., Shull, C. G., *J. Phys. Chem. Solids* **3**, 303 (1957).
(55) Yakel, H. L., *Acta Cryst.* **11**, 46 (1958).
(56) Zachariasen, W. H., *Ibid.*, **6**, 393 (1953).

RECEIVED September 6, 1962.

Neutron and X-Ray Diffraction Studies of Nonstoichiometric Metal Hydrides

S. S. SIDHU, N. S. SATYA MURTHY[1], F. P. CAMPOS, and D. D. ZAUBERIS
Argonne National Laboratory, Argonne, Ill.

The zirconium-deuterium system in addition to α-Zr consists of three deuteride phases: γ, δ, and ϵ. Each phase exists over a wide range of compositions. The γ phase is tetragonal. The δ phase is cubic (CaF_2-type). The ϵ phase is tetragonal. Its lattice constants vary with composition as it approaches stoichiometry of ZrD_2. The unit cell contains $4ZrD_2$ with atoms in similar positions as in the δ phase. The γ phase retains its structure over long periods of time at room temperature. The $\delta + \epsilon$ region has a finite width. The sizes of interstitial octahedral and tetrahedral voids in α-Zr are calculated and shown to be larger or smaller, respectively, than those of tetrahedral sites actually occupied by deuterium atoms in the deuterides to permit interstitial solid solution.

A systematic diffraction study was made with both neutrons and x-rays of metal-hydride systems in the composition range of 2 to 66.5 atomic % hydrogen of hafnium, titanium, and zirconium, and a nuclear null-matrix consisting of 62 atomic % titanium and 38 atomic % zirconium, with emphasis on the metal-rich regions. A nuclear null-matrix as defined here consists of two or more types of nuclei in which some of the nuclei scatter thermal neutrons 180° out of phase with others, such that the resultant structure factor is zero.

The samples studied were in the form of polycrystalline deuterides. The substitution of deuterium for hydrogen gave the advantage of the higher nuclear coherent scattering amplitudes and lower spin diffuse scattering of deuterium for neutron diffraction studies. The phases formed in any two corresponding metal-hydride and metal-deuteride systems of a given metal are usually the same, although the lattice constants of a phase of the same composition in the two systems are slightly different; this arises from the fact that the lattice of a metal hydride contracts (5) when deuterium atoms replace those of hydrogen. Since the zirconium-hydrogen system is representative of the systems studied here and is of considerable interest to investigators in the field, data and discussion are presented

[1] On leave from Atomic Energy Establishment, Trombay, India, under sponsorship of Agency for International Development.

which aid in determining the number of phases formed in the system, their crystal structures and nonstoichiometric nature, the evaluation of existing concepts of interstitial solid solution of hydrogen in metals, and the mechanism of transformation of metal into a hydride and one hydride into another.

Experimental Procedure

Samples of metal deuterides were prepared from crystal bar purity metals in two ways. In one case the rolled metal strip, about 5 mils thick, was prepared and deuterated as described previously (6). In the second case the metal was filed to produce maximum absorbing surface area. The filings were carefully searched with a magnet to remove any particles from the file, etched by dipping in an acid solution of 40% HNO_3, 5% HF, and 55% H_2O, removed when they appeared bright, washed in running water, rinsed in acetone, and air-dried. The x-ray diffraction pattern of the metal thus treated showed lines of the metal only. The samples were weighed, then heated and outgassed in an evacuated Vycor tube (10^{-6} mm. of Hg) at 1073° K. for 4 hours. The outgassing temperature was below the α-β transformation of the metal to avoid sintering of the filing. A measured volume of deuterium gas was introduced into the tube at 1073° K. and at a known pressure. The gas was absorbed in the range 973° to 1073° K. To assure a thoroughly reacted sample it was cycled three times between 773° and 1073° K., held for 16 hours at the lower temperature, and then cooled at the rate of approximately 1° per minute in the furnace to room temperature. The composition of the sample was calculated from the weight of the metal and the volume of absorbed deuterium.

For a thorough study of the zirconium-deuterium system, several samples were prepared in each of the following composition ranges: (1) 0 to 10, (2) 10 to 50, (3) 50 to 60, (4) 60 to 62, (5) 62 to 63, and (6) 63 to 66.5 atomic % deuterium in zirconium. Neutron and x-ray diffraction patterns of these samples were made at room temperature and repeated for some of the samples at several elevated temperatures to determine transformation or crystal structure changes in deuterides. A few neutron patterns were also made at liquid nitrogen temperature to determine the effect of increased ordering on intensities of reflections. The effect of aging or slow decomposition on deuteride phases was determined by repeating their neutron patterns at room temperature after a period of over two years. For neutron patterns at temperatures below and above room temperature the samples were sealed in vanadium tube holders.

To ascertain identical crystallographic form of the metal before absorption of deuterium gas and after complete desorption, a sample of zirconium was deuterated to $ZrD_{1.98}$ and then desorbed to $ZrD_{0.}$ and its diffraction patterns were made at room temperature.

Results

As summarized in Table I, the results obtained from these studies show that the zirconium-deuterium system, at room temperature, like the zirconium-hydrogen system, contains in addition to α-Zr three deuteride phases: γ, δ, and ϵ. The composition range in which each phase exists, however, differs somewhat from the range of the corresponding phase of the zirconium-hydrogen system as given in a composite phase diagram (Figure 1) by Libowitz (3), and elsewhere in the literature. Other significant differences in the results presented here and those given in the literature are discussed below.

γ-**Phase.** The γ-phase has been reported by Gulbransen (1) and others, and its nature was described (3) as probably being "a high temperature hydride which coexists with β-Zr at high temperature and is metastable at room temperature."

From the published phase diagrams and the description of its nature one gets the impression that either the γ phase does not exist at room temperature or, if it

Table I. Structure Constants of Phases in Zirconium-Deuterium System

Composition, Atomic % D	Phases and Intensity	Phase and Crystal Structure	Lattice Constants	Interatomic Distances, A.	Vol. of Unit Cell, 10^{-24} Cc.	Calcd. Density, G./Cc.
0–10	α-Zr (s) +γ (w)	α-Zr, hexagonal	$a_0 = 3.227$ A. $c_0 = 5.157$ A. $C = 1.598$	About Zr: 6 at 3.181 A. 6 at 3.227 A. 6 at 4.531 A.	46.51	6.51
10–50	α-Zr (w) +γ (s) +δ (m)	γ, tetragonal	$a_0 = 4.586$ A. $c_0 = 4.948$ A. $C = 1.08$	About Zr: 4D at 2.039 A. 4Zr at 3.243 A. 8Zr at 3.373 A. 8D at 3.831 A. 4D at 4.050 A. 4D at 5.019 A. About D: 4Zr at 2.039 A. 2D at 2.474 A. 4D at 3.243 A. 8Zr at 3.831 A. 4Zr at 4.050 A. 8D at 4.078 A.	104.06	5.87
50–60	γ (w) + δ(s)					
60–62	δ	δ, face-centered cubic	$a_0 = 4.768$ A.	About Zr: 8D at 2.065 A. 12Zr at 3.372 A. 24D at 3.953 A. About D: 4Zr at 2.065 A. 6D at 2.384 A. 12D at 3.372 A. 12Zr at 3.953 A. 8D at 4.129 A.	108.39	5.78
62–63	δ (s) + ε (w)					
63–66.5	ε	ε, tetragonal	$a_0{}^a = 4.943$ A. $c_0 = 4.463$ A. $C = 0.903$	About Zr: 8D at 2.074 A. 8Zr at 3.330 A. 4Zr at 3.495 A. 8D at 3.776 A. 16D at 4.063 A. About D: 4Zr at 2.074 A. 8D at 3.291 A. 4D at 3.495 A. 4Zr at 3.776 A. 8Zr at 4.063 A.	109.05	5.79

s = strong; m = medium; w = weak.

[a] Lattice constants of ε phase vary with composition. Values given are for sample containing 66.5 atomic % D.

does, it coexists with α-Zr and the δ phase. Neutron and x-ray diffraction studies and metallographic examinations of the samples in the composition range 0 to 10 atomic % deuterium showed that the γ phase was formed in this range and coexisted with α-Zr at room temperature, as shown in Figure 2. There was no evidence of the δ phase in this range. As the concentration of deuterium atoms was increased in the zirconium metal, however, the δ phase was formed, and α-Zr, γ, and δ phases coexisted in the composition range 10 to 50 atomic % deuterium. The amount of unreacted metal decreased with increasing concentration of

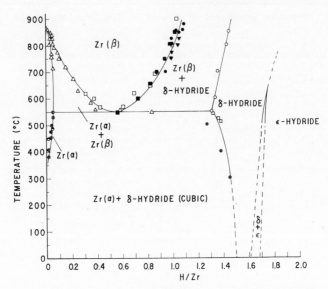

Figure 1. Composite phase diagram of zirconium-hydrogen system

From Figures 1 and 5 (3). Courtesy of Journal of Nuclear Materials

deuterium atoms, and a sample of composition 50 atomic % deuterium consisted mostly of the γ and δ phases and a small amount of α-Zr, the γ phase having maximum intensity. Similar studies of the samples prepared in the composition range 50 to 60 atomic % deuterium showed that it contained mostly the γ and δ phases, and the relative proportion of the δ phase increased as the concentration of deuterium increased. Neutron diffraction patterns of the sample containing γ and δ phases were made in the range between room temperature and 605° K. The pattern obtained at about 523° to 535° K. consisted of a single phase deuteride and a trace of unreacted α-Zr. As shown in Figure 3, *b* and *c*, this deuteride pattern is identical with that of the δ phase, indicating that the γ phase transforms to the δ phase at the above temperature.

Diffraction data obtained from x-ray and neutron patterns for the γ phase are given in Table II. The reflections in the x-ray pattern could be indexed by assuming face-centered tetragonal structure in which the Miller indices are either all even or all odd, but the extra reflections in the neutron pattern of the same sample could be indexed only by mixed Miller indices. The structure derived from these data is shown in Figure 4. Its space group is:

$P\,4_2/n$ with
4 Zr (*c*) at: 　0 0 0; 　1/2 1/2 0; 　1/2 0 1/2; 　0 1/2 1/2
2 D (*a*) at: 　1/4 1/4 1/4; 　3/4 3/4 3/4
2 D (*b*) at: 　1/4 1/4 3/4; 　3/4 3/4 1/4

and for which the structure factors take the following forms:

(1) 　$F_{\text{nuc}} = \pm\,4b_{\text{D}}$ for *h*, *k*, and *l* indices mixed
(2) 　$F_{\text{nuc}} = 4b_{\text{Zr}}$ for indices all odd
(3) 　$F_{\text{nuc}} = 4(b_{\text{Zr}} + b_{\text{D}})$ for $h + k + l = 4n$
(4) 　$F_{\text{nuc}} = 4(b_{\text{Zr}} - b_{\text{D}})$ for $h + k + l = 4n + 2$

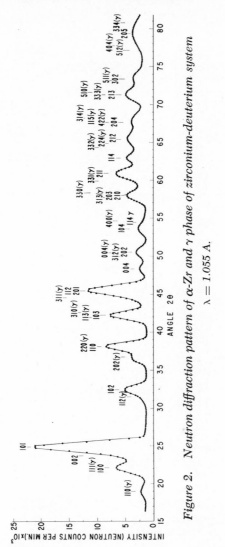

Figure 2. *Neutron diffraction pattern of α-Zr and γ phase of zirconium-deuterium system*

λ = 1.055 A.

where b_{Zr} and b_D are the nuclear coherent scattering amplitudes of zirconium and deuterium, respectively.   The relative intensities for cylindrical samples were calculated from the following equations:

$$\text{For x-rays, } I \propto |F|^2\, m\, \frac{1 + \cos^2 2\theta}{\sin^2\theta\, \cos\theta} \qquad (1)$$

$$\text{For neutrons, } I \propto |F|^2\, m\, \frac{1}{\sin^2\theta\, \cos\theta} \qquad (2)$$

The face-centered tetragonal unit cell can be transformed to body-centered tetragonal in which the lattice sites occupied are:

2 Zr at: 0 0 0;   1/2 1/2 1/2

2 D at: 1/2 0 1/4;   1/2 0 3/4

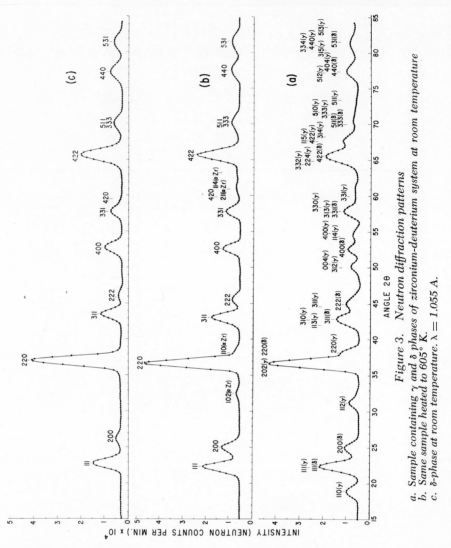

Figure 3. Neutron diffraction patterns

a. Sample containing γ and δ phases of zirconium–deuterium system at room temperature
b. Same sample heated to 605° K.
c. δ-phase at room temperature. λ = 1.055 Å.

and the lattice constants and the Miller indices are obtained by the usual transformations.

$$a_{0_{(B.C.T.)}} = a_0/\sqrt{2} \text{ (F.C.T.) and } c_{0_{(B.C.T.)}} = c_0 \text{ (F.C.T.)}$$

$$h_{B.C.T.} = 1/2(h + k)_{F.C.T.}; \quad k_{B.C.T.} = 1/2(h - k)_{F.C.T.}; \quad l_{B.C.T.} = l_{F.C.T.}$$

Neutron patterns of a sample consisting of α-Zr and the γ phase (Figure 2) and of a sample consisting of γ and δ phases (Figure 3, a) were repeated after about 3 years to determine if γ was a metastable phase which slowly converted to α-Zr or the δ phase during this period. [We have never proposed that the γ is a metastable phase (7).] No such change was observed.

Since the γ phase is formed in the composition range 0 to 10 atomic % deuterium with a crystal structure which differs from that of zirconium, and the lattice constants of unreacted metal are the same as of α-Zr, the correct expression for the reaction between zirconium and deuterium would be:

$$Zr + yD \rightarrow Zr(1 - x) + Zr_x D_y \tag{3}$$

rather than:

$$Zr + yD \rightarrow Zr D_y \tag{4}$$

which is usually given in the literature.

Table II.   Interplanar Spacings (d), Calculated and Observed X-Ray and Neutron Diffraction Relative Intensities (I/I_0) for γ-Phase

	X-Rays			Neutrons		
hkl	d, A.	I/I_0 (calcd.)	I/I_0 (obsd.)	d, A.	$I/I_0{}^a$ (calcd.)	I/I_0 (obsd.)
110	—	—	—	3.242	10.0	10.0
111	2.713	100	v s	2.722	19.0	22.6
002	2.473	19.0	m	—	—	—
200	2.292	30.5	m+	—	—	—
112	—	—	—	1.968	7.8	7.3
202	1.686	23.1	m+	1.684⎫	39.1	44.1
220	1.624	10.2	w+	1.624⎭		
113	1.474	14.5	m	1.471⎫	10.3	10.9
310	—	—	—	1.452⎭		
311	1.389	23.7	m+	1.383	10.7	8.2
222	1.359	10.6	w+	—	—	—
312	—	—	—	1.252⎫	10.5	7.6
004	1.241	1.9	v w	1.238⎭		
114	—	—	—	1.156⎫	7.6	5.7
400	1.148	3.3	v w	1.147⎭		
313, 204	1.093	16.9	m	1.090	7.0	6.5
331	1.057	5.2	w	1.056	3.3	2.5
402	1.040	5.0	w	—	—	—
420	1.026	5.0	w	—	—	—
332, 224	0.985	4.7	w	0.983	12.5	10.5
422, 115	0.947	9.5	w+	0.947⎫	26.1	18.3
314	—	—	—	0.941⎭		
333	0.907	5.0	w	0.908⎫	7.6	6.9
511	0.885	10.4	w+	0.886⎭		
315	0.819	14.5	m			
424	0.790	23.0	m+			

v = very; s = strong; m = medium; w = weak.
$R = \Sigma |I_0 - I_c| \div \Sigma I_0 = 0.065$.

$^a b_D = 0.65 \times 10^{-12}$ cm.; $b_{Zr} = 0.71 \times 10^{-12}$ cm. (experimentally determined recent value); not corrected by temperature factor.

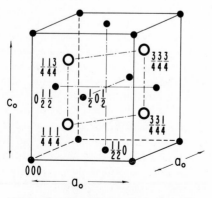

Figure 4.   Crystal structure of γ phase in zirconium-deuterium system

○ *Deuterium*
● *Zirconium*

δ Phase. As seen in Table I, the δ phase at room temperature extends over a composition range of 10 to 63 atomic % deuterium. In the range from 10 to 50 atomic % deuterium it coexists with α-Zr and the γ phase, in 50 to 60 atomic % deuterium with the γ phase, and in 62 to 63 atomic % deuterium with the ε phase. It is a single phase only in a narrow range of 60 to 62 atomic % deuterium. Its crystal structure as derived from the diffraction data given in Table III is cubic, probably CaF_2-type, and the space group is:

F_{m3m} with

4 Zr (a) at: 0 0 0;   1/2 1/2 0;   1/2 0 1/2;   0 1/2 1/2

8 D (c) at: ± (1/4 1/4 1/4;   3/4 3/4 1/4;   3/4 1/4 3/4;   1/4 3/4 3/4)

However, as in the case of a cubic phase in the hafnium-deuterium (6) system, only about 75% of the normal deuterium sites in the above structure were filled and the structure factors for the intensities of neutron diffraction peaks were calculated from the statistical occupancy of these sites.

Table III. Interplanar Spacings (d), Calculated and Observed X-Ray and Neutron Diffraction Relative Intensities (I/I_0) for δ-Phases

		X-Rays		Neutrons	
hkl	d, A.	I/I_0 (calcd.)	I/I_0 (obsd.)	I/I_0 (calcd.)	I/I_0 (obsd.)[a]
111	2.744	100.0	v s	10.0	10.0
200	2.384	48.1	s	0.8	1.6
220	1.683	33.5	m	30.2	33.1
311	1.438	38.0	m+	7.6	7.6
222	1.376	10.5	w	0.3	0.4
400	1.192	5.1	v w	7.0	7.2
331	1.093	16.2	m −	4.1	4.6
420	1.067	15.2	m −	0.6	0.6
422	0.974	14.1	m −	17.4	19.9
333, 511	0.919	19.2	m −	3.6	4.1
440	0.844	8.9	w	6.1	6.6
531	0.808	48.6	s	3.9	4.8
442, 600	0.796	33.7	m	0.4	—
620	0.755	—	—	9.4	10.1
533	0.731	—	—	1.5	1.7

v = very;   s = strong;   m = medium;   w = weak.

[a] Intensities obtained at 185° K.   R = 0.084.

ε Phase. The ε phase extends over a composition range 62 to 66.5 atomic % deuterium. It coexists with the δ phase in the two-phase region of 62 to 63 atomic % deuterium, but it is a single phase from 63 to 66.5 atomic % deuterium, and approaches stoichiometry of ZrD_2. The crystal structure of a sample of composition ZrD_2, determined by neutron diffraction techniques, has been reported (4). The present study, however, covers the entire range of compositions in which the ε phase exists. Neutron diffraction data for $ZrD_{1.76}$ and $ZrD_{1.98}$, given in Table IV, confirm the tetragonal crystal structure previously published. However, as the amount of deuterium is increased in the composition range of the phase, not only the intensities of reflections to which deuterium atoms contribute are increased but the lattice constants also vary. As shown in Figure 5, a_0 increases and c_0 decreases. The relation between the structures of the δ and the ε phases, the mechanism of transformation from the one to the other, and the continuous increase in the tetragonality of the ε phase with increasing deuterium concentration are under further investigation.

Table IV.   Calculated and Observed Neutron Diffraction Relative Intensities (I/I_0) for ZrD$_{1.76}$ and ZrD$_{1.98}$

	ZrD$_{1.76}$			ZrD$_{1.98}$	
hkl (f.c.t.)	I/I_0 (calcd.)	I/I_0 (obsd.)	hkl (f.c.t.)	I/I_0 (calcd.)	I/I_0 (obsd.)
111	10.0	10.0	111	10.0	10.0
200	1.4	1.8	200	2.6	2.9
002	0.6	0.8	002	1.0	1.0
220	12.9	14.8	220	15.4	16.1
202	23.2	25.2	202	27.1	26.8
311	5.4	6.1	311	5.5	5.8
222	0.7⎱	3.4	222	1.4⎱	3.2
113	2.3⎰		113	2.3⎰	
400	5.9	6.2	400	7.1	7.3
331	1.5⎫	4.4	331	1.8⎫	4.8
004	2.4⎬		004	2.8⎬	
420	0.4⎭		420	0.8⎭	
402	0.4⎱	3.2	402	0.8⎱	3.2
313	2.7⎰		313	2.7⎰	
204	0.3⎱	16.7	204	0.6⎱	19.5
422	13.8⎰		422	16.8⎰	
511	2.0⎱	9.1	511	2.1⎱	8.9
224	6.1⎰		224	7.3⎰	
333	0.9	1.0	333	0.9	0.9
			440	3.1	3.5
440	2.5⎱	4.3	115	0.8⎱	2.5
115	0.8⎰		531	1.5⎰	
531	1.5⎫	6.9	404	5.3⎱	6.6
404	4.4⎬		600	0.2⎰	
600	0.1⎭				
442	0.1⎱	2.0	442	0.3⎱	2.0
513	1.4⎰		513	1.4⎰	
424	0.3⎫	8.0	424	0.6⎫	9.6
620	3.7⎬		620	4.7⎬	
315	1.2⎪		602	4.5⎪	
602	3.6⎭		315	1.3⎭	

$R = 0.092$ $R = 0.014$

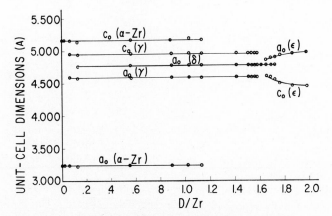

Figure 5.   Lattice constants vs. composition for α-Zr, γ, δ, and ε phases in zirconium-deuterium system

Discussion

The results obtained here show several points of interest.

Interstitial Solubility. The γ phase, as shown in Figure 5, could be observed by x-ray diffraction methods in the pattern of a sample which contained as low as 2 atomic % deuterium, and metallographically in samples which contained still lesser amounts. The fact that a zirconium deuteride with a crystal structure different from that of the metal is formed at a very low concentration of deuterium indicates that the solubility of deuterium in the metal at room temperature is very small, if it exists at all. The reason seems to be this: A hexagonal unit cell provides one octahedral and two tetrahedral voids for each interlayer translation, as given in Table V.

Table V. Interstitial Voids in Unit Cell of α-Zirconium

		Location (2)		*Diameter*	
Interlayer Translation	*Change*	*Octahedral void*	*Tetrahedral voids*	*Octahedral void, A.*	*Tetrahedral void, A.*
2/3, 1/3, C/2	+	1/3, 2/3, C/4	2/3, 1/3, C/8 0, 0, 3C/8	1.336	0.725 0.725
1/3, 2/3, C/2	—	2/3, 1/3, C/4	1/3, 2/3, C/8 0, 0, 3C/8	1.336	0.725 0.725

Unit cell dimensions: $a_0 = 3.227$A.; $c_0 = 5.157$ A.; $C = 1.598$.

The diameter of the octahedral void is 0.4142 a_0 and that of the tetrahedral void 0.2247 a_0, where a_0 is the distance of nearest approach of atoms in the unit cell. With $a_0 = 3.227$ A. for the hexagonal unit cell of α-Zr, the diameter of the bonded atom which can be accommodated in the octahedral void would be 1.336 A. and in the tetrahedral void 0.725 A. The diameters of the bonded deuterium atoms as derived from the nearest metal-metal and metal-deuterium atom distances in the crystal structures of each of the deuteride phases on the other hand are as given in Table VI.

Table VI. Diameters of Bonded Deuterium Atoms in Crystal Structures of γ, δ, and ϵ Phases

Phase	*Nearest Metal-Metal Atom Distance, A.*	*Nearest Metal-Deuterium Atom Distance, A.*	*Diameter of Bonded Deuterium Atom, A.*
γ	3.243	2.040	0.835
δ	3.372	2.065	0.758
ϵ	3.330	2.074	0.818

The latter diameters are either smaller or larger than those of the octahedral and the tetrahedral voids in the metal structure. If interstital solubility were dependent upon the comparable diameters of the voids available in the solvent metal and of the actually bonded solute atoms, then the solubility of deuterium atoms in α-Zr should be as it is found.

Mechanisms of Transformation. As shown in Figure 4, the zirconium atoms occupy face-centered positions in the unit cell of the γ phase. The transformation from the close-packed hexagonal unit cell of the metal to the face-centered tetragonal or cubic structure of the deuteride is the usual transformation for the two structures. The whole groups of atoms in one plane or one direction, in contrast to single atoms, move simultaneously, which accounts for the planes and lines of densest atomic packing in both structures being parallel. A mere shear movement of the atom layers resulting from bonding of deuterium and metal atoms in this case can cause the transformation.

The transformation of the tetragonal structure of the γ phase to the cubic structure of the δ phase takes place when the concentration of deuterium atoms is increased, and also by heating the samples which contained the γ and δ phases to 538° K. The mechanisms of this transformation appears to be this. The atom sites in the two structures are:

γ phase (a) 4 Zr at: 0 0 0; 1/2 1/2 0; 1/2 0 1/2; 0 1/2 1/2
         (b) 4 D at: 1/4 1/4 1/4; 3/4 3/4 1/4; 1/4 1/4 3/4; 3/4 3/4 3/4

δ phase (a) 4 Zr at: 0 0 0; 1/2 1/2 0; 1/2 0 1/2; 0 1/2 1/2
         (b) 8 D at: 1/4 1/4 1/4; 3/4 3/4 1/4; 1/4 1/4 3/4; 3/4 3/4 3/4;
                1/4 3/4 1/4; 3/4 1/4 1/4; 3/4 1/4 3/4; 1/4 3/4 3/4

The structure of the γ phase is characterized by diffraction lines which are indexed by mixed Miller indices, such as (110), (112), (310), (114), etc. The expression for the structure factor is:

$$|F_{hkl}| = b_{Zr}\{1 + e^{\pi i(h + k)} + e^{\pi i(h + l)} + e^{\pi i(k + l)}\} + b_D\{e^{\pi i(h + k + l)/2} + e^{\pi i(3h + 3k + l)/2} + e^{\pi i(h + k + 3l)/2} + e^{\pi i(3h + 3k + 3l)/2}\} \quad (5)$$

and the structure factor for (110) reflection, for example, is

$$|F_{110}| = -4\,b_D \quad (6)$$

The expression for the δ phase structure is the same as for the γ phase when the last four deuterium sites are not filled. As these sites begin to fill—that is, if 1/4 3/4 1/4 site was filled in addition—the structure factor for (110) becomes:

$$|F_{110}| = -3\,b_D \quad (7)$$

and when 1/4 3/4 1/4 and 3/4 1/4 1/4 are both filled it becomes

$$|F_{110}| = -2\,b_D \quad (8)$$

As the other sites in (b) 8 D are also filled, the structure factor for (110) and other reflections with mixed Miller indices becomes zero. The transformation is complete and the resultant structure is of the δ phase. Similar transformation can be produced by heating the γ phase and randomizing the sites occupied by deuterium atoms.

It is apparent that the sites occupied by deuterium atoms in the tetragonal structure of the γ phase, which give rise to the characteristic diffraction lines, are unique. This structure, therefore, is not the same as of the δ or the ϵ phase with only half of the tetrahedral sites randomly occupied.

Nonstoichiometry. The crystal structure of each phase studied here remains the same in the entire composition range of the phase. The observed neutron diffraction intensities, however, vary with the amount of deuterium present in the sample. This means that at least some of the lattice sites were unfilled when the unit cell was formed and are filled later when the concentration of deuterium is increased, except that if the structure of the δ phase is taken as of CaF_2 type, the normal deuterium sites in this structure are never filled. The δ phase transforms to the ϵ phase when the occupancy of deuterium sites exceeds 75%. In general, nonstoichiometry seems to be the rule rather than an exception in these structures.

Acknowledgment

Thanks are due to Melvin H. Mueller, LeRoy Heaton, Kenneth D. Anderson, and Harold W. Knott for help in obtaining experimental data and helpful discussions.

Literature Cited

(1) Gulbransen, E. A., Andrew, K. F., *J. Electrochem. Soc.* **101,** 4 (1954).
(2) "International Tables for X-Ray Crystallography," J. S. Kasper and Kathleen Lonsdale, eds., Vol. II, p. 344, Kynoch Press, Birmingham, England, 1959.
(3) Libowitz, G. G., *J. Nucl. Mater.* **5,** 228 (1962).
(4) Rundle, R. E., Shull, C. G., Wollan, E. O., *Acta Cryst.* **5,** 22 (1952).
(5) Sidhu, S. S., *J. Chem. Phys.* **22,** 1062 (1954).
(6) Sidhu, S. S., Heaton, LeRoy, Zauberis, D. D., *Acta Cryst.* **9,** 607 (1956).
(7) Sidhu, S. S., Heaton, L., Mueller, M. H., *Am. Phys. Soc. Bull.* **5,** 461 (1960).

RECEIVED September 6, 1962. Work performed under the auspices of the U. S. Atomic Energy Commission.

Nonstoichiometric Hydrides

Interstitial-Atom, Proton, and Hydride-Anion Models

THOMAS R. P. GIBB, Jr.

Department of Chemistry, Tufts University, Medford 55, Mass.

Metallic hydrides are usually nonstoichiometric compounds, as expected from their relatively low heats of formation and the mobility of hydrogen. They are ordinarily described, chemically, in terms of any of three models in which hydrogen is considered a small interstitial atom, a proton, or a hydride anion. These models are discussed critically with particular reference to the group V metal hydrides. The interstitial atom model is shown to be useful crystallographically, the protonic model is questioned, and the hydridic model is shown to be the most useful at present. The effect of hydrogen content on the lattice parameter of VH_n and the structural and magnetic properties of several hydrides are discussed in terms of these models.

Only about 20 metals are not known to form reasonably stable hydrides, and this number is getting smaller every year as new techniques are developed for hydride preparation. When one considers the intermediate electronegativity of H (2.1 on Pauling's scale) and the high heat of dissociation of molecular hydrogen, it is surprising that many metals form hydrides exothermically by direct synthesis. The heats of formation are considerably less than those of fluorides or oxides, and hydrogen does not encourage the utilization of the higher valencies of the metals—e.g., TiH_2 is the limiting compound, rather than TiH_4. One would expect the solid hydrides, at least to dissociate more readily than oxides or halides, and to be less ionic and more prone to form defect structures. The latter statement is qualitatively rationalized by the relative magnitude of the entropy term, TS, compared to H in the general expression for free energy.

The hydrides show the chemical and physical properties one would anticipate from the position of the metal in the periodic table and from the foregoing. The strongly electropositive metals of the first two groups give saline hydrides which physically resemble the corresponding fluorides. The transition metals form metallic or semimetallic hydrides, presumably because of their ability to use d or d-hybrid orbitals which are delocalized into a conduction band. Apart from their metallic character, however, there are no unexpected differences in properties between the saline and metallic (or semimetallic) hydrides. The heats of formation, equilibrium-pressure isotherms, crystal structures, molar volumes, etc., of the metallic hydrides are very nearly what one would predict on the basis of the saline hydrides. The observation that a net contraction accompanies the formation of saline hydrides from the metals—e.g., LiH is more dense than Li—whereas a net expansion accompanies metallic hydride formation, does not imply a fundamental difference between the two types, but is merely a consequence of the looser packing of the metals of the first two groups (except beryllium). Uranium trihydride shows a surprising physical resemblance to the metallic-appearing UF_3, and in general the metallic hydrides have many physical properties in common with the comparable suboxides or lower halides.

This paper presents and compares current ideas about the nature of metallic hydrides contained in three somewhat overlapping but basically different models of metallic hydrides, which are referred to according to the postulated nature of the hydrogen as interstitial-atomic, protonic, and hydridic.

Interstitial-Atomic Model

This model takes hydrogen to be a small atom (0.3- to 0.7-A. radius), occupying interstitially (4, 13) certain sites in the metal structure, which are ordinarily a little too small to accommodate it without an expansion of the structure. The H-metal bonding is considered covalent-metallic (43) or resonating-covalent (37). In either case, hydrogen is considered to be more protonic than hydridic, and the arguments given below for the protonic model are to some extent pertinent. A related model in which nonbonded hydrogen atoms are trapped in the holes of metal structure (38) may be mentioned here, but it does not explain the fairly high heat of formation of many hydrides. Any model, of course, must provide a sufficient source of energy to pay for the dissociation of molecular H_2 and the endothermic dilation of the metal structure in forming the hydride. This requirement appears less formidable, however, when one notes that the heat of sorption of hydrogen on metals (41) is frequently comparable to the heat of formation of the hydrides (18).

The hydrogen atom is considered to be spherical, and its effective radius to vary as the logarithm of its coordination number (36, 37). An empirical modification of Pauling's approach has been suggested (12), where the single-bond radius of H is taken as 0.37 A. or half the internuclear distance in H_2. This model rationalizes satisfactorily the M-H distances in both saline and metallic hydrides, but requires some arbitrariness in the assignment of valences and coordination numbers. For the group V monohydrides, the metal valence is taken as 5 and the coordination number as 4. The latter is defensible because of the distortion of the octahedral holes. The effective radius of H is 0.55 A. for CN = 4 and 0.60 A. for CN = 6. On the basis of this model, the structure of a metallic hydride should be dictated by both efficient packing and the nature of the directed orbitals of the metal (1, 42). The model explains satisfactorily the nonexistence of ThH_3 [analogous to known UH_3 (47)] and the expansion of metals in forming hydrides.

It is of interest to note the relationship of the effective size of H on the distension of a *BCC* metal and the symmetry of the hydride. If one assumes occupancy by H of a typical group of octahedral holes, arbitrarily $(^1/_2, ^1/_2, 0)$ and $(0, 0, ^1/_2)$, then the development of a tetragonal structure as a function of the radius of a hard spherical H atom may be calculated by simple geometry with the

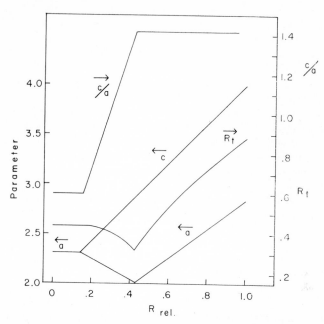

Figure 1. Calculated properties of hydride of BCC metal (atomic radius unity) as a function of radius R of hydrogen in octahedral sites (1/2, 1/2, 0) and (0, 0, 1/2)

Radius of unoccupied tetrahedral site R_t and axial ratio refer to right-hand ordinate

result shown in Figure 1.   If one takes into account the "softness" of the H atom and the fact that an octahedral hole in a *BCC* metal is fitted by an oblate spheroid rather than a sphere, a similar calculation gives Figure 2.   If the tetrahedral holes, one in each vertical face, alternating top and bottom at $(0, 1/2, 3/4)$ and $(1/2, 0, 1/4)$ are each occupied by spherical H, there is a rapid and drastic expansion along one vertical axis, as shown in Figure 3.   The relatively small dimensional changes (usually about 10% on a volume basis) observed in metals as hydrogen is taken up, limit the effective size of R to a value only slightly larger than the size of the interstice.

A preliminary report on the actual variation of lattice parameter with H content indicates the possible relation to the theoretical ideas referred to.   The shape of the graph in Figure 4 (*25*) is at least qualitatively in agreement with the idea that two pairs of opposite octahedral sites—e.g., $(1/2, 1/2, 0)$ and $(0, 0, 1/2)$—are occupied more or less successively with resulting anisotropic expansion, and that before these four sites are filled at $VH_{0.75}$—e.g., in alternate (110) planes—the tetrahedral sites may start to fill rather than the remaining octahedral sites.   Thus, the limiting phase is not NaCl-type, but probably resembles a CaF_2-type.   Figure 4 requires rejection of the oblate spheroid model shown in Figure 2, and renders unlikely the initial occupation of tetrahedral holes according to Figure 3.   The sites occupied by H are chosen arbitrarily for Figures 1 to 3, but they are chosen in such a way that each H is surrounded by the maximum number of accessible vacant sites.   The reason for this is twofold.   In several metallic hydrides, including Ta (*10*), V (*33*), and Pd (*31*), the narrow NMR line (proton resonance here) at room temperature indicates that the hydrogen is highly mobile. It therefore follows that H will favor sites where it can have the maximum choice of neighboring available sites. Secondly, neutron diffraction studies (39), confirmed by recent repetition (15), indicate that in $VD_{0.7}$ the deuteriums are in (110) planes, or at least separated by $a_0 \sqrt{2}$ where a_0 is the vanadium BCC lattice parameter. Several arrangements of deuteriums in a super-lattice are also possible, and these may involve octahedral or tetrahedral sites or both in the original BCC lattice. Until the results of low temperature neutron diffraction measurements have been interpreted, however, further speculation appears not warranted.

There are 42 sites in a BCC unit cell, 24 of which are tetrahedral. If these are allocated to the unit cell by accounting for their sharing with surrounding unit cells, then there are six octahedral sites (three in the edge centers and three in the crystallographically equivalent face centers) and 12 tetrahedral sites per original unit cell. The statistical-mechanistic treatment of a hydrogen-BCC metal system requires that one know the number of hydrogen sites made unavailable by each hydrogen site occupied. It is evident that the ratio of sites occupied to sites available and the differentiation of octahedral and tetrahedral sites are necessary to both the statistical-mechanistic development and any consideration of configurational entropy, heat capacity, lattice vibrations, hydrogen jumping, and diffusion. This ratio may be calculated by a somewhat tedious enumeration based on the relative size of the interstitial hydrogen and on the lattice distension as given (typically) in Figures 1 to 3. The mutual exclusion of sites is a function of the size of the interstitial atom as it governs both the dimensions of the structure and its overlap of neighboring sites. Thus, if the radius

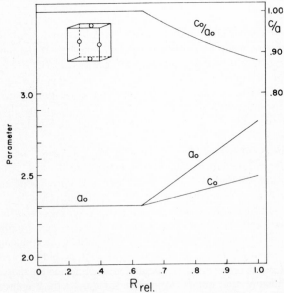

Figure 2. Calculated properties of hydride of BCC metal (atomic radius unity) as a function of major axis R of an oblate spheroidal hydrogen just filling octahedral sites indicated

Ratio of major to minor axis taken as 4.11

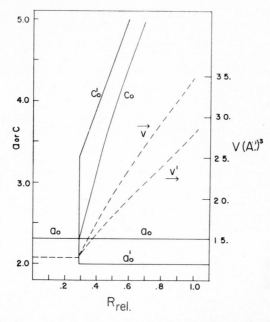

Figure 3. Calculated properties of hydride of BCC metal (atomic radius unity) as a function of relative radius R of hydrogen in one tetrahedral site on face, alternating (0, 1/2, 3/4) and (1/2, 0, 1/4)
Unprimed numbers refer to case where metal atoms are at minimum separation; primed numbers to case of minimum molar volume

of a hard-sphere H atom is 0.3 (relative to the radius of metal atom as unity and with reference to Figure 1) in a *BCC* cell, occupancy of an octahedral site located in a face center prevents, by overlap, occupation of the four tetrahedral sites in the same face. If the interstitial H has a relative radius of 0.2, however, the four tetrahedral sites are still available. It is evident that the statistical-mechanistic interpretation of hydrides must include such considerations.

One might also suggest that the structure of a hydride, according to this spherical atom model, is governed by at least three factors: the shape of the metal-metal bonding orbitals or, more broadly, of the electron density distribution; packing or geometrical requirements; and the availability of neighboring vacant sites. One may argue that site-site interaction (vacancy aggregation) and H—H interaction (proton clumping) are more reasonably interpreted as a dipole-dipole interaction in which the dipoles result from synchronized movement of the two hydrogens to and from vacant sites. The evident mobility of H and the presence of a conduction band of electrons in the matrix suggest that such interaction should be significant.

Protonic Model

The objections to the presence of protons, as such, in metallic hydrides are included as the major portion of this discussion of the protonic model merely to emphasize that while the model may be partly correct; most of the historical reasons for adopting it are questionable. If the model is appraised, however, by its utility, it is found to lead only with great difficulty to such useful conclusions as the prediction of internuclear distances, heats of formation, or gross magnetic behavior. The model does appear useful, however, for the rationalization of the very rapid diffusion of hydrogen in many metals. Hydrogen in a lattice site and hydrogen jumping from one site to another may have to be treated as two quite different entities.

When H atoms penetrate a hydride-forming metal and occupy a lattice site, the over-all process starting from H_2 gas is exothermic. The question is: Which

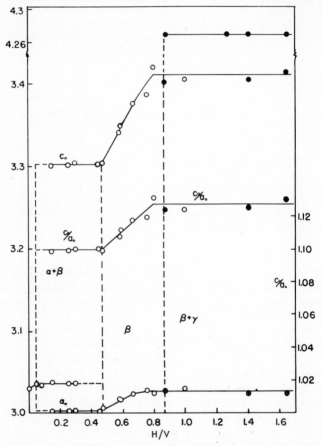

Figure 4.   Lattice parameter (A) and axial ratio for VH_n
as a function of H/V

From data of A. Maeland.

Alpha phase.   Solution of H in V

β-phase.   *Body-centered tetragonal hydride (with reference to*
V positions only)
Gamma phase.   *Face-centered cubic hydride, presumably*
fluorite-type

Vertical dashed lines indicate composition at which novel phase
appears as H content is increased

of two alternatives is more exothermic: to remove, wholly or in part, the $1s$ electron of H and give it to the electron sea of the metal? or to allow the rather loosely held electrons of the metallic sea to center on the hydrogen?   Certainly all of the rule-of-thumb theories, such as electronegativity, screening of nuclear charge, etc., suggest the latter.   However, recent PMR studies, referred to below, may indicate the former.

The protonic model for $PdH_{0.7}$ has been generally accepted since the work of Oxley (*30, 34*), and accordingly, is not described here.   It seems appropriate, however, to look at the older evidence for this model to see if this evidence is unequivocal.

The argument that in $PdH_{0.7}$ the zero paramagnetic susceptibility reflects donation of electrons by the hydrogen to pair the 0.7 unpaired electron in the d-band of Pd is open to the following questions: the strong temperature-dependence of the limiting H content of PdH_n where n approaches unity (actually 0.9+) at low temperature (*21*), and the apparently confirmed (*5, 7*) observation of Michel and Gallissot (*27*) that the zero paramagnetic susceptibility of $PdH_{0.7}$ is due entirely to lattice distension.

The theoretical conclusion of Isenburg (*17*) that H should ionize to H^+ in metals applies, under the assumptions used, only to dilute and undistended solid solutions of hydrogen.   This conclusion may also mean that the field of the proton under these conditions is completely screened by the conduction electrons.   Additional work is needed to show that this condition indeed implies lack of a bound state rather than what amounts to a σ orbital or helium-like distribution of electrons around the proton in an actual hydride.

The electromigration of hydrogen in several metals to the negative end of a filament, as reported by many workers (*16, 46*), need not constitute evidence of predominantly protonic character.   The transport number is very low, and the result is that expected if the current carriers are largely positive holes—i.e., if the conduction is by an electron-deficient mechanism.   The direction of electromigration of metal components in alloys is not attributed to the sign or magnitude of the charge only, but is a function of atomic size, composition of the alloy, and other factors (*2*).   While the experimental work on electromigration of hydrogen has been elegant, it fails to yield definitive evidence here.

Recent work by Gutowsky and Stalinski (*8, 40*) using proton resonance techniques leads them to the tentative conclusion that H carries a partial positive charge in $TiH_{1.607}$ to $TiH_{1.969}$.   The large negative Knight shift of -3×10^{-4} is interpreted to mean that the spins of electrons in the conduction band are paired with the spins of electrons centered on protons.   The line widths below $0°$ C. indicate a rigid lattice, with motional narrowing above this temperature more marked for $TiH_{1.607}$ than for $TiH_{1.969}$.   A much larger Knight shift of the opposite sign has been reported for $VH_{0.66}$ (*33*), indicating the latter to be less ionic.   The chemical shifts for CaH_2 (presumably tending towards $Ca^{+2}2H^-$) (*8*) and $TaH_{0.33}$ (*33*) are negligible; thus the technique does not differentiate the saline hydride, CaH_2, from the metallic hydride, $TaH_{0.33}$.   The chemical shifts for $VH_{0.66}$ and TiH_2 are both negative relative to water as a standard.   Interestingly, the chemical shift for $PdH_{0.66}$ is of opposite sign.

A further piece of evidence indicates that hydrogen sorbed on metals is not protonic, as generally believed; this is provided by measurement of the work function of electrons passing through a sorbed layer of hydrogen (*28*).   Measurements for several metals show that the work function is increased and the initially sorbed hydrogen is therefore negative.   [In the discussion accompanying Mignolet's paper (28) the secondary role of sorbed H_2^+ and the electrical resistance of metal films are stated to be pertinent to the above.]

Hydridic Model

The presence of H^- in metallic lanthanide hydrides was proposed by Dialer (9), and the idea later extended to other metallic hydrides (11, 23). As at present interpreted the model suggests that H is associated with a helium-like configuration of electrons, in a rather low-density electron sea. The metal is considered to be the inert-gas core (or a stable non-inert-gas core) with a localized net positive charge derived from the stoichiometry of the hydride. The remaining electrons of the metal are considered to be in the usual directed hybrid orbitals, whose directions help determine the crystal structure and whose bonding to nearest metal neighbors stabilizes the structure. Electrons in these directed orbitals are sufficiently delocalized to provide a conduction band and metallic or semimetallic properties. [Compare the model of TiO and VO proposed by Morin (29).]

The hydridic model is also naïve, yet it provides a useful rationalization of internuclear distances in hydrides (as does the atomic model), and it permits estimation of their lattice energies. The latter is true only because the calculation of lattice energies by the method of Born et al. (11) works reasonably well for solids which are not very ionic.

The estimation of lattice energies is based on the calculation of the coulombic (Madelung) energy, which comprises most of the lattice energy, to which an additional bonding energy due to metal-metal attractive interaction—for example, as in some rutile type oxides (26)—is added. The latter may be obtained empirically or by use of ligand field theory (11).

The number of electrons available for empirical evaluation of metal-metal bonding has been taken as the Pauling metallic valence less the number of H^- ions per metal. In this connection the valence numbers of Borelius (6) give somewhat better correlations—e.g., in differentiating Pd from Ag (valences ~ 7 and ~ 1, respectively). Heats of formation calculated from the lattice energies by the Born-Haber cycle are not yet sufficiently accurate to be useful numerically, but they provide an interesting rationalization of the formation of many hydrides. This is the principal reason for considering such a naïve model.

It might be said in extenuation of the hydridic model that, according to the ideas of Kimball (19), the H atom should enter a more or less spherical electron cloud representing an unpaired electron associated with a metal atom. Thus, LiH is represented in Kimball's theory as a pair of tangent "electron cloud" spheres, or spheroids, each comprising two electrons of opposite spin centered about a $+3$ and a $+1$ nucleus, respectively. This picture is equally applicable to the hydrogen in CH_4, HCl, or a metallic hydride—i.e., in all cases hydrogen is surrounded by a pair of electrons.

The coexistence of O^{-2} with hydrogen in oxygen-contaminated metallic hydrides is more acceptable if H tends to be negative, and indeed, mutual repulsion of H^- and O^{-2} and the large bulk of H^- help to interpret the exclusion of hydrogen from a dozen or so lattice sites surrounding oxygen as reported by Kofstad, Wallace, and Hyvonen in the $Ta-H_2$ system (20). The crystallographic similarity of suboxides and hydrides may be attributed to the similar radii of the ions (radius of O^{-2} is ~ 1.40 A.)

Of the many difficulties which beset the hydridic model, six are discussed here:

1. Screening of the nuclear charge by conduction electrons. Actually this should be rather small in many stoichiometric hydrides, and one may argue that screening is also neglected in estimating the Madelung energy of semimetallic suboxides, sulfides, etc.

2. The metallic character of YH_3. Certainly if both of the s and the one d electron are removed by hydrogen atoms to form H^-, one should be left with substantially a nonconductor. The conductivity of bluish, metallic-appearing YH_3 is not yet known, however, and only a very small fraction of an electron or a minute departure from stoichiometry is needed to give a reasonable conductivity. In the case of somewhat analogous YbH_2, the infrared absorption spectrum is strikingly similar to that of saline CaH_2 *(14)*.

3. The model necessitates some interpenetration of H^- ions in TiH_2, UH_3, etc. This is true, but H^- with a nuclear charge of 1 and an effective radius of 1.2 to 1.4 A. is a rather tenuous ion and some interpenetration is not unreasonable. Compare the penetration of oxide ions in the 001 planes of rutile, for instance.

4. The size of H^- also implies that H nuclei cannot be close to each other as, for example, in adjacent octahedral or tetrahedral sites in $VH_{0.75}$. This is also a valid comment, but it accounts correctly for the single occupancy of faces in such unit cells by hydrogen, thus eliminating the assumption made earlier that hydrogen tended to surround itself by vacant sites.

5. Bulky H^- should not diffuse or show marked oscillational movement as indicated by magnetic resonance studies. The hydridic model actually provides a reasonable explanation for the mean amplitude of H vibrations (ca. 0.2 A.) and is noncommittal about diffusion. Conceivably, the barrier to diffusion comprising an $1s^{2-}$ configuration about the proton is in effect lowered by the distance of the barrier from the mean position of the nucleus. If the movement of hydrogen is quasitautomeric—for example, in keto-enol tautomerism—one may consider that it moves from one potential well to another as a proton.

6. The long-accepted interpretation of the drop in paramagnetic susceptibility of Pd with increasing H content is not in accord with the loss of electrons by Pd. This objection may be a serious one, but tentatively it is refuted by the work of Michel and Gallissot *(27)*, whose measurements should be confirmed further. Libowitz has pointed out that H^- is more likely to couple metal spins antiferromagnetically by superexchange than any other form of hydrogen *(22)*.

The relation of H content, n, to lattice parameter for VH_n is interpreted readily by the hydridic model as indicated in Figure 5, which represents a portion of a hypothetical unit cell in which H^-, of radius 1.22 A., is located in an octahedral site in a *BCC* V^{+5} cell. The radius of V^{+5} is 0.48 A., both ionic radii being corrected for fourfold coordination *(12)*. The V-H distance is, of course, the same as that given by the atomic model shown on the right, where the metal and hydrogen radii are, respectively, 0.93 and 0.56 A. (see also Figure 6).

A serious limitation of (but not an objection to) the hydridic model is its inability to rationalize the nonstoichiometry of metallic hydrides. The difficulty arises in part because of the use of the Madelung constant (or an approximate equivalent) and a Born-Lande or exponential repulsion term. It is not yet clear how these may be calculated for a defect structure where ions are randomly missing from their sites. It is reasonable that mutual repulsion of outer electrons will be less in such a structure, but no quantitative interpretation has been made.

The ligand field theory has not been applied to univalent compounds of the transition metals, largely because of the paucity of examples. Preliminary treatment by Orgel *(32)* suggests that d-s mixing will provide the large stabilization needed to rationalize the formation of VH, NbH, $TaH_{<1}$, $PdH_{<1}$, etc. This mixing is selective with regard to the nature of the d-orbitals (d_{x^2}, $d_{x^2-y^2}$) and

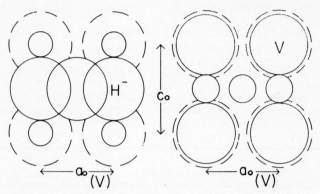

Figure 5. Schematic comparison of geometry of VH_n as
given by hydridic model (left) and atomic model (right)

Dashed circles represent V diameters in pure metal

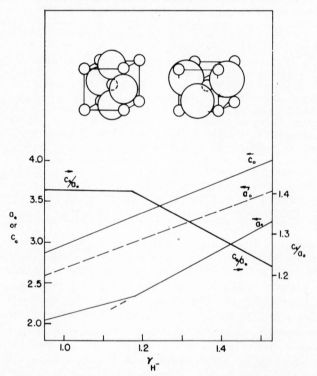

Figure 6. Geometric properties of two hydridic (H—)
models

Structural unit on left represents one quarter of a tetragonal
unit cell with H^- (large spheres) in selected octahedral sites.
Structural unit on right shows occupation of selected tetrahedral
sites (note larger H^-). Corresponding lattice parameters a_o, and
a'_o, are shown for the two units, the latter by a dashed line.
Left-hand structural unit is tetragonal and values of c_o and axial
ratio are also shown. Crystal radius of 0.48A. is assumed for
vanadium ion; abscissa is H^- radius. c_o/a_o ratio is larger than
shown in Figure 4 but is in agreement with Figure 4, if $a_o \cong$
parameter for vanadium metal $= 3.02A.$, and r_H 1.22A.

tends to distort the coordination polyhedron, to increase the amplitude of vibration, and to allow the lattice to accommodate interstitial ions more easily.

The classical interpretation of defect structures includes a rapid electron exchange between identical ions of two different charges—e.g., Fe^{+2} and Fe^{+3} in Fe_3O_4 (*3*), or Ag^{+1} and Ag^{+3} in AgO (*24*). A similar exchange is implicit in the two ionic models of metallic hydrides. The rate of this exchange is thought to be more rapid than the Larmor frequency in magnetite (*3, 44, 45*). A similar exchange involving a neutral metal atom and one of its positive ions is proposed in the hydridic model for metallic hydrides.

Conclusion

Each of the three models discussed has a certain degree of internal consistency which makes one suspect that a rigorous development of any one of them would achieve reasonable success. At the moment, the hydridic model is the most useful, in that it provides approximate lattice energies, but the atomic model promises to be better adapted to the treatment of lattice vibrations and electrical properties.

Acknowledgment

Diffraction data on VH_n were provided by A. Maeland and K. Hardcastle who, with D. P. Schumacher, W. A. Norder, and E. R. Skaw, read the manuscript and made useful suggestions.

Literature Cited

(1) Altman, S. L., Coulson, C. A., Hume-Rothery, W., *Proc. Roy. Soc. (London)* **240**, 145 (1957).
(2) Angus, J. C., Hucke, E. E., *J. Phys. Chem.* **65**, 1549 (1961); cf. their references 6, 13, 14.
(3) Bauminger, R., *et al., Phys. Rev.* **122**, 1447 (1961).
(4) Benard, J., Proc. Xth Solvay Conference Brussels, pp. 83–108, 1956.
(5) Benard, J., Talbot, J., *Compt. rend.* **222**, 493 (1946).
(6) Borelius, G., *Arkiv Fysik* **16**, 413 (1959).
(7) Chaudron, G., Portevin, A., Moreau, L., *Compt. rend.* **207**, 235 (1938).
(8) Coogan, C. K., Gutowsky, H. S., *J. Chem, Phys.* **35**, 110 (1962).
(9) Dialer, K., *Monatsh.* **79**, 296 (1948).
(10) Garstens, M. A., *Phys. Rev.* **79**, 397–398 (1950).
(11) Gibb, T. R. P., Jr., *J. Inorg. Nuclear Chem.* **24**, 349 (1962).
(12) Gibb, T. R. P., Jr., Schumacher, D. P., *J. Phys. Chem.* **64**, 1407 (1960).
(13) Hägg, G., *Z. phys. Chem.* **B 12**, 33 (1931).
(14) Hardcastle, K., Ph.D. thesis, Univ. of Southern California, 1961.
(15) Hardcastle, K., unpublished results from work carried out with R. Ferrier in C. G. Shull's laboratory at MIT.
(16) Hillig, W. B., Ph.D. thesis, Univ. of Michigan; *Univ. Microfilms* **11**, 293 (1955).
(17) Isenburg, I., *Phys. Rev.* **79**, 736 (1950).
(18) Jolly, W. L. *et al.*, U. S. At. Energy Comm., **UCRL 4519** (1955).
(19) Kimball, G., *J. Chem. Educ.* **36**, 233 (1959).
(20) Kofstad, P., Wallace, W. E., Hyvonen, L. J., *J. Am. Chem. Soc.* **81**, 5015 (1959).
(21) Levine, P. L., Weale, K. E., *Trans. Faraday Soc.* **56**, 357 (1950).
(22) Libowitz, G. G., *Acta Met.* **6**, 133 (1958).
(23) Libowitz, G. G., Gibb, T. R. P., Jr., *J. Phys. Chem.* **60**, 510 (1956).
(24) McMillan, J. A., *J. Inorg. Nuclear Chem.* **13**, 28 (1960).
(25) Maeland A., Hardcastle, K., Tufts University, unpublished work.
(26) Magneli, A., Sundholm, A., Andersson, S., Marinder, B., *Acta Chem. Scand.* **12**, 13 (1958).
(27) Michel, A., Gallissot, M., *Compt. Rend.* **208**, 434 (1939); **221**, 551 (1945).
(28) Mignolet, J. C. P., "Étude theorétique et experimentale de quelques problemes d'adsorption," Univ. of Liége, Belgium, 1958.
(29) Morin, F. J., *Phys. Rev. Letters.* **3**, 34 (1959).

(30) Mott, N. F., Jones, H., "Theory of the Properties of Metals and Alloys," Oxford Univ. Press, London, 1936.
(31) Norberg, R. E., *Phys. Rev.* **86**, 745–52 (1952).
(32) Orgel, L. E., *Phys. Chem. Solids* **7**, 276 (1958); *J. Chem. Soc.* (1958), 4186.
(33) Oriani, R. I., McCliment, E., Youngblood, J. F., *J. Chem Phys.* **27**, 330 (1957).
(34) Oxley, A. E., *Proc. Royal Soc. (London)* **101, A**, 264 (1922).
(35) Pauling, L., "Nature of the Chemical Bond," Cornell Univ. Press, Ithaca, N. Y., 1960.
(36) Pauling L., *J. Am. Chem. Soc.* **69**, 542 (1947).
(37) Pauling, L., Ewing, F. J., *Ibid.,* **70**, 1660 (1948).
(38) Reiss, H., *J. Chem. Phys.* **25**, 681 (1956).
(39) Roberts, B., *Phys. Rev.* **100**, 1257 (1955).
(40) Stalinski, B., Coogan, C. K., Gutowsky, H. S., *J. Chem. Phys.* **33**, 933-4 (1960); **34**, 1191–206 (1961).
(41) Trapnell, B. N. W., *Proc. Roy. Soc. (London)* A **218**, 566 (1953).
(42) Trost, W. R., *Can. J. Chem.* **37**, 460 (1959).
(43) Ubbelohde, A. R., *Proc. Roy. Soc (London)* **A159**, 295, 306 (1937).
(44) Verwey, E. J. W., de Boer, J. H., *Rec. Trav. Chim.* **55**, 531–40 (1936).
(45) Verwey, E. J. W., Heilmann, E. L., *J. Chem. Phys.* **15**, 174–80 (1947).
(46) Wagner, C., et al., *Z. Physik. Chem.* **B46**, 242 (1948).
(47) Zachariasen, W. H., *Acta Cryst.* **6**, 393 (1953).

RECEIVED September 6, 1962. Research based on work supported by the U. S. Atomic Energy Commission. Contribution 262.

Solutions of Hydrogen in Palladium

J. G. ASTON and **PAUL MITACEK, Jr.**
Cryogenic Laboratory, College of Chemistry and Physics, The Pennsylvania State University, University Park, Pa.

The heat capacity curves of solutions of hydrogen in palladium of certain compositions are used to throw light on the structures in the palladium-hydrogen system. The warming rate of the solutions after heating has been used to identify two processes of diffusion. A peak in the heat capacity curve at 55° K. is connected with an anomaly in the resistivity for solutions with the hydrogen-palladium ratio greater than H/Pd = 0.5. This connection, together with a change from metallic conduction below this ratio to semiconduction behavior above, is used as the basis for a model which also explains the diffusion processes.

A real understanding of the behavior of hydrogen in palladium (*13*) was not possible until the positions occupied by entering hydrogen atoms in the palladium lattice were established. This has been done by Worsham, Wilkinson, and Shull in reasonable detail by neutron diffraction (*15*). Their work has been extended by Schindler (*11*).

The Model

It is hypothesized that below the composition Pd_2H no corner palladium atom can have more than four nearest neighbor hydrogen atoms, all of which must lie on a line between corner atoms. Only above the composition Pd_2H is the number of nearest neighbors increased and then the number becomes six, the configuration five nearest neighbors practically never occurring below and near room temperature. This applies to any of the phases present. (There are, of course, four ways of choosing the corner atoms, but once the choice is made the system perpetuates itself through the crystal.)

Figure 1 gives details of a portion of the lattice with one possible arrangement of hydrogen atoms in the model proposed for the beta phase based on the neutron diffraction data (*15*). The face-centered atoms are omitted. Each cube of eight corner palladium atoms must have eight and only eight hydrogen atoms lying on a line between corner palladium atoms. The wavy lines with arrows show how hydrogen atoms can be shifted and still obey these rules. Hydrogen atoms are

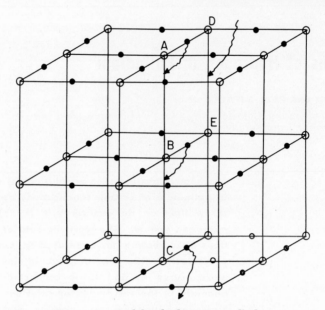

Figure 1. Model of hydrogen in palladium

shifted from between A and D to between A and B and from between B and E to between B and C.

The beta phase consists of a combination of arrangements in which each corner and each face-centered palladium atom is surrounded by four and only four nearest neighbor hydrogen atoms.

In this way the hydrogen atoms define a family of irregular surfaces, each separated by a topologically similar surface containing all the face-centered palladium atoms with only two nearest neighbors. These surfaces cannot cross, although they change direction randomly by $\pi/2$.

For the composition Pd_2H there are no atoms in the alpha phase. We have set the composition 0.5 H/Pd ratio as the limit of the beta phase in accord with the numerology of the model. Consideration of the d-band places this figure at 0.60. However, the hydrogen atoms themselves will modify the lattice and it is difficult to get a consistent model of the beta phase which gives it a composition other than $H/Pd = 0.5$ *(6)*. Obviously the neutron diffraction data require a composition $Pd/H = 0.5$.

At a composition $Pd/H_{0.75}$ all positions between the corner palladium atoms are full. This explains the rapid rise in equilibrium pressure of hydrogen at this composition.

For compositions below Pd_2H a structure is proposed which is formed from the assembly described above by removing the required number of hydrogen atoms at random. If this is done completely at random, the assembly is not at equilibrium because of the energetics of the system.

Above the composition Pd_2H hydrogen atoms go into positions in the irregular surfaces which have been assigned to the face-centered palladium atoms and which below this composition contain no hydrogen atoms. This produces configurations which can no longer be thought of as the beta phase.

The alpha phase consists of hydrogen in any parts of the lattice other than described above. Therefore, each corner palladium atom in the alpha phase cannot have more than three nearest neighbor hydrogen atoms and therefore no alpha can exist between beta-phase surfaces. Thus the alpha phase is possible only for compositions below Pd_2H (except at high temperatures). At room temperature the composition of the alpha phase corresponds to a H/Pd ratio of less than 0.04, according to the data of Worsham, Wilkinson, and Shull (*15*).

General Thermodynamic Properties of Lattice

Neglecting the face-centered atoms and considering hydrogen bonding between corner palladium atoms, it is obvious that the model of the beta phase ($H/Pd = 0.5$) is numerologically analogous to that for ice. This should give rise to a zero point entropy of $R \ln 3/2$ (equal to 0.82 cal. deg.$^{-1}$ mole^{-1}) for each unit (*10*) containing three face-centered and one corner palladium along with two hydrogen atoms (Pd_4H_2). The experimental value found was 1.16 ± 0.36 cal. deg.$^{-1}$ mole^{-1} (*7*).

At low temperatures the hydrogen atoms in a hydrogen-palladium system would be expected to form a Debye sublattice, but at higher temperatures when the well known, but little understood, diffusion processes set in, heat capacities characteristic of hindered translation for the hydrogen atoms might be expected. Rapid cooling of a mobile system of hydrogen atoms would be expected to produce nonequilibrium conditions. Experimentally the system does behave somewhat as expected, but some unusual consequences of this situation became evident only after the experimental observations.

The Heat Capacity Results

Figure 2, *A*, represents the experimental heat capacity data in the temperature range between 20° and 360° K. for H_2 in Pd_4H_2—i.e., Pd_4H_2 minus the heat capacity of the palladium atoms in palladium black (*7*) and block palladium (*5*). In Figure 2, *B*, *C*, and *D* represent the similarly calculated experimental contributions for H_2 in the other samples studied which had H/Pd ratios of 0.75, 0.25, and 0.125. Above 120° K. the results for palladium black are noticeably different from all of the others. This is apparently due to the fact that in palladium black, owing to the smallness of the particles, the lattice is somewhat more mobile. In Figure 3 all the experimental contributions of two hydrogen atoms to the heat capacity for alloys of compositions $H/Pd = 0.75, 0.50, 0.25$, and 0.125 are plotted between 35° and 85° K. (*5*). All the points lie on a single curve, within experimental error. Such a situation is difficult to conceive unless the hydrogens are similarly located with respect to each other in all samples.

Thus for compositions up to 0.50 H/Pd a single phase is involved. This is evidently the beta phase. The fact that the heat capacity per mole of hydrogen at any temperature is the same below a H/Pd ratio of 0.75 is, at first glance, somewhat startling. It can only mean that here the hydrogens are in surfaces of the beta phase which cross the surface of the beta phase at right angles and are behaving in the same manner. This automatically limits the choice of a mechanical situation which will explain the data. Any order-disorder process, in the usual sense of the term, is unlikely, since such a mechanical situation would be expected to give heat capacities which would be concentration-dependent. The hydrogen atoms must form a second Debye lattice of torsional modes of the type proposed originally to explain the heat capacities below the peak (*8*).

In Figure 4, *A* gives a graph of the contribution due to three torsional Debye modes with $\theta = 200°$ K., while *B* represents the heat capacity contribution of three hindered rotational degrees of freedom with:

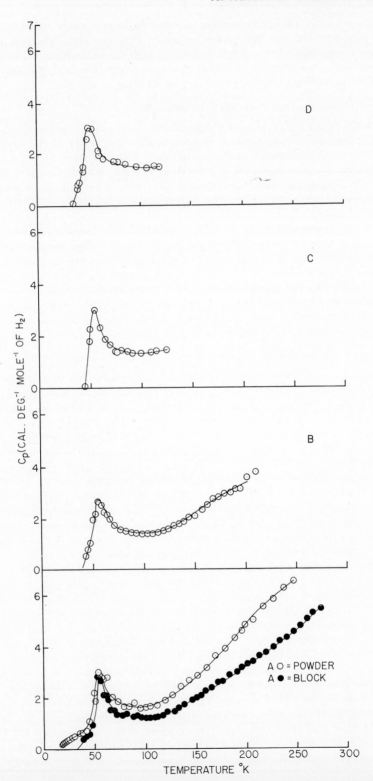

$$V = 390(1 - \cos 3\varphi)/2 \qquad (1)$$

This assumption is made arbitrarily to fit the maximum in the heat capacity curve. Rotation of four hydrogens is required to get the right heat capacity at the maximum. Curve C of Figure 4 represents the Debye lattice contribution of the

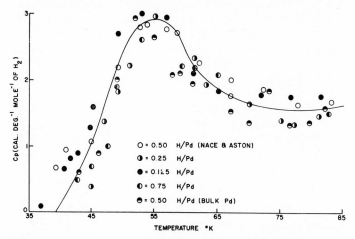

Figure 3.   *Experimental heat capacity of a mole of hydrogen in block palladium samples of ratio 0.75, 0.50, 0.25, and 0.125 H/Pd and palladium powder sample of 0.50 H/Pd ratio between 35° and 85° K.*

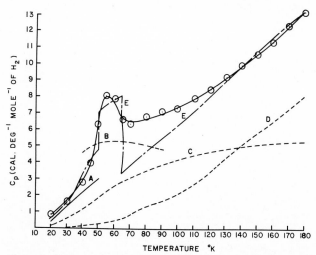

Figure 4.   *Experimental and calculated C_p of PdH_4 model from 10° to 180° K.*

◀   Figure 2.   *Experimental heat capacity of a mole of hydrogen*

   A. *In powder and block samples of 0.50 H/Pd ratio*
   B. *In block palladium sample of 0.75 H/Pd ratio*
   C. *In block palladium sample of 0.25 H/Pd ratio*
   D. *In block palladium sample of 0.125 H/Pd ratio*

motions of the centers of gravity with $\theta = 275°$ K., which is the experimental value for pure palladium, while D represents the heat capacity of a Debye lattice containing 4 gram atoms of hydrogen, each with three translational degrees of freedom (12 degrees of freedom in all) with $\theta = 950°$ K.

The points in Figure 4 are the corresponding experimental values for H/Pd = 0.5 in palladium black in the temperature region 10° to 180° K. These points were calculated on the basis of PdH_4 by adding the experimental heat capacity of one palladium atom to the experimental heat capacity contribution of four hydrogen atoms in Pd_2H (palladium black) (8).

The dashed curve, E, below 50° K. is the sum of curves A and C; between 50° and 65° K. it is the sum of curves B and C. Up to 50° K., it is assumed that the hydrogen atoms oscillate cooperatively in groups of four about an axis perpendicular to the surfaces and about two mutually perpendicular axes in the surfaces as a Debye sublattice. The group of four hydrogen atoms also suffers translational motion along with the palladium atoms and, being of negligible mass, does not change the θ for the palladium. In the unit PdH_4, with 15 degrees of freedom, three go to the palladium Debye lattice and three to the torsional Debye lattice of the hydrogen. The remainder are unexcited vibrations. Between 50° and 65° K., the cooperation is broken and it is assumed that at first each group forms a three-dimensional hindered rotor with a barrier of 390 cal. about each axis.

Between 65° and 180° K, the dashed curve, E, is the sum of C and D. This assumes that after the cooperative transition the hydrogen atoms are hindered translators. The barrier is sufficiently high that the effective motion is vibration in a Debye sublattice. Figure 5 gives a theoretical curve calculated in a similar manner between 100° and 300° K. In this case the curve is calculated on the

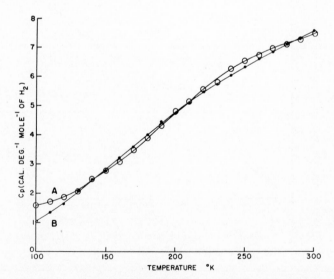

Figure 5. Heat capacity of a mole of hydrogen in 0.50 H/Pd ratio, powder sample, and calculated C_p

$\theta = 950°$ K. from 100° to 300° K.

A. Calculated
B. Experimental

basis of two hydrogen atoms—i.e., the Debye contribution for the accompanying four palladium atoms is omitted. The experimental points are accordingly twice the measured values for Pd_2H, from which the contributions of the four palladium atoms have been subtracted (7). This mode of plotting is employed to demonstrate that above 65° K., the mechanical situation is different from that below.

In the system deuterium-palladium with D/Pd = 0.5, it is obvious that the heat capacities should be fitted by a similar curve with θ equal to the value for hydrogen divided by $\sqrt{2}$. Figure 6 gives the heat capacities calculated for the contribution of two deuterium atoms to the heat capacity of Pd_2D along with the experimental points between 20° and 300° K. (7). The experimental points below 100° K., are included to show the peak which is shifted to higher temperatures. Such a behavior has been noticed for the transition in deuteromethane (3) when the peak splits into two parts. Since no good explanation has been given for this behavior, obviously none can be attempted for the PdD_4 unit, which is square planar.

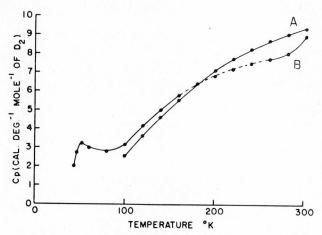

Figure 6.   Experimental and calculated C_p of deuterium from 20° to 300° K.

A. Calculated
B. Experimental

Diffusion Processes

Between 105° and 200° K. warm drifts in the calorimeter were noted for samples with H/Pd = 0.125 and 0.25, after a period when equilibrium was usually obtained. Similarly, drifts in the calorimeter were noted in the region 200° to 250° K. for the same samples and also for the sample with H/Pd = 0.75. This is due to some process in which hydrogen migrates from one part of the lattice to another. It is concluded that the process occurring at the lower temperature is diffusion of hydrogen from one lattice point to another lattice point in a neighboring face-centered unit—i.e., in a unit with six face-centered atoms. The process occurring at the higher temperature is long-range diffusion to a unit farther away.

In all cases where the warm drift was studied, the calorimeter had been quickly quenched. It can then be assumed that the system is sufficiently far away from equilibrium that, during the process of observing the drifts at various temperatures, as the temperature of the calorimeter is raised, no appreciable change in the concentration in the various regions has occurred. In such a case, the time rate of change of concentration is proportional to the rate constant, since, where C is the concentration of the disappearing species:

$$\frac{dC}{dt} = -kC^n \text{ (with } C \text{ practically constant)} \tag{2}$$

The time rate of heat evolution is proportional to the time rate of change of concentration and, therefore, to the rate constant. Figure 7 gives a graph of the log of the rate of heat evolution against the reciprocal of absolute temperature in the region between 150° and 200° K. for the composition H/Pd = 0.125 and between 200° and 250° K. for the compositions H/Pd = 0.125 and 0.75. In all cases there are at least three points on the graph. If, during any runs, the system has progressed to equilibrium to an appreciable extent, these graphs would obviously not be straight lines.

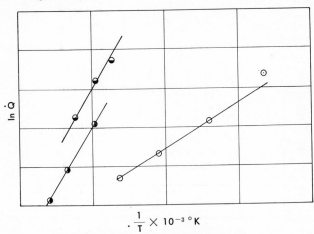

Figure 7.   Reciprocal of T vs. ln rate of heat evolution to give activation energies for three samples

    ○   *0.125 H/Pd from 150° to 200° K.*
    ◑   *0.125 H/Pd from 200° to 250° K.*
    ◒   *0.75 H/Pd from 200 ° to 250° K.*

Table I summarizes the activation energies obtained from the slope of these graphs using Equation 3 where $\dot{Q}$ is the time rate of heat evolution.

$$\frac{d \ln k}{dT} = \frac{d \ln \dot{Q}}{dT} = \frac{\Delta E}{RT^2} \tag{3}$$

Table I.   Energies of Activation for Diffusion Processes

(Kcal.)

	H/Pd			
Range, °K.	*0.125*	*0.25*	*0.50*	*0.75*
150–200	2.9	2.9	No drift	No drift
200–250	6.5	6.4	No drift	5.5

The activation energy for the process occurring at the lower temperatures is 2.9 kcal. per atomic mole of hydrogen. This process was not evident in the heat capacity determination for H/Pd = 0.50 and 0.75. There is an obvious reason for this. In the composition H/Pd = 0.5 there are no vacancies in the surfaces. No matter how rapidly the system is cooled, it will therefore always be in equilibrium with respect to any process of diffusion in the surfaces. For H/Pd ratios below 0.5, where there are vacancies in the surfaces, as can occur at temperatures above about 150° K., rapid cooling does not allow these vacancies to be filled.

The activation energy for the process occurring between 200° and 250° K. is 6.4 kcal. This process is associated with long-range diffusion. It seems curious at first sight that no drifts in this region were noted for the composition H/Pd = 0.50 while they were observed above this composition, yet above H/Pd = 0.5, there were no drifts in the low temperature region. As the composition goes above H/Pd = 0.50, positions between the surfaces are filled and the energy liberated in this process is apparently much lower than for the corresponding process in the surfaces.

To explain the results it must be assumed that the extra resonance energy gained in forming continuous cross surfaces is necessary to overcome the extra repulsive energy. Thus there are no vacancies in the cross surfaces and no drift toward the equilibrium can be observed for the cell to cell process of low activation energy. For the long-range diffusion process, the situation is obviously different. As the temperature is raised, some of the units in the lattice in which face-centered units have every position between the corner hydrogens filled, will become smaller because equilibrium will be shifted in the direction of units of higher surface (surface tension effect). As the temperature is lowered, these units will tend to become larger by a diffusion-controlled rate process. If a sample is rapidly chilled, equilibrium in this process is frozen and as it returns to its equilibrium gives rise to the observed drift.

This explanation assumes that units with vacancies in the face-centered units above H/Pd = 0.5 have insufficient attractive energy for hydrogen to overcome the repulsive forces—e.g., as a liquid is formed in continuous spherical drops when it is condensed from the saturated vapor.

The activation energy for long-range diffusion is roughly the same as the measured activation energy (6 to 8 kcal.) for the diffusion of hydrogen through palladium (*1*), as it should be. A value of 5300 cal. was measured by NMR line narrowing for the process by Burger, Poulis, and Hass (*2*). Spalthoff (*14*) gave an activation energy of 2300 cal. at 115° K., which is obviously for the cell to neighboring cell diffusion. The early NMR work of Norberg is also in agreement (*9*).

Electrical Resistivity

Figure 8 is a graph of the electrical resistivity between 35° and 85° K. for hydrogen-palladium alloys of composition H/Pd = 0.48, H/Pd = 0.54, and H/Pd = 0.60, taken from the data of Schindler, Smith, and Kramer (*12*). On the same graph are included the best curve fitting and heat capacity data. There is little doubt that the change in behavior from that of almost metallic conduction below the ratio H/Pd = 0.5 to the behavior of a semiconductor above this ratio is connected with hydrogen atoms between the surfaces. Above this composition, hydrogen atoms go between corner palladium atoms, between the surfaces in positions completely vacant below this composition. It also seems reasonable to believe that the peak in the electrical resistivity for H/Pd = 0.6 is connected with

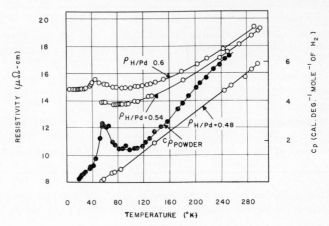

*Figure 8. Resistivity and heat capacity vs. temperature
for samples of hydrogen in palladium*

the peak in the heat capacity curve and is due to a change in the behavior of the
phonons below the temperature of the heat capacity peak.

Hysteresis

On attempting to remove hydrogen from hydrogen-palladium alloys with
H/Pd ratios between 0.30 and 0.50, the equilibrium pressure of hydrogen drops
to a value equal approximately to that in equilibrium with alloys of compositions
H/Pd = 0.03. It is likely that this process removes hydrogen rapidly from the
positions not in the sheets, where it exists as the alpha phase. For the hydrogen
in the alpha phase there is less no-bond resonance and presumably therefore a
lower energy of activation required to remove it. Therefore, the transfer of
hydrogen from the alloy to the gas phase must be rapid and involve only the
hydrogen not in the sheets (alpha-phase hydrogen). Equilibrium is established
rapidly in the part of the isotherm involving only the alpha phase. Pumping removes the alpha-phase hydrogen from the lattice and the true equilibrium pressure is not re-established until the equilibrium concentration of these hydrogen
atoms has been reached again. A pseudo-equilibrium exists at all times between
the alpha-phase hydrogen and the gas. The transfer of hydrogen from beta to
alpha is slow, since it involves the long-range diffusion discussed above.

The Isotherms

The model described is far too elaborate to use in detail to calculate a partition function. However, the average resonance energy can be assigned to pairs
of neighboring hydrogen atoms. The calculation of the equilibrium pressure now
becomes that of the quasichemical approximation. Lacher (4) has used the
quasichemical approximation to calculate the isotherms without justifying the
attractive potential between the hydrogen atoms. The partition function assumed
lacks the detail to explain either the heat capacities or the hysteresis.

Literature Cited

(1) Barrer, R. M., "Diffusion in and through Solids," Cambridge Univ. Press, Cambridge,
     1941.

(2) Burger, J. P., Poulis, N. J., Hass, W. P., *Physica* **27**, 514 (1961).
(3) Clusius, K., Rapp, L., Frank, A., *Ibid.*, **4**, 1105 (1937).
(4) Lacher, J. R., *Proc. Roy. Soc. (London)*, **161**, 525 (1937).
(5) Mitacek, Paul, Aston, J. G., *J. Am. Chem. Soc.*, in press.
(6) Mott, N. F., Jones, H., "Theory of the Properties of Metals and Alloys," Clarendon Press, Oxford, England, 1956.
(7) Nace, D. M., Aston, J. G., *J. Am. Chem. Soc.* **79**, 3623 (1957).
(8) *Ibid.*, p. 3627.
(9) Norberg, R. E., *Phys. Rev.* **86**, 745 (1952).
(10) Pauling, L., "Nature of the Chemical Bond," Cornell University Press, Ithaca, N. Y., 1959.
(11) Schindler, A. I., unpublished work.
(12) Schindler, A. I., Smith, R. J., Kramer, E. W., Proceedings of 10th International Congress on Refrigeration, Copenhagen, 1959.
(13) Smith, D. P., "Hydrogen in Metals," University of Chicago Press, Chicago, Ill., 1948.
(14) Spalthoff, W. J., *J. Phys. Chem.* **29**, 258 (1961).
(15) Worsham, J. E., Jr., Wilkinson, M. K., Shull, C. G., *J. Phys. Chem. Solids* **3**, 303 (1957).

RECEIVED September 6, 1962. Contribution 154 from Cryogenic Laboratory, Pennsylvania State University.

11

Magnetic Characteristics of Gadolinium, Terbium, and Ytterbium Hydrides in Relation to the Electronic Nature of the Lanthanide Hydrides

W. E. WALLACE, YOSHIO KUBOTA, and R. L. ZANOWICK

Department of Chemistry, University of Pittsburgh, Pittsburgh 13, Pa.

Hydrogenation of the heavy lanthanides leads to formation of cubic dihydrides and hexagonal trihydrides, which exist over a considerable composition range. Metallic conduction is exhibited by the dihydrides but not trihydrides, suggesting that the latter lack conduction electrons, a conclusion also indicated by absence of magnetic ordering at low temperatures. Since the atomic moment is essentially unchanged by hydrogenation, the number of core electrons is unchanged in the process. One concludes that the conduction electrons are absorbed by the dissolving hydrogen to form the H⁻ ion and hence the trihydrides are essentially ionic. The dihydrides exhibit metallic conduction and order at low temperatures considerably below the point at which ordering begins in the corresponding metal.

The lanthanide metals react readily with hydrogen to form a series of hydrides in which the hydrogen-metal atom ratio varies over rather wide limits. These hydrides (of all the lanthanides, including La and Y, except radioactive promethium) have been examined by conventional x-ray diffraction techniques with the following conclusions (4, 9): All of the lanthanides form dihydrides; in the majority of cases the dihydride will readily absorb extra hydrogen, approaching or reaching a composition corresponding to a trihydride; and the metal ion cores in the di- and trihydrides of the light lanthanides are in a face-centered cubic arrangement, whereas for the heavier lanthanides beginning with Sm the metal ion cores in the trihydrides are in a close-packed hexagonal arrangement. The dihydrides of Eu and Yb are exceptional in that they absorb extra hydrogen with reluctance, if at all (*14*), and the metal ion cores are in an orthorhombic structure (*5*), which can, however, be regarded as a rather simple distortion of hexagonal close packing. Eu and Yb behave unlike the other lanthanide metals in many ways, because they are divalent whereas the others are trivalent. Experiment shows nonstoichiometry to be the rule, rather than the exception, for the lanthanide hydrides. The metal-hydrogen atom ratio, Me/H, is found to extend from about 1.8 to 2.5 in the dihydride phases and from roughly 2.5 to 3.0 for the trihydrides.

In recent years a considerable body of information has been accumulating, bearing upon the presumed electronic nature of these hydrides. The point of view has been held in many quarters for a number of years that the bonding in the lanthanide hydrides is essentially coulombic in character—that is, these hydrides are saline in nature, with the hydrogen, of course, present as an anion. Suggestive evidence in support of this point of view has been provided by the magnitude of the heats of hydrogenation (*2*) and the ideal stoichiometry of the hydrides—trihydrides easily form with trivalent metals, whereas normally only dihydrides form with the divalent metals Eu and Yb. Additional and more powerful support for this point of view has been and is currently being provided by the observed electrical and magnetic properties of the lanthanide hydrides. In this laboratory it has been found that when Dy, Ho, and Yb are hydrogenated to saturation, their conductivities diminish by five or more orders of magnitude (*10*). Similar observations have been made by Warf and Hardcastle (*13*) for the Pr-H system and by Stalinski for the La- and Ce-H systems. Moreover, Stalinski noted that the resistivities of LaH_3 and CeH_3 decreased with increasing temperature, indicating that the conductivity in these materials was nonmetallic in nature (*11*). The observed conductivity behavior clearly indicates that the fully hydrogenated lanthanide metal is lacking in conduction band electrons. This leads to the conclusion that the hydride ion is formed by absorbing electrons from the conduction band and the hydrogen-saturated metal represents the situation in which this process has led to the complete depopulation of the conduction band.

Support for the thesis that the hydrogen in the lanthanide hydrides is anionic and the fully hydrogenated lanthanide metal is devoid of conduction electrons is also provided by the study of the magnetic properties of the lanthanide hydrides carried on in this laboratory in recent years. The elemental lanthanides are known to order magnetically at reduced temperatures and it is generally believed the localized 4*f* electrons in adjacent metal ion cores do not overlap appreciably. The interactions which produce ferromagnetism and antiferromagnetism in the lanthanides are hence not due to direct exchange. Instead they result from indirect exchange—that is, exchange via the conduction band electrons. It follows, therefore, that hydrogenating these metals will have strong implications as regards their tendencies to order magnetically. Hence studies of the magnetic behavior of the lanthanide hydrides, particularly the strength of their tendency to order, provide further evidence in support of the presumed electronic nature of these hydrides. This provided the original incentive for investigating the magnetic behavior of this group of hydrides. Earlier investigations have dealt with the magnetic characteristics of holmium (*6*) and europium hydrides (*15*). The present paper is concerned with a similar study of gadolinium, terbium, and ytterbium hydrides and the utilization of the results obtained to document further the thesis set forth above.

Experimental Details

The lanthanide metals were obtained from the Nuclear Corp. of America, Burbank, Calif. They were analyzed spectroscopically by the supplier and found to be 99% pure or better. The hydrogen was obtained from a commercial cylinder and purified by passing through a Deoxo unit and a liquid nitrogen trap and finally by diffusion through a heated palladium tube.

In preparing the metal for hydrogenation 0.1- to 0.4-gram samples were cut from the stock supply, the cutting being done under mineral oil. The samples were then polished under mineral oil with progressively finer abrasive papers, ending with Type 600A. They were then washed successively with CCl_4, acetone, and ether. After weighing, the sample was introduced into the preparation train (vacuum system and appropriate gas metering equipment) and evacuated to high vacuum for at least 4 hours. It was then heated gradually to 500° and hydrogen was admitted. Hydrides with compositions approximating the dihydride formed rapidly in most cases. For higher hydrogen contents the temperature had to be lowered and higher pressures (up to 1 atm.) had to be applied. After the desired composition had been attained, the temperature was reduced and the sample was annealed at 200° to 300° for at least 4 hours. Upon removal, the hydrides were either placed under oil and kept there to retard oxidation and/or decomposition or were introduced immediately into the equipment used to measure susceptibilities.

Susceptibilities were measured from 4° K. to room temperature using the Faraday method. A Varian 6-inch magnet provided with a Sucksmith gap (*12*) was used and the forces were measured with the automatic recording balance which has been described in detail (*1*). The field gradient was calibrated using $NiCl_2$ solution and elemental iron. Measurements were always made at several field strengths to test for possible field dependencies of the measured susceptibilities. The observed susceptibility can vary with the field strength for either of two reasons: (1) the presence of ferromagnetic impurity which tends to saturate at higher fields and (2) an intrinsic property of the sample under investigation. The latter occurs only under conditions of very high field and very low temperatures (<4° K.) or at temperatures close to the Curie or Néel point.

Results

It has been tacitly assumed to this point that the dissolving hydrogen acquires its supernumerary electron from the conduction band of the metal. There is, of course, another possibility—that some or all of the electrons are taken from the core. If so, the atomic moment would change. For terbium the alteration in moment is rather large; for a loss of 1 electron from the core its moment would decrease by 1.7 μ_B (Bohr magnetons). Terbium hence is a favorable case for verifying that the number of core electrons is essentially invariant during the hydrogenation process, and its hydrides were studied rather thoroughly. The gadolinium and ytterbium hydrides were studied somewhat less thoroughly.

Terbium Hydrides. The measured susceptibilities at 300° K. of eleven terbium hydrides at a variety of field strengths are given in Table I. These values can be compared with the value 8.7×10^{-4} e.m.u. per gram obtained for elemental Tb. Thus the hydrides are seen to be very strongly paramagnetic materials but not quite so strongly paramagnetic as the parent metal. The temperature dependence of the susceptibilities of a number of the samples is represented in Figures 1, 2, and 3. Over most of the temperature range the susceptibilities of the hydrides are represented by the Curie-Weiss law, $\chi = C/(T - \theta)$. This is also true for the parent metal for temperatures above its Curie point. Below a certain temperature, T_d, however, the χ values show significant departures from the Curie-Weiss law.

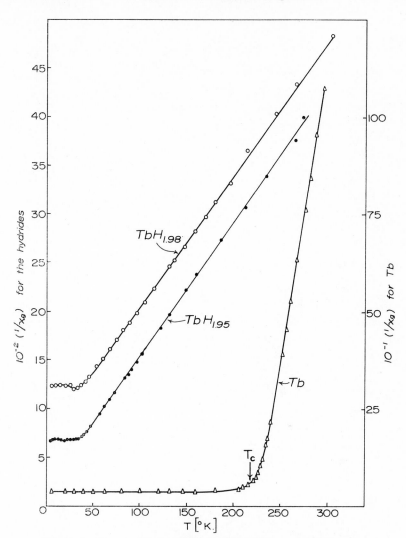

Figure 1. Inverse susceptibility of Tb, TbH$_{1.95}$, and TbH$_{1.98}$
vs. temperature

G./e.m.u.
Data for TbH$_{1.98}$ for clarity displaced upward by 5 units. Arrow indicates Curie
temperature, T$_C$, for Tb

Values of T_d, the Weiss constant, Θ, and the atomic moment computed from the Curie constant, C, are given in Table II.

For most of the hydrides in the region of the dihydride the susceptibility rises to maximum 40° and 50° K. (Figures 1, 2, and 3). For TbH$_{2.08}$ there is in addition a minimum χ at about 20° K. The maximum implies the onset of some type of antiferromagnetic ordering and the temperature at which this begins is the Néel point, T_N. The values of T_N are also given in Table II.

GdH$_2$ and GdH$_3$. The susceptibilities of GdH$_2$ and GdH$_3$ at 300° K. were found to be 1.56×10^{-4} and 1.36×10^{-4} e.m.u. per gram, respectively. The temperature dependence of their susceptibilities is shown in Figure 4. Here again one

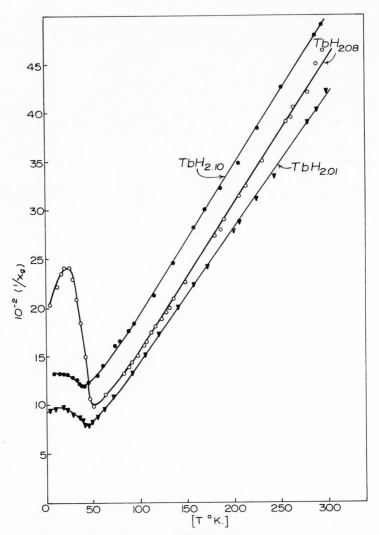

Figure 2. Inverse susceptibilities vs. temperature for
$TbH_{2.01}$, $TbH_{2.08}$, $TbH_{2.10}$

G./e.m.u.
Data for $TbH_{2.08}$ and $TbH_{2.10}$ displaced upward by 2 and 4 units, respectively

Table I.   Susceptibilities of Terbium Hydrides at 300° K

$10^4 \chi_g$, e.m.u./g.

Field Strength, Koe.	$TbH_{1.95}$	$TbH_{1.98}$	$TbH_{2.01}$	$TbH_{2.10}$	$TbH_{2.21}$	$TbH_{2.40}$	$TbH_{2.88}$	$TbH_{2.92}$	$TbH_{2.95}$	$TbH_{2.97}$
8.5	2.19	2.16	2.18	2.20	2.05	2.17	2.18	2.17	2.20	2.17
10.5	2.20	2.15	2.17	2.18	2.06	2.16	2.16	2.11	2.18	2.16
13.4	2.18	2.16	2.17	2.19	2.07	2.15	2.17	2.16	2.19	2.16
15.4	2.20	2.15	2.19	2.20	2.08	2.18	2.19	2.10	2.17	2.19
16.8	2.18	2.14	2.18	2.21	2.06	2.15	2.15	2.14	2.18	2.16
18.2	2.17	2.17	2.18	2.19	2.05	2.17	2.16	2.15	2.20	2.16
18.9	2.19	2.18	2.19	2.21	2.08	2.18	2.18	2.18	2.21	2.18
19.6	2.20	2.19	2.20	2.21	2.09	2.19	2.19	2.19	2.22	2.19
20.0	2.19	2.18	2.20	2.21	2.09	2.19	2.19	2.19	2.22	2.19

notes a wide range of temperature over which Curie-Weiss behavior is obeyed and a Néel point for the dihydride. Values for the atomic moment, T_N, T_d, and Θ, for these materials are also listed in Table II.

Yb and YbH$_2$. Information on these two materials was only semiquantitative, since the equipment employed was designed for use with either strongly paramagnetic or ferromagnetic materials. Lock showed that elemental ytterbium is weakly paramagnetic and its susceptibility is nearly independent of temperature (7). Results obtained for Yb in this study were similar. Measurements showed that YbH$_2$ was even more weakly paramagnetic than Yb and may even be diamagnetic. χ was of the order of 10^{-6} e.m.u. per gram for both Yb and YbH$_2$.

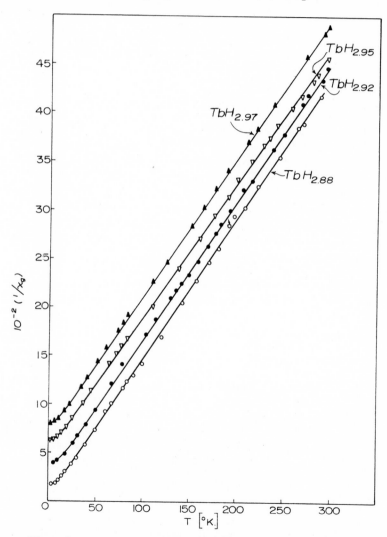

Figure 3. Inverse susceptibilities vs. temperature for TbH$_{2.88}$.
TbH$_{2.92}$, TbH$_{2.95}$, and TbH$_{2.97}$

G./e.m.u.
Data for TbH$_{2.92}$, TbH$_{2.95}$, and TbH$_{2.97}$ displaced upward by 2, 4, and 6 units respectively

Table II.   Results of Magnetic Studies of Terbium and Gadolinium Hydrides

Sample	$T_N,^a$ °K.	$T_d,^a$ °K.	$\Theta,^a$ °K.	μ_{eff}, Bohr Magnetons
Tb	235	240	230	9.85
TbH$_{1.95}$	?	40	−11	9.8
TbH$_{1.98}$	40	38	−13	9.7
TbH$_{2.01}$	46	70	−6	9.8
TbH$_{2.08}$	50	75	+7	9.4
TbH$_{2.10}$	40	55	−7	9.4
TbH$_{2.21}$	N.O.	b	b	9.3
TbH$_{2.40}$	N.O.	b	b	9.4
TbH$_{2.88}$	N.O.	8	−2	9.5
TbH$_{2.92}$	N.O.	8	−2	9.5
TbH$_{2.95}$	N.O.	8	−5	9.7
TbH$_{2.97}$	N.O.	8	−7	9.7
GdH$_2$	21	55	+3	7.7
GdH$_3$	N.O.	9	−3	7.3

^{a} T_N. Néel temperature (N.O. means not observed). T_d. Temperature below which departures from Curie-Weiss law become noticeable. Θ. Weiss constant. μ_{eff}. Effective moment. ^{b} Below about 160° K. linearity of $1/\mu$ vs. T is only approximate for these two samples. The data between 75° and 160° K. show small but significant systematic negative deviations from the straight line which represents the results well above 160° and between 40° and 75° K. The cause of these deviations is unknown but TbH$_{2.40}$ is known to be a two-phase mixture of the di- and trihydrides. TbH$_{2.21}$ is close to the phase boundary and it, too, may be two-phase (see 9). The anomalous magnetic behavior may in these cases be due to the fact that they are mixtures.

Discussion.   The exchange interactions between the highly localized 4f electrons in the lanthanide metals take place via the delocalized electrons in the conduction band (3). Hence, in the fully hydrogenated metal, if the conduction electrons are absorbed the tendency for magnetic alignment is expected to be greatly suppressed as compared to the parent metal or perhaps removed entirely. Earlier work gave no indication of ordering in fully hydrogenated holmium (6)—i.e., HoH$_3$—and a similar situation is indicated in the present work for GdH$_3$ and TbH$_3$. Stalinski (11) studied the magnetic properties of CeH$_3$, and found that it remains paramagnetic to the lowest temperatures studied. However, his measurements extended to only 80° K. If magnetic ordering occurs at all, it is expected to develop at temperatures considerably lower than this. Hence, Stalinski's results are not conclusive. It seems likely that if ordering at lower temperatures were sought, results would be negative. Since the packing of the metal ion cores in the element and in the trihydride is essentially the same (9), the absence of magnetic ordering in the latter strongly suggests that they lack conduction electrons. Furthermore, the lanthanide moment is nearly the same in the hydride and in the corresponding element [(10) and Table II], indicating that the conduction electrons have not been absorbed into the lanthanide core. It thus appears that they have been consumed by the dissolving hydrogen to form the H$^-$ ion.

The results for Yb and YbH$_2$, even though only semiquantitative, are consistent with the ideas in the preceding paragraph. The susceptibility of a paramagnetic metal can originate in at least two ways—from the electrons in the conduction band (Pauli paramagnetism) and from the core electrons, if the core contains an unfilled shell or subshell (Langevin paramagnetism). If the latter predominates, χ varies with temperature according to either Curie's law, $\chi = C/T$, or the Curie-Weiss law, $\chi = C/(T-\Theta)$. If, however, the susceptibility originates largely with the conduction electrons, χ is essentially independent of temperature. This, as pointed out above, is the situation for Yb, suggesting that χ for Yb derives in the main from the conduction electrons. Hence, hydrogenation, which absorbs these electrons, should produce a decrease in χ. This is observed to happen.

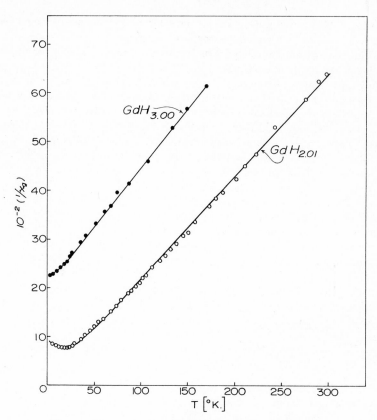

Figure 4. Inverse susceptibilities vs. temperature for
GdH₂.₀₁ and GdH₃.₀₀
G./e.m.u.

Data for GdH₂.₀₁ displaced upward by 40 units

The foregoing remarks do not hold, of course, for the dihydrides of the trivalent lanthanides. They exhibit metallic conduction (*10*), as would be expected, since their conduction band is only somewhat depleted. One would expect them to display a tendency to order at low temperatures, but it seems not unreasonable to expect that this tendency would be weaker than the corresponding element, in view of the decreased electron concentration, and the ordering would hence occur at lower temperatures. This was in fact observed for HoH_2, which exhibits (*6*) a Néel point at 8° K., as compared to 135° K. for Ho. It is also observed in the present work for the terbium dihydrides, whose Néel points are 40° to 50° K., whereas that for the element is 241° K. These properties are compatible with the notion that hydrogen in all the lanthanide hydrides is anionic. On this basis the dihydrides appear as an intermediate form between the truly metallic elements on the one hand and the truly ionic or saline trihydrides on the other.

Most, but not all, of the observed magnetic behavior of the lanthanide hydrides fits in with the notion that the hydrogen-saturated metal lacks conduction electrons. The hydride of europium is an exception; $EuH_{1.86}$, the highest hydride that has been formed in this laboratory, has been shown (*15*) to be ferromagnetic below 25° K. This would ordinarily imply the existence of electrons in the conduction band. However, EuO, a known insulator, also exhibits ferromagnetism at low temperatures (8). Elemental europium is atypical in many respects and perhaps in the case of europium dihydrides the interactions can occur without the intervention of the conduction electrons.

Two aspects of the properties of the hydrides reported in the present paper merit attention. First, GdH_2 exhibits a Néel point, despite the fact that it derives from a metal which alone among the strongly magnetic lanthanides never becomes antiferromagnetic. Second, $TbH_{2.08}$ shows an increase of susceptibility with decrease of temperature at temperatures below 20° K. This implies a change in the nature of the ordering in this material at this point, seemingly toward ferromagnetic ordering. $TbH_{2.08}$, alone among the terbium hydrides, shows a positive Weiss constant, which is a further indication of a tendency toward ferromagnetic ordering. Change from antiferromagnetic to ferromagnetic ordering at the lowest temperature is the rule for the elemental lanthanides but heretofore has not been observed for the lanthanide hydrides. The point of greatest interest is the extreme sensitivity of this effect to the hydrogen content, and hence conduction electron concentration, of the sample. The rise in susceptibility is not observed for $TbH_{2.01}$ nor $TbH_{2.10}$. Evidently the electron concentrations and/or the Tb-Tb spacing in these materials is not favorable for the formation of the ferromagnetic structure at low temperatures, whereas the conditions in $TbH_{2.08}$ are conducive to this type of ordering. The fact that so slight a change in composition can produce so radical a change in behavior is probably no more than another indication of the very slight difference in energy of the ferromagnetic and antiferromagnetic modes of coupling.

Literature Cited

(1) Butera, R. A., Craig, R. S., Cherry, L. V., *Rev. Sci. Instr.* **32**, 708 (1961).
(2) Dialer, K., Rothe, W., *Z. Elektrochem.* **59**, 970 (1955).
(3) Elliott, R. J., *Phys. Rev.* **124**, 346 (1961).
(4) Holley, C. E., Jr., Mulford, R. N. R., Ellinger, F. H., *J. Phys. Chem.* **59**, 1226 (1955).
(5) Korst, W. L., Warf, J. C., *Acta Cryst.* **9**, 452 (1956).
(6) Kubota, Y., Wallace, W. E., *J. Appl. Phys. Suppl.* **33**, 1348 (1962).
(7) Lock, J. M., *Proc. Phys. Soc. (London)* **70B**, 476 (1957).
(8) Matthias, B., Bozorth, R. M., Van Vleck, J. H., *Phys. Rev. Letters* **7**, 160 (1961).
(9) Pebler, A., Wallace, W. E., *J. Phys. Chem.* **66**, 148 (1962).
(10) Peltz, T., Wallace, W. E., unpublished measurements.
(11) Stalinski, B., *Bull Acad. Polon. Sci.* **5**, 1001 (1957); **7**, 269 (1959).
(12) Sucksmith, W., *Proc. Roy. Soc. (London)* **A170**, 551 (1939).
(13) Warf, J. C., Hardcastle, K., Final Report, Office of Naval Reserve, Contract Nonr 228(15), August 1961.
(14) Warf, J. C., Hardcastle, K., *J. Am. Chem. Soc.* **83**, 2207 (1961).
(15) Zanowick, R. L., Wallace, W. E., *Phys. Rev.* **126**, 536 (1962).

RECEIVED September 6, 1962. Work assisted by a contract with the U. S. Atomic Energy Commission. Portions taken from a thesis presented by R. L. Zanowick to the Graduate Faculty, University of Pittsburgh, in partial fulfillment of the requirements for the Ph. D. degree, January 1962.

Phase Studies in the Zirconium-Hydrogen-Uranium System

H. H. KRAUSE, H. E. BIGONY, and J. R. DOIG, Jr.[1]

Battelle Memorial Institute, Columbus, Ohio

Hydrogen-absorption isotherms were measured over the range 535° to 835° C. by Sievert's method for alloys of zirconium containing 1 and 25 weight % uranium. High-temperature x-ray diffraction studies were made over approximately the same temperature range for the zirconium–1, –25, and –50 weight % uranium alloys. In general, these studies support the interpretation that, as hydrogen is absorbed, the alloys break down into uranium and zirconium, and the latter absorbs the hydrogen. Heats of solution of hydrogen were found to range from −25.9 to −47.9 kcal. per mole for the 1 weight % alloy, and from −30.7 to −50.6 kcal. per mole for the 25 weight % alloy. Proposed isothermal sections of the ternary diagram at 627°, 675°, and 750° C. are included.

This study has been concerned with the phase relationships in the ternary system zirconium-hydrogen-uranium in the temperature range 500° to 800° C. To examine the concept of a fueled moderator for nuclear reactors, the absorption of hydrogen by two zirconium-uranium alloy compositions was measured.

There is adequate information in the literature on the three binary systems involved. Libowitz and colleagues (*12*) have shown that uranium forms the single hydride, UH_3, at temperatures below 450° C. The zirconium-hydrogen system includes several hydride phases; the delta hydride, having a composition in the range $ZrH_{1.5}$ to $ZrH_{1.7}$ at elevated temperatures, is of the greatest interest for moderator purposes. The zirconium-hydrogen system has been described (*1–5, 7, 8, 10, 11, 13, 16, 18–21*). The uranium-zirconium system has also been studied in detail (*15*).

The earliest study of the ternary system was by Gulbransen and his associates (*6, 17*), who obtained data on the 50 weight % uranium alloy. Their chief concern was the possible weakening effects of hydrogen absorption by such alloys in a pressurized-water reactor. More recently, La Grange *et al.* (*9*) examined

---

[1] Present address, Boeing Aircraft Co., Wichita, Kan.

a series of hydrided zirconium-uranium alloys for fueled moderator reactor applications.

In the present investigation, the hydrogen-absorption data have been supplemented by high-temperature x-ray diffraction. By this means the solid-state reactions indicated by the hydrogen-solubility data could be identified. Furthermore, x-ray examination of the samples at the absorption-isotherm temperature is desirable in the system where transformations can occur even on rapid cooling from elevated temperatures. The high diffusivity of hydrogen makes this system particularly susceptible to such changes, so quenching of samples was avoided in this work. Selected alloys with hydrogen contents near the terminal phases and the eutectoid composition were examined.

Experimental Procedures

The hydrogen-absorption isotherms were measured over the temperature range 535° to 835° C. for both the 1 and 25 weight % uranium alloys. Nine alloy compositions were selected for x-ray study: zirconium-base alloys containing 1, 25, and 50 weight % uranium, each with 10, 30, and 50 atomic % hydrogen, based on the zirconium content. The 10 and 50 atomic % hydrogen contents correspond to positions near the terminal phases in the zirconium-hydrogen system, and the 30 atomic % hydrogen addition approximates the eutectoid composition.

Materials and Fabrication Techniques. The zirconium used in this work was iodide metal and the uranium was center-cut from biscuit stock. Both 1 and 50 weight % uranium alloys were double-melted by consumable-electrode arc-melting, as part of large batches prepared for other studies. The 25 weight % uranium alloy was prepared by a tungsten-electrode arc-melting method. The alloys were hot-rolled at 1500° F., cleaned, and cold-rolled to a final thickness of 0.125 inch. Vacuum fusion analysis showed that these alloys contained from 300 to 450 p.p.m. of oxygen, and less than 30 p.p.m. of hydrogen or nitrogen.

Pure hydrogen for the isotherm determinations, and also for hydriding the alloys used in the x-ray study, was obtained by the thermal decomposition of uranium hydride. Table I gives the composition of the hydrides used in this program, as obtained by vacuum-fusion analysis.

Table 1.   Hydrogen Content of Hydrided Alloys Used in X-Ray Diffraction Study

	Uranium Concentration, Weight %		
	1	25	50
Hydrogen concn.	10.4	10.8	10.0
per atom, at. %	31.7	31.6	34.1
	49.3	48.4	48.4

Individual wire sections chosen for straightness and desirable cross-sectional shape were cut to desired length and etched in a nitric acid–hydrofluoric acid–water solution to remove the inevitable scale that occurs on closed heating. The bright sample was then rinsed in 1 to 1 nitric acid to remove any green deposit that might have formed during etching.

Each alloy was examined by x-ray at temperature levels about 100° C. apart, starting at either 400° or 500° C., and extending to 800° C. The 400° or 500° C. level was preceded by room-temperature examination, and the sample was sometimes re-examined at room temperature after the elevated-temperature excursion. Each x-ray photogram was obtained by a 2-hour exposure to unfiltered nickel radiation.

The 800° C. examination was seldom considered useful because of apparent reaction with the capillary wall. The diffraction photograms at that temperature level indicated the presence of uranium dioxide, cristobalite from devitrification of the silica capillary, and an unknown corrosion product. These effects were sometimes noted to a mild degree at 700° C. also. In most cases of the 800° C. examination, the silica capillary split open during exposure.

Apparatus. The hydrogen-absorption system, a modified Sievert's apparatus, consisted of three self-contained units. The first unit provided a source of, and storage facilities for, pure hydrogen, which was obtained by the thermal decomposition of uranium hydride. The second unit provided precise metering of hydrogen at a known temperature, for delivery to the reaction system. The third unit was a constant-volume section in which the reaction of hydrogen with the zirconium-uranium alloy occurred at a controlled temperature ($\pm 3°$ C.). The equilibrium pressures of hydrogen were measured in this section also.

The x-ray studies were made with a high-temperature x-ray diffraction camera of Hume-Rothery design. This camera had a 9-cm. diameter and employed the Straumanis film setting. A fine Chromel-Alumel thermocouple within the furnace cavity and adjacent to the sample served to measure and control temperature. The sample temperature was calibrated against the thermocouple e.m.f. through a series of lattice-constant measurements on pure silver.

Experimental Methods. The absorption of hydrogen by the zirconium-uranium alloys was measured isothermally, using the constant-volume section of the system. An Autovac gage was used to measure pressures below 2 mm., and a large-bore manometer was used for higher pressures. A cathetometer was employed for the manometer readings. Possible contaminants such as mercury and stopcock grease were excluded from the reaction vessel by means of a $-78°$ C. trap. The alloy samples were placed in an Inconel container to prevent possible reaction with the mullite tube in which the hydriding was effected.

At each temperature successive additions of hydrogen were made and the equilibrium pressures measured. Equilibrium was reached in minutes at temperatures above 700° C., but several hours were required at lower temperatures. Additions of hydrogen were continued until the amount of hydrogen absorbed per gram of zirconium approximated 60 atomic %. The volume of hydrogen taken up by the sample was determined as the difference between that added and the volume remaining in the reaction system at equilibrium. Corrections were made for the differences in manifold temperatures encountered during the experiments.

For the x-ray work, "wire" samples were prepared by shearing 0.010-inch sheet of the desired uranium-zirconium alloy composition, keeping the width as close to the thickness as possible. A small batch of these wires was then hydrided at 600° C. to the desired hydrogen content along with a small block of the same alloy to bring the sample weight to a feasible value. The hydrided material of each composition was then sealed in an evacuated Vycor capsule and homogenized at 1000° C.

Results and Discussion

The absorption-isotherm method provides a very useful approach to the study of a gas-solid system. Inflection points in the isotherms locate phase boundaries, and a plot of log P vs. $1/T$ (Arrhenius plot) permits calculation of heats of solution and estimation of the eutectoid temperature. The shape of the isotherms depends only on those phases which affect the hydrogen absorption, rather than all phases present. The actual phases present were identified by high-temperature x-ray diffraction. The designation of the phases follows terminology commonly used in U. S. Atomic Energy Commission studies:

α_{Zr} = hexagonal close-packed zirconium
β_{Zr} = body-centered cubic form of zirconium
δ = face-centered cubic zirconium hydride
ϵ = face-centered tetragonal zirconium hydride
α_U = orthorhombic uranium
β_U = tetragonal uranium

γ_U = body-centered cubic uranium
γ_1 = uranium-rich series of solid solutions formed between γ_U and β_{Zr}
γ_2 = zirconium-rich series of solid solutions formed between γ_U and β_{Zr}
δ_{UZr2} = solid solution of γ_U and α_{Zr}

The phase diagrams of the uranium-zirconium and uranium-hydrogen systems employed in this work were those given by Rough and Bauer (15). The zirconium-hydrogen phase diagram used is a composite of data found in the various references to that system, and is presented in Figure 1.

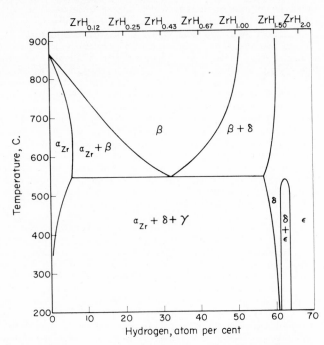

Figure 1. Phase diagram of zirconium-hydrogen system

Zirconium-1 Weight % Uranium Alloy. Isotherms for the 1 weight % uranium alloy were run at six temperatures, covering the range 534° to 802° C. The x-ray diffraction studies on this alloy were made at room temperature and from 500° to 800° C. The general effect of the addition of the uranium is to shift the phase boundaries of the zirconium-hydrogen system to slightly lower hydrogen percentages. The eutectoid temperature is also lowered from 547° to 541° C.

HYDROGEN-ABSORPTION ISOTHERMS. The isotherms determined for the zirconium–1 weight % uranium alloy are shown in Figure 2. Solid solution of hydrogen in the alloy is represented by the initial portions of all the curves, which show a rapid change of pressure with the volume of hydrogen absorbed. The inflection points of the curves represent phase boundaries, and the transition from α-zirconium to a multiphase region is indicated by the first such point on each curve. The vertical portions of the curves, which indicate hydrogen uptake at constant pressure, show the extent of the multiphase regions.

The isotherm at 534° C. has a very sharp inflection, followed by an almost vertical portion, as the multiphase region is tranversed. The second inflection in

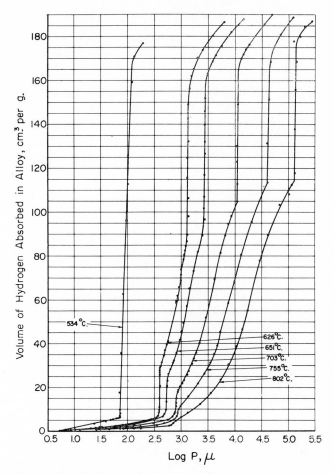

*Figure 2. Hydrogen-absorption isotherms for zirconium–
1 weight % uranium alloy*

the 534° C. isotherm indicates the transition to the single hydrogen-absorbing phase, δ-zirconium hydride. Because this isotherm lies below the eutectoid temperature, only two phase boundaries are crossed.

The four isotherms at 626°, 651°, 703°, and 755° C. have similar shapes, but the transition back to solid solution is not so sharply defined as the other transitions.

The 802° C. isotherm differs slightly from the others, in that the inflections at low hydrogen absorptions are not very pronounced. However, when the data are plotted on the phase diagram, a narrow multiphase region appears. Extrapolation indicates that above 875° C. this multiphase region would not exist. The remainder of the isotherm is the same as the others.

The phase boundaries which are indicated by these isotherms represent slight shifts from those of the zirconium-hydrogen system, and show that no unexpected change results from small uranium additions.

X-Ray Diffraction Study. The intensities of the phase patterns observed for the 1 weight % uranium alloy are presented in Table II. The intensity is indicative of the quantity of a given phase that is present, but the amount present is not necessarily proportional to the intensity. These data show that α_{Zr} was present in all three alloys up to 600° C., indicating either that at the 30 and 50 atom % hydrogen levels reaction was incomplete, or the sample was below the solvus surface on the α_{Zr} side of the ternary eutectoids. The lattice constant of the γ phase increased from 3.62 A. at 10 atom % hydrogen to 3.66 A. at 30 atom % and to 3.69 A. at 50 atom %.

Table II.   Phases Detected by X-Ray Diffraction Examination of Hydrided Zirconium–1 Weight % Uranium Alloy

Hydrogen Content, At. % in Zr	Temp.,° C.	α-Zr	γ-UZr	δ-ZrH$_x$	Unknown A
10	26	S	O	VVF-VF	O
	500	S	O	VVF-VF	O
	600	S	O	VVF-VF	O
	700	S	M	O	MF
	800	O	O	O	S
30	27	S	O	M	O
	500	VS	O	MS	O
	600	MS	S	F	O
	720	O	VS	O	O
	815	O	VS	O	MF
50	28	M	O	MS	O
	515	M	O	S	O
	600	M	MF	M	O
	700	O	VS	O	O
	815	O	S	O	MF

The column header *Intensities of Phase Patterns Observed[a]* spans the α-Zr, γ-UZr, δ-ZrH$_x$, and Unknown A columns.

[a] S = strong, M = medium, F = faint, V = very, O = absent.

An unidentifiable phase, designated as Unknown A, was detected in moderate intensity at 700° C. This material was observed in several samples at 700° and 800° C., and is believed to be a surface contamination resulting from a reaction with the silica container. This unknown phase remains when the sample is cooled to room temperature.

Zirconium–25 Weight % Uranium Alloy. Thirteen hydrogen-absorption isotherms covering the range 572° to 835° C. were run on the 25 weight % uranium alloy. The x-ray diffraction patterns were taken at room temperature and at 500°, 600°, 700°, and 800° C. The effect of the uranium on the zirconium-hydrogen system in this case is appreciable below 40 atomic % hydrogen. The phase boundaries of the zirconium-hydrogen system which define the α-zirconium plus β-zirconium hydride region are shifted to much higher hydrogen contents. Similarly, the eutectoid shifts from 32 to 38 atomic % hydrogen, and its temperature boundary rises from 547° to 601° C.

HYDROGEN-ABSORPTION ISOTHERMS. The isotherms for the 25 weight % uranium alloy constitute a family of curves closely resembling each other. Seven of the 13 isotherms which were measured are plotted in Figure 3. Isotherms intermediate between each adjacent pair were omitted to reduce the complexity of the plot. The isotherms at 572° C. (not shown) and at 601° C. cross only two phase boundaries, because they are below the eutectic temperature.

When the isotherms for the 25 weight % uranium alloy are compared with those for the 1 weight % alloy, significant differences are noted. The region of solid solution of hydrogen in the alloy is much broader in the 25 weight % alloy, as a large amount of uranium is being precipitated from the alloy. The result is to shift the first two phase boundaries to compositions of greater hydrogen content. The third and fourth phase boundaries are practically unchanged, since they are in a region in which δ-zirconium hydride predominates, and precipitation of uranium is no longer occurring.

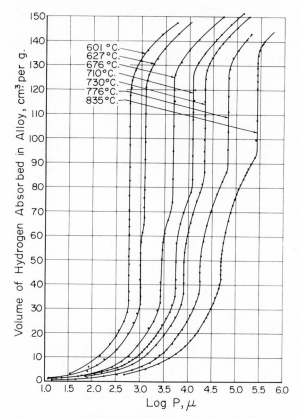

Figure 3. Hydrogen-absorption isotherms for zirconium–25 weight % uranium alloy

The vertical portions of the isotherms for the 25 weight % alloy, representing hydrogen uptake at constant pressure, show no variation of pressure with composition, indicating that in this slower hydrogen absorption, equilibrium of three solid phases has been reached.

X-Ray Diffraction Study. The x-ray diffraction data for the 25 weight % uranium alloy are presented in Table III. For the most part, the phases detected in the material containing 10 atom % hydrogen were what would be expected from the uranium-zirconium phase diagram. However, in addition there was found a phase which was either δ_{UZr2} or an omega-type phase with the same structure. The latter phase is difficult to differentiate from the δ_{UZr2}, and in uranium-zirconium alloys it decomposes into α_{Zr} and δ_{UZr2} upon annealing.

With 30 atom % hydrogen present, α_{U} and δ-zirconium hydride appeared as expected. However, at 720° and 815° C., the gamma phase was split into two portions having the lattice constants 3.68 and 3.64 A., respectively. A new phase, which has been designated as Unknown B, also appeared at 720° C. These results were verified in three different samples at 700° C. level. It is suspected that the two different gamma phases were of high hydrogen and low hydrogen contents, respectively. The high-hydrogen phase is probably the enlargement of the gamma field of the zirconium-hydrogen eutectoid, and the phase of low hydrogen content is probably a similar effect at the zirconium-uranium eutectoid. Unknown B may be a complex uranium-zirconium hydride.

Table III.   Phases Detected by X-Ray Diffraction Examination

| | | | | *Intensities* |
Hydrogen Content, At. % in Zr	Temp., ° C.	α-Zr	α-U	ω or δ-UZr_2
10	26	O	O	S
	500	VF	O	S
	600	MS	VF	O
	700	VF	O	O
	815	O	O	O
30	26	S	F	O
	515	S	F	O
	620	MS	M	O
	720	O	F	O
30	815	O	O	O
50	26	O	F	O
	515	O	F	O
	600	O	MF	O
	700	O	F[d]	O

[a] S = strong, M = medium, F = faint, V = very, O = absent.
[b] Duplex gamma phase observed.
[c] Unknown B.
[d] β-uranium rather than α-uranium.

Table IV.   Phases Detected by X-Ray Diffraction Examination

| | | | | *Intensities* |
Hydrogen Content, At. % in Zr	Temp., ° C.	α-Zr	α-U	δ-UZr_2
10	28	O	O	VS
10	500	MF	MF	S
10	600	M	MS	O
10	700	M	VF	O
30	28	O to VF	MS	O
30	515	O to VF	M	O
30	620	O to VF	M	O
30	720	O	O	O
30	815	O	O	O
50	28	O	MF	O
50	515	O	M	O
50	620	O	M	O
50	720	O	MF[c]	O
50	800	O	O	O

[a] S = strong, M = medium, F = faint, V = very, O = absent.
[b] Faint patterns for both UO and UO_2 were obtained.
[c] β-uranium.

In the alloy having 50 atom % hydrogen, β_U patterns appeared at 700° C., and the unidentified pattern previously designated as Unknown A was found at 815° C. Some faint UO_2 patterns were also observed, probably resulting from slight surface contamination with oxygen.

Zirconium–50 Weight % Uranium Alloy. This system was examined by Gulbransen and his associates (6, 17), but their x-ray studies were made on quenched samples, so there has been uncertainty as to the exact nature of the phases present at the higher temperatures. Consequently, x-ray diffraction patterns of the 50 weight % uranium alloy were taken over the range 500° to 800° C. (Table IV).

A 50 weight % uranium alloy, free of interstitial impurities such as hydrogen, would consist of the intermetallic compound UZr_2, designated as the delta phase.

of Hydrided Zirconium–25 Weight % Uranium Alloy

of Phase Patterns Observed[a]

| γ-UZr | ZrH$_x$ | Unknown | | UO$_2$ | Lattice Parameter of Cubic Gamma Phase, A. |
		A	Other		
MS	O	O	VVF	VVF	3.56
O	VF	O	VVF	O	...
S	O	O	VF	O	3.631
S	O	O	VVF	O	3.639
S	O	M	MF	O	3.615
O	M	O	O	O	...
F	M	O	VVF	O	...
MF	MS	O	F	O	3.68
S and M[b]	VVF	VF	M[c]	O	3.68 and 3.64
S and M[b]	O	VS	O	O	3.68 and 3.64
O	S	O	VVF	O	...
O	S	O	O	VF	...
M	MS	O	VVF	VVF	3.68
S	MF	O	VVF	VF	3.712

of Hydrided Zirconium–50 Weight % Uranium Alloy

of Phase Patterns Observed[a]

| γ-UZr | ZrH$_x$ | Unknown | | UO$_2$ | Lattice Parameter of Cubic Gamma Phase, A. |
		A	Other		
O	O	O	VVF	O	...
O	VF	O	VVF	O	...
MF	O	O	VVF	O	3.61
S	O	M	VVF	O	3.608
O	M	O	VVF	O	...
O	M	O	VVF	F	...
O	MS	O	VF	F	...
MS	F	VF	VF	F[b]	3.696
M	O	MS	VF	S	3.710
O	MS	O	VF	O	...
O	S	O	O	VF	...
O	S	O	O	VVF	...
O	S	VF	VF	VF	...
O	S	S	VF	F	...

This was also found to be the case for the alloy with 10 atomic % hydrogen at room temperature. However, at 500° C. medium-faint patterns of α_{Zr} and α_U appeared, although a large amount of the delta UZr$_2$ remained. At 600° C., the delta phase disappeared completely, and the α_{Zr} and α_U phases were correspondingly increased in intensity. Despite the difficulty in distinguishing between small amounts of gamma and delta phase (the delta pattern resembles merely a superlattice pattern of the gamma), a minor amount of gamma phase was detected. At 700° C., the gamma phase predominated, but a considerable quantity of α_{Zr} was also present, with possibly a trace of α_U. The results for this alloy show that hydrogen at a concentration of 10 atomic % (based on the zirconium present) reduces the stability of the delta compound. At the higher hydrogen concentrations the delta phase was not observed at all. These facts are a verification of similar results obtained by Gulbransen and associates (17). The effect of hydrogen on the stability of the delta phase is therefore comparable to the effect of oxygen and nitrogen on the uranium-zirconium system (14). The delta phase is possibly a nonequilibrium structure produced by the transformation of the gamma phase.

At 30 and 50 atomic % hydrogen the alloy consisted essentially of α_U and the face-centered cubic zirconium hydride. β_U replaced α_U at 720° C. for the 50 atom % hydrogen alloy. The unidentified phase previously designated as Unknown A appeared above 700° C. at all hydrogen levels in this alloy.

Heats of Solution. The heat of solution of hydrogen in these zirconium-uranium systems was determined from the Arrhenius plots of the isotherm data (log P vs. $1/T$). The average ΔH values, calculated from the slopes of the isochors, increase with the hydrogen content until the system has been completely converted to δ-zirconium hydride and uranium, after which the value drops slightly. These results, presented in Table V, indicate that the hydrogen is held more strongly as it passes through the solid-solution stage into compound formation. The uranium-zirconium alloy is broken down in the process and the hydrogen reacts with the zirconium. The heat of solution in uranium is about +1 kcal. per mole as compared to −35 kcal. per mole for pure zirconium, indicative of the much greater stability of the zirconium hydride.

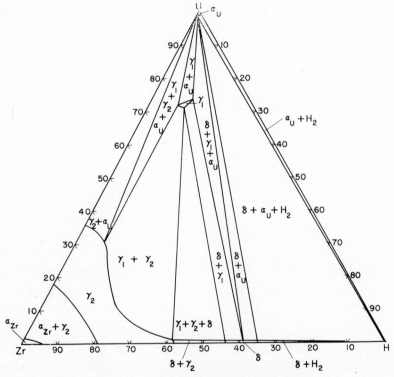

Figure 4. Proposed Zr-H-U phase diagram

627° C. section

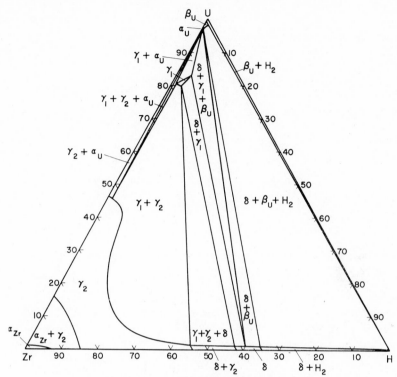

Figure 5.   Proposed Zr-H-U phase diagram

675° C. section

Table V.   Heats of Solution of Hydrogen in Zirconium-Uranium Alloys

Zirconium-Hydrogen Phases	$-\Delta H$, *Kcal. per Mole*	
	1 wt. % uranium	*25 wt. % uranium*
α_{Zr} + H_2 solid solution	25.9	30.7
α_{Zr} + β_{ZrH} two-phase region	29.5	35.2
β_{ZrH} + H_2 solid solution	33.4	39.1
β_{ZrH} + δ_{ZrH} two-phase region	47.9	50.6
δ_{ZrH} + H_2 solid solution	41.2	47.2

For the 1 weight % uranium alloy, the values of the heat of solution range from −25.9 to −47.9 kcal. per mole, whereas the values in corresponding parts of the system are higher for the 25 weight % alloy. The range is −30.7 to −50.6 kcal. per mole, indicating that the rejection of a larger amount of uranium has only a small effect on the energy requirements for hydriding.

Ternary Diagrams.   Proposed isothermal sections of the zirconium-hydrogen-uranium ternary diagram at 627°, 675°, and 750° C. are shown in Figures 4, 5, and 6. The isotherm and x-ray diffraction data from this study, when combined with those of previous investigators and the known binary diagrams, permit deduction of these sections. The exact extent of some of the very narrow regions is in doubt, because of the difficulty in pinpointing these small areas.

The single-phase fields of α-zirconium, the γ_2 uranium-zirconium solid solution, and δ-zirconium hydride have well-defined phase boundaries. However, the exact limits of the single-phase fields of the γ_1 uranium-zirconium solid solution, α-uranium, and β-uranium are not as certain.

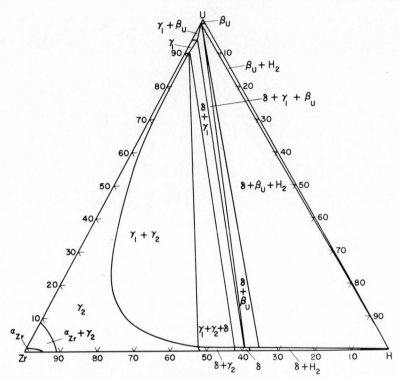

Figure 6.   Proposed Zr-H-U phase diagram

750° C. section

The rather narrow two-phase fields such as the delta hydride $+\alpha$-uranium in the 627° section, and the corresponding delta hydride $+\beta$-uranium in the 675° and 750° sections have somewhat uncertain limits.   Other two-phase fields are well defined.

Similarly, the limits of the broader areas having three solid phases are fairly certain, whereas those of extremely narrow regions such as the $\gamma_1 + \gamma_2 + \alpha$-uranium in the 675° C. section and the delta hydride $+ \gamma_1 + \beta$-uranium in the 675° and 750° C. sections are subject to question.   Additional x-ray data would be helpful in defining these phase fields.

Literature Cited

(1) Edwards, R. K., Levesque, P., Cubiciotti, D., *J. Am. Chem. Soc.* **77**, 1307 (1955).
(2) Ells, C. E., McQuillan, A. D., *J. Inst. Metals* **85**, 89 (1956–57).
(3) Espagno, L., Azon, P., Bastien, P., *Compt. Rend.* **248**, 2003-5 (1959).
(4) Gulbransen, E. A., Andrew, K. F., *J. Electrochem. Soc.* **101**, 474 (1954).
(5) Gulbransen, E. A., Andrew, K. F., *Trans. AIME* **203**, 136 (1955).
(6) Gulbransen, E. A., Andrew, K. F., Ruka, R. J., "Solubility of Hydrogen in the 50 w/o Uranium-Zirconium Alloy," Westinghouse Research Laboratories Rept. **100 FF1010-P1** (Oct. 16, 1956).
(7) Hagg, G., *Z. physik. Chem. (Leipzig)* **11B**, 433 (1930–31).
(8) Hall, M. N., Martin, S. L., Rees, A. L., *Trans, Faraday Soc.* **41**, 306 (1945).
(9) La Grange, L. D., Dykstra, L. J., Dixon, J. M., Merten, U., *J. Phys, Chem.* **63**, 2035 (1959).
(10) Libowitz, G. G., *J. Nucl. Mater.* **2**, 1–22 (1960).
(11) Libowitz, G. G., U. S. At. Energy Comm. Rept. **NAA-SR-5015** (June 30, 1960).

(12) Libowitz, G. G., Goon, E. J., Rice, M. J., *Ibid.,* NYO-3919 (March 17, 1955).
(13) Mallett, M. W., Albrecht, W. M., *J. Electrochem. Soc.* 104, 142 (1957).
(14) Rough, F. A., Austin, E. A., Bauer, A. A., Doig, J. R., U. S. At. Energy Comm. Rept. BMI-1092 (May 28, 1956).
(15) Rough, F. A., Bauer, A. A., "Constitutional Diagrams of Uranium and Thorium Alloys," Addison-Wesley Publishing Co., Reading, Mass., 1958.
(16) Schwartz, C. M., Mallett, M. W., *Trans. ASM* 46, 640 (1954).
(17) Singleton, J. H., Ruka, R. J., Gulbransen, E. A., "Reaction of Hydrogen with a 50 w/o Alloy of Uranium and Zirconium between 542° C. and 798° C.," Westinghouse Research Laboratories Rept. AECU-3630 (Nov. 16, 1956).
(18) Vaughan, D. A., Bridge, J. R., *Trans. AIME* 206, 528 (1956).
(19) Vetrano, J. B., Atkins, D. F., *Nucl. Metallurgy* 7, 57–61 (October 1960).
(20) Whitwham, D., *Mem. Sci. Rev. Met.,* 57, 1–15 (1960).
(21) Whitwham, D., Huber, M. A., Herenguel, J., *Acta Met.,* 7, 65–8 (1959).

RECEIVED September 6, 1962. Work supported by the U. S. Atomic Energy Commission, under Contract W-7405-eng-92.

13

Nonstoichiometry in Intermetallic Compounds

GUY R. B. ELLIOTT and **JOE FRED LEMONS**

The University of California, Los Alamos Scientific Laboratory, Los Alamos, N. M.

Defect equilibria in intermetallic compounds are inferred from measured changes of vapor pressure with composition and from other experimental information. Equilibria analogous to those in aqueous solution are found in dissociation, complexing, and random solution; other equilibria connected with the ordering of defects show a distinctly intermetallic flavor. Techniques for calculating the equilibria are described. Cerium-cadmium phase information is collected.

As an introduction to nonstoichiometry, particularly in intermetallic compounds, the vapor pressure and free energy relationships may be considered first. Each partial molal free energy is related to the vapor pressure, or more exactly the fugacity, of the individual component:

$$\bar{F}_i = RT \ln P_i + \text{constant}_i \tag{1}$$

The sum of the partial molal free energies multiplied by their appropriate mole fractions gives the total molal free energy:

$$N_1 \bar{F}_1 + N_2 \bar{F}_2 + + + = F \tag{2}$$

The total free energy measures the factors holding the whole phase together. In this sense the vapor pressures are bulk properties reflecting the stability of the condensed phase.

But in another sense the vapor pressure of a component is related closely to *deviations* from ideal stoichiometry rather than to gross composition. Consider a sodium chloride crystal in equilibrium at room temperature with metallic sodium, and also consider the same crystal in equilibrium with chlorine gas at a pressure of 1 atm. This system is also discussed by Brewer (2). Under the first conditions, there will be a very slight excess of sodium atoms in the crystal, and in the second case, a very slight deficiency of these atoms. Data from Pitzer and Brewer (16) indicate that the sodium vapor pressure of the crystal in the first case will be 10^{68} times that of the crystal in equilibrium with chlorine, and the partial molal free energy difference of the sodium between the two crystals will be 92,000 cal. Yet the total free energy of the crystals is different by at most a few calories, because the total bonding is little changed. Thus the vapor pressure difference reflects not so much the total bonding of the system as the bonding of the relatively few defects.

The idea of considering defect concentrations in a solid lattice is far from new. Wagner (21) was writing on the subject 30 years ago. Recently much work has been done in correlating composition variation with specific defects. Several papers of this symposium treat this correlation. The semiconductor people have considered regular solutions (20) and even solutions of electrons and holes (17) in their semiconductors.

Aim of Work

The work of this laboratory extends the defect treatment to intermetallic compounds. The experiments measure simultaneously both the cadmium vapor pressure and the composition at equilibrium for a series of only slightly different alloy compositions. The precision and the relative accuracy of the measurements are high; the absolute values suffer from any starting composition uncertainty and from errors in the absolute vapor pressure of cadmium as determined by other techniques. The experimental method is described elsewhere in this symposium (6). It has proved possible to infer the concentration and identity of lattice defects by analyzing the experimental data following the analytical techniques described below.

Establishing Defect Equilibria

Aqueous or gaseous species and solution equilibria are often deduced from mass action relationships. Experimental data for the isotherms of product concentration *vs.* total composition are compared with the predicted shapes of the isotherms based on various potentially valid assumed reactions. Frequently with simple reactions the appropriate reaction may readily be selected.

The technique requires the measurement of some property which is proportional to a product concentration—e.g., pH, color, or electrical conductivity. In the cerium-cadmium system the cadmium vapor pressure is one such measurable property.

Once the principal net reaction and equilibrium constant are established, standard total free energies, entropies, and heat contents become corollary. In the case of the cadmium vapor pressure one can therefore calculate total thermodynamic quantities from the established reactions as well as partial thermodynamic quantities from the vapor pressures directly.

Some of the defect equilibria which we have deduced by this type of analysis were not surprising—a parent lattice may dissociate into interstitials and vacancies in conformity with appropriate equilibrium constants; defects may associate, again consistent with an equilibrium constant; or the lattice may dissolve excess atoms in simple solubility. (When we speak of a solvent or parent lattice we mean the crystallographic lattice, as it would be determined by x-ray analysis, stoichiometrically perfect, and free of vacancies or interstitials. We call the process of vacancy and interstitial formation "lattice dissociation." Simple solution adds interstitials or fills voids in the parent lattice).

There has been one unexpected though perhaps not too surprising result: While a solid solution range for an ordered compound may be achieved by randomly dissolving defect atoms into an otherwise ordered lattice, these random defect atoms may themselves order and break the compound into a multitude of new true phases (microphases) separated by two-phase regions.

Species Mole Fractions

Consider that an intermetallic compound, A_2B, acts as a solvent. Just as nearly pure (but strongly cross-linked) H_2O units exist in equilibrium with a few

OH− and H+ units, so also one may anticipate that nearly pure (and even more strongly cross-linked) A_2B units will exist in equilibrium with a few A and AB units. In each case one can expect to describe the equilibrium by a constant of the form:

$$K = \frac{(A)\,(AB)}{(A_2B)} \tag{3}$$

where constant activity coefficients are included in K. By common usage interstitials are indicated by Δ and vacancies by $\square$. Using $\mathfrak{N}$ to describe a mole fraction:

$$K = \frac{(\mathfrak{N}_{A_\Delta})(\mathfrak{N}_{A_\square})}{(\mathfrak{N}_{A_2B})} \tag{4}$$

$\mathfrak{N}$ indicates that the mole fractions are based on species concentrations rather than atom concentrations. For example,

$$\mathfrak{N}_{A_\Delta} = \frac{n_{A_\square}}{n_{A_\Delta} + n_{A_\square} + n_{A_2B} + + +} \tag{5}$$

where n refers to the total moles of a species in the sample. The moles of A_2B refer to units which have not dissociated.

Relationship between Vapor Pressure and Defect Concentration

When the lattice dissociates, the bulk of the A product atoms may be expected to appear at equivalent sites next lower in bonding energy than the ideal sites. Similarly, if the lattice departs from stoichiometry by adding excess A atoms, these atoms will also be expected to appear first at the same type of site. Adding excess A atoms will decrease the A-vacancy concentration according to the equilibrium constant. An excess of B atoms will decrease A .

If the bulk of the A atoms are in random solution within a particular type of site, one may anticipate that their concentration will be proportional to the vapor pressure of A according to Henry's law:

$$P_A = k\mathfrak{N}_{A_\Delta} \tag{6}$$

Constant Activity Coefficients

All systems which we have studied behaved in a manner consistent with a constant species activity coefficient for the random defect solutes and the solvents. With the microphases the bulk of the defect atoms order to make a new parent structure, while the remainder of the defects appear in random solution.

Calculation of Equilibria

For purposes of discussion the dissociation of A_2B was chosen as the principal net reaction. In practice dissociation will always occur, but it may be masked by other reactions. At higher concentrations of A_Δ, the simple random solution of A_Δ in A_2B might be the principal net reaction, the vacancy concentration having become insignificant. On the other hand, at high A_Δ concentrations the A_Δ might cluster to extend the parent lattice while creating a B-vacancy.

In calculating the equilibrium constants from imperfect experimental data, it is often convenient to assume successive approximate values to find the best fit to the experimental data. If species activity coefficients are constant (as we have found them to be), the principal net reaction may often be determined by inspection of the plot of vapor pressure on the ordinate *vs.* composition on the abscissa. Simple solution yields a straight line; dissociation gives a shallow U; complexing, such as to form a B-vacancy, gives an unsymmetrical, inverted U; the combination of dissociation and complexing gives a bent-fishpole shape.

Defects in Real Intermetallics

Much of our work has been on the cerium-cadmium system. In Figure 1 the width of each CeCd$_{\sim 6}$ and CeCd$_{\sim 4.5}$ line above room temperature indicates the true stable range of the compound (including microphases).

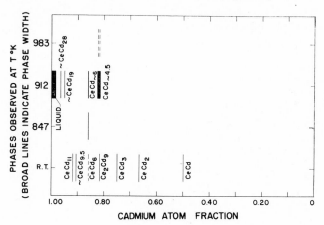

Figure 1. Collected phase information for cerium-cadmium system

Collected Phase Information for Cerium-Cadmium Alloys. A partial phase diagram for the cerium-cadmium system is presented in Figure 1. The room temperature results are based on x-ray studies by Iandelli and Ferro (9), who studied slowly cooled samples. However, their CeCd$_6$ is shown as a dashed line because nuclear magnetic resonance studies by Jackson and the authors (10) have shown that the compound is unstable at room temperature and can decompose to metallic cadmium and CeCd$_{\sim 4.5}$. Because of probable kinetic barriers, the absence of compounds intermediate between cadmium and CeCd$_{\sim 6}$ does not indicate that these intermediates are unstable at room temperature.

At the elevated temperatures the line width for CeCd$_{\sim 6}$ and CeCd$_{\sim 4.5}$ indicates the phase widths approximately. Because microphases of different stability may be produced in CeCd$_{\sim 4.5}$, there is a variability to both phase widths. Elliott and Lemons (6, 7) give more complete composition ranges. In particular Table I (6) may be used to calculate phase limits for CeCd$_{\sim 6}$ in the presence of different CeCd$_{\sim 4.5}$ structures.

The existence of structures approximating CeCd$_{28}$ and CeCd$_{19}$ and the liquidus for equilibrium with CeCd$_{28}$ are based on unpublished preliminary studies. The existence of these high cadmium compounds seems clear-cut, since the system showed different two-phase equilibrium pressures on either side of each compound and a continuous variation of vapor pressure with composition within each phase region. However, the assigned solid and liquidus compositions are sensitive to the "available" cerium from the material added and the assigned compositions may later be revised. Single-crystal x-ray studies of a composition approximately $CeCd_{9.5}$ by Olsen and the authors (*14*) indicate that it has a hexagonal structure different from any reported structures. Similar studies of $CeCd_{\sim4.5}$ samples by Cromer and the authors (*4*) indicate that there is a hexagonal structure with faint spots doubling the hexagonal axis; this structure is isomorphous with $PuZn_{4.5}$. Based on analysis of filtered samples, a cerium-cadmium liquidus assumed to correspond to equilibrium between $CeCd_{11}$ and the liquid has been reported by Johnson and Anderson (*11*). An extrapolation of their measurements to 912° K. predicts a liquidus near 0.043 mole fraction cerium, where our liquidus is closer to 0.01 mole fraction. On the basis of our vapor pressure measurements we would conclude that at 912° K. and to considerably lower temperatures a $CeCd_{11}$-liquid equilibrium would be metastable relative to the intermediates discussed.

Lattice Dissociation

The variation of cadmium activity with composition for the metastable broad solid solution range of $CeCd_{\sim4.5}$ is shown in Figure 2. Additional $CeCd_{\sim4.5}$ data are presented elsewhere (*6*).

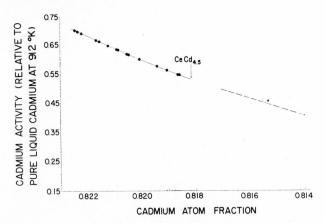

Figure 2. Metastable broad single-phase region in $CeCd_{\sim4.5}$

Microphases not included

A calculated composition differing by no more than 1/50,000 from the experimental value at any cadmium activity may be found by the equations:

$$K = \frac{(\mathfrak{N}_{Cd_\Delta})(\mathfrak{N}_{Cd_\square})}{(\mathfrak{N}_{CeCd_{4.5}})} = 2.6376 \times 10^{-3} \tag{7}$$

$$a_{Cd} = 10.872\mathfrak{N}_{Cd_\Delta} \tag{8}$$

Equation 7 describes the relationship between the solvent lattice and dissociation products, assuming constant species activity coefficients: Cd_Δ designates cadmium atoms in less tightly bound sites—e.g., interstitials; $Cd_\square$ refers to solvent units lacking a cadmium atom (cadmium vacancies). The cadmium activity,

α_{Cd}, is directly proportional to $\mathfrak{N}_{Cd_\Delta}$. $\mathfrak{N}$ refers to species, not atom, fractions based on species concentrations. In calculating concentrations it is assumed that cadmium atoms in excess of $CeCd_{4.5000}$ enter Cd_Δ positions or annihilate vacancies.

The excellent agreement between model and experiment suggests strongly that a dissociation reaction plus composition changes determine the cadmium activity. At $CeCd_{4.5000}$, $\mathfrak{N}_{Cd_\Delta} = \mathfrak{N}_{Cd \square} = 0.04879$ according to the equation. It is possible to rule out complexing reactions from the shape of the curve. A less likely alternative is that a $CeCd_4$ lattice dissolves excess cadmium atoms in random solution with slightly varying activity coefficient. With this model the curve would have approximately followed the dashed line in Figure 2, had not more stable phases interfered.

Lattice Dissociation Plus Complexing

Our data on $CeCd_{\sim 6}$ at two temperatures are presented in Figure 3. The data are less precise than the $CeCd_{\sim 4.5}$ data, so there is more uncertainty as to the shape of the curves, but their bent-fishpole shape seems distinct. The data do not fit the straight line associated with simple solubility or the bow accompanying dissociation alone. By assuming two equilibria the curves shown through the data were calculated: dissociation of a parent $CeCd_6$ lattice to cadmium interstitials and cadmium vacancies, and association of groups of six cadmium interstitials to form a cerium vacancy.

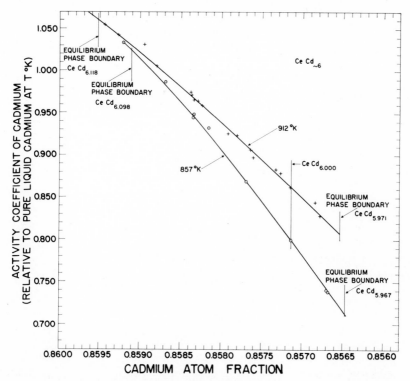

Figure 3. Composition-activity coefficient measurements and calculations for $CeCd_{\sim 6}$

Again as with $CeCd_{\sim 4.5}$, there is a large amount of dissociation. For $CeCd_{6.000}$ at 847° and 912° K. there are, respectively, 2.0 and 3.4% dislocated atoms.

Calculations of total thermodynamic quantities for the formation of various defects have been presented (7). The calculations are based on the assumed reactions and on constant (not unit) species activity coefficients.

Random Substitution at Specific Sites

Both U_2Zn_{17} (12) and Pu_2Zn_{17} (3) have the same structure. Chemical analyses have been made of high zinc liquid solutions in equilibrium with presumably the surface of precipitated U_2Zn_{17}, Pu_2Zn_{17}, or three-component solid solutions between them (5). When plotted as log solubility vs. reciprocal temperature, the individual actinide solubilities in the liquid have the same constant slope within experimental error. This statement applies for the precipitation of Pu_2Zn_{17}, U_2Zn_{17}, and $Pu_{1.6}U_{0.4}Zn_{17}$ from liquid solution. For the three-component system each individual actinide solubility is depressed consistent with an ideal solution of U_2Zn_{17} in Pu_2Zn_{17} in the solid. In other words, the Pu_2Zn_{17} departs from its ideal stoichiometry by randomly replacing plutonium atoms by uranium atoms, the zinc sites being unchanged.

The plutonium-uranium ratio in liquid solution was not consistent with that added. There seems little doubt that this discrepancy resulted from the precipitation of two different compounds as the alloy cooled from higher temperatures. Pu_2Zn_{17} decomposes peritectically at 1083° K. to form $PuZn_8$ and liquid (3). Presumably the $PuZn_8$-based three-component form dissolves and reprecipitates on the U_2Zn_{17} matrix near this temperature, as the temperature is lowered. The selected data of P/540 (5) show slightly different slopes for the plots of log solubility vs. reciprocal temperature for Pu-Zn and U-Zn. This variance probably reflects difference in technique by the two groups of experimenters, since it does not show in parallel Pu-Zn and U-Zn experiments by Elliott and coworkers on which that part of P/540 was based.

Out-of-Steps

The interesting alloy, CuAu(II), has been studied for many years. It is an example of so called out-of-steps, in which the types of atoms occupying lattice planes reverse abruptly and regularly. Only recently, as a result of the electron microscope and electron diffraction studies by Watanabe, Ogawa, and coworkers (13), is it apparently rather clearly understood. The results have pertinence to us because they represent an intermediate situation between distinctly single-phase regions (such as the $CeCd_{\sim 4.5}$ single-phase range just discussed) and ordered defects which yield distinctly different phases (discussed as microphases). Before ordering, the alloy is face-centered cubic. It orders to form alternate layers of gold and copper. However, at every five cube widths distance in one direction, the planes of gold and of copper alternate positions in out-of-steps. If the composition departs from ideal stoichiometry, plates six cube widths thick stack randomly with the five-cube-width plates. Presumably the two types of plates have different compositions and their relative frequency reflects the over-all composition.

This interpretation is not universally accepted. We find it convincing. We see no more feasible way to reconcile: the observed nonstoichiometry, the x-ray and electron diffraction spots which appear to indicate non-whole-numbers of atoms aligned to give a non-whole-number plate thickness, and the impossibility of any real reaction involving fractional atoms. Pashley and Presland (15) have reported uniform plate thicknesses $5^1/_2$ units thick, or 11 atoms through the plate. This possibility is also reasonable, but some other plate thickness would also have to be invoked to account for such x-ray-based apparent thicknesses as 5.7 units. In their theory of out-of-step ordering, Sato and Toth (18) calculate a single electron-atom ratio corresponding to an average non-whole-number plate thickness but appear not to explain its physical meaning.

Microphases

The random solution of defects caused by lattice dissociation and nonstoichiometry has been discussed for $CeCd_{\sim 4.5}$. In addition to this random solution in an otherwise ordered lattice, these defects can themselves order to create very many new and complex ordered lattices which we have named microphases. Structures with very similar properties appear at cadmium concentrations both greater and less than that of $CeCd_{4.5}$; if the $CeCd_{4.5}$ structure were the common base of all the microphases, discontinuities would be expected at $CeCd_{4.5}$ where the composition shifted from excess cadmium to deficient cadmium. $CeCd_4$, however, is a reasonable common base. The microphases are the subject of another paper (6).

Electrons as Alloy Components

If a Brillouin zone is nearly full or nearly empty, the electron concentration may become an important factor in determining alloy stability. This factor forms the basis of the Hume-Rothery rules (8) and is of great importance in intermetallic semiconductors.

Defect Interaction Term

As the concentration of defects becomes large, the assumption of constant activity coefficients becomes invalid. Anderson (1) has treated defect interactions by evaluating a constant interaction term between defect neighbors coupled with a term for the probability of occurrence of defect neighbors. Thorn (19) intends to look at metallic solid solution in this way.

Table I summarizes some observed types of nonstoichiometry in intermetallic compounds. The types are not mutually exclusive.

Table 1. Some Observed Types of Nonstoichiometry in Intermetallic Compounds

Types	Examples
Lattice dissociation	$CeCd_{\sim 4.5}$ in Fig. 2
Lattice dissociation with complexing	$CeCd_{\sim 6}$ in Fig. 3
Random substitution at particular sites	Actinide sites in $(U\text{-}Pu)_2Zn_{17}$
Different out-of-step distances	CuAu(II)
Ordered defects	Microphases in $CeCd_{\sim 4.5}$
Solution based on unstable parent solvent	Microphases in $CeCd_{\sim 4.5}$ (based on $CeCd_4$?)
Brillouin zone influences	Electron compounds

None of these types of nonstoichiometry establishes a specific phase boundary. The phase limits are determined by a competition between possible (and nucleated) phases for the available atoms.

Literature Cited

(1) Anderson, J. S., *Proc. Roy. Soc.* (*London*) **A185**, 69 (1946).
(2) Brewer, L., *J. Chem. Educ.* **38**, 90 (1961).
(3) Cramer, E. M., Ellinger, F. H., Land, C. C., "Extractive and Physical Metallurgy of Plutonium and Its Alloys," p. 169, W. D. Wilkinson, ed., Interscience, New York, 1959.
(4) Cromer, D. T., Elliott, G. R. B., Lemons, J. F., unpublished studies.
(5) Elliott, G. R. B., Feder, H. M., Kesser, G. M., Sweezer, R. U., as reported in part in Proceedings of United Nations Second International Conference on Peaceful Uses of Atomic Energy (Geneva), P/540, **17**, 383 (1958).
(6) Elliott, G. R. B., Lemons, J. F., ADVAN. CHEM. SER., No. **39**, 153 (1963).
(7) Elliott, G. R. B., Lemons, J. F., *J. Phys. Chem.* **64**, 137 (1960).
(8) Hume-Rothery, W., Raynor, G. V., "Structure of Metals and Alloys," Institute of Metals, London, 1956.
(9) Iandelli, A., Ferro, R., *Gazz. Chim. Ital.* **84**, 463 (1954).
(10) Jackson, J., Elliott, G. R. B., Lemons, J. F., unpublished studies.
(11) Johnson, I., Anderson, K. E., Argonne Natl. Lab., Rept. **ANL-6029** (1959).
(12) Makarov, E. S., Vinogradov, S. I., *Kristallografiya* **1**, 634 (1956).
(13) Ogawa, S., Watanabe, D., Watanabe, H., Komada, T., *Acta Cryst.* **11**, 872 (1958).
(14) Olsen, C. E., Elliott, G. R. B., Lemons, J. F., unpublished studies.
(15) Pashley, D. W., Presland, A. E. B., "Structure and Properties of Thin Films," Wiley, New York, 1959.
(16) Pitzer, K. S., Brewer, L., revision of G. N. Lewis, M. Randall, "Thermodynamics," 2nd ed., McGraw-Hill, New York, 1961.
(17) Reiss, H., Fuller, C. S., Morin, F. J., *Bell System Tech. J.* **35**, 535 (1956).
(18) Sato, H., Toth, R. S., *Phys. Rev.* **124**, 1833–40 (1961).
(19) Thorn, R. J., private communication.
(20) Thurmond, C. D., *J. Phys. Chem.* **57**, 827 (1953).
(21) Wagner, Carl, "Thermodynamics of Alloys," Addison-Wesley Press, Cambridge, Mass., 1952.

RECEIVED September 20, 1962.

Nonstoichiometry, Order, and Microphases in CeCd$_{\sim 4.5}$ Solid Solutions

GUY R. B. ELLIOTT and JOE FRED LEMONS

University of California, Los Alamos Scientific Laboratory, Los Alamos, N. M.

Both a very large number of phases (microphases) and a comparatively broad single phase have been observed in the same composition region near CeCd$_{\sim 4.5}$ using vapor pressure measurements with a bithermal, isopiestic equilibrator-balance. The broad single-phase range results from random defects dissolved in an ordered parent lattice. Further ordering by the defects creates the many different microphases. Family similarities exist in the activity coefficients of the microphases and in the two-phase regions between them. The two-phase ranges cover as little as 125-p.p.m. addition of cadmium to the alloy. In some cases a periodicity in allowed compositions is observed. Free energy data for CeCd$_{\sim 4.5}$ structures and for two-phase mixtures with CeCd$_{\sim 6}$ and with CeCd$_{\sim 3}$ are reported. Sources of bonding energy for the ordering reactions are discussed.

Cadmium vapor pressure measurements on cerium-cadmium alloys have been extended to include CeCd$_{\sim 4.5}$. As first reported, this alloy was called Ce$_2$Cd$_9$ (8). Designating it as CeCd$_{\sim 4.5}$ indicates that it has an experimentally measurable composition range. These measurements have disclosed the existence of many phases in what had appeared to be a single-phase region. The complexity of this system is greater than has been reported for any other metal system.

Experimental

General Method. The method has been described in detail (4).

At a selected alloy temperature the vapor pressure of cadmium is determined as a function of alloy composition; the cerium solvent has a negligible vapor pressure. The alloy, located in one leg of a sealed inverted U-tube, is subjected to various specific pressures of cadmium from a supply of pure cadmium at selected temperatures in the second leg of the tube. The U-tube is freely suspended at its midpoint and connected to a balance, so that the transfer of cadmium from one leg of the tube to the other can be measured. This gives information as to the change in alloy composition and phase equilibrium.

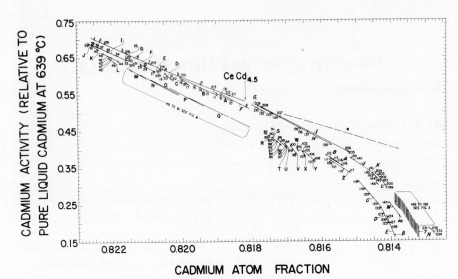

Figure 1.   Microphases observed in CeCd~4.5 region at 639° C.

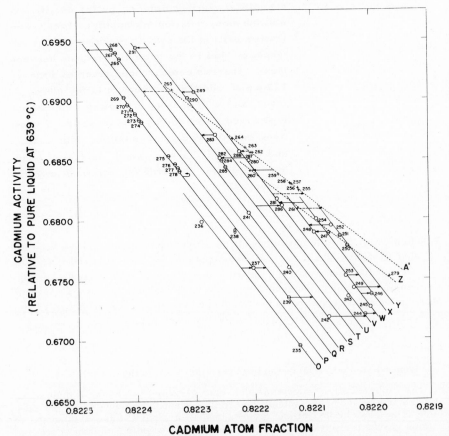

Figure 2.   Microphases observed in run III
Bold faced letters correspond to bold italic in text

Materials. The materials were equivalent to those used previously; however, there was an evident amount of intergranular oxide in the cerium used in run III. Approximately 4 grams of $CeCd_{\sim 4.5}$ was formed *in situ* by evaporating cadmium from $CeCd_{\sim 6}$. Three separate alloy charges in different equilibrators were used for three series of measurements: run I, points 1 to 128, and run II, points 129 to 234, in Figure 1; run III, points 235 to 297, in Figure 2. Each terminal alloy was observed to have been a single, porous, chunk of alloy. Metallography indicated clean crystals with enough pipes and cavities so that cadmium solid diffusion distances were in the range 0.01 to 0.1 mm.

Equilibrium Criteria. The experimentally practical criterion of equilibrium used in runs I and II was that neither composition nor temperature should change observably for $1/2$ hour. Experience with the equipment and sample observations for much longer periods of time (days in some cases) indicated that this time was adequate. In the composition-structure region represented in Figure 3 the alloy composition did not change detectably within limited ranges of cadmium vapor pressure. For these measurements the criterion of equilibrium adopted was that a composition should not have shifted detectably for at least $3/4$ hour and the cadmium condensate temperature should not have shifted detectably for $1/3$ hour. Once a pattern of behavior had been established, some measurements were accepted in which the procedure or conditions varied in minor detail from that described. Such points are not indicated in Figure 1, but are indicated by a bar through the datum circles in other figures.

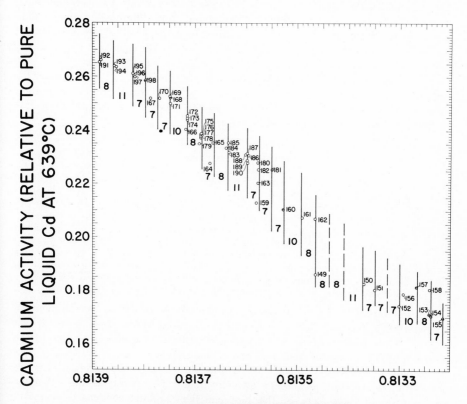

Figure 3.   Enlargement of microphase family observed in points 149 to 198

A second procedure was adopted for some of the points in run III. When the system was thought to be near equilibrium, the cadmium condensate temperature was allowed to drift at a rate of approximately 0.002 degree per minute in a direction which would tend to decrease the rate of cadmium transfer between alloy and condensate. A reversal of the direction of drift of alloy weight then indicated that the equilibrium vapor pressure of the alloy had been observed.

A small change in cadmium temperature resulted in a slow continuous change in alloy weight corresponding to a linear relationship between activity and cadmium mole fraction. Such a relationship could be followed for days at a time. The nucleation of a new structure resulted in an easily recognized sharp departure in composition which was completed in about $1/2$ hour. The system composition would reflect even the small temperature fluctuations associated with change of ambient conditions in the room. The effect tended to randomize the direction of approach to equilibrium for a particular point.

For the larger temperature changes, composition equilibrium lagged temperature equilibrium by perhaps an hour, but the temperature readjustment was slow enough normally to require some 8 hours between measurements.

Precision of Measurements. Reading the balance to ± 0.25 mg. for a 4-gram alloy (and including the approximately sixfold sensitivity multiplication because of differences in the balance and U-tube torque arms) resulted in knowing changes in the alloy composition to about $\pm 1/100,000$ or to ± 0.000008 in relative cadmium mole fractions. For the readings to ± 0.10 mg. the cadmium mole fraction was indicated to ± 0.000003. The temperature differences between alloy and cadmium were read to $\pm 0.01°$ C., which corresponds to about $3/10,000$ in the cadmium activity. Only in Figure 2 is the activity the major source of uncertainty.

The relative nature of the data needs to be emphasized. Corrections for oxide and other impurities have been applied (4), but the absolute composition uncertainty is perhaps 30 times as great as the relative uncertainty. For this reason runs I and II were superimposed as follows:

Points 1 and 12 were assumed to correspond at their observed activities to the upper curve of run II, which had been evaluated as described in "Improvements." The compositions so determined were used with the observed balance readings to establish the two calculation constants used in the evaluation of all other data in run I. Point 128 was confirmed within analytical error by a chemical analysis. The compositions associated with run III (Figure 2) could not be determined directly because of the unknown amount of oxide present. However, since the absolute composition-activity relationships for $CeCd_{\sim 6}(4)$ are known approximately, an estimate of the composition was possible. The resulting calculated values for $CeCd_{\sim 4.5}$ were increased by 0.05%, in order to be consistent with the position of the upper structure in Figure 1. The resulting composition values should not be assumed to correspond precisely to those in Figure 1; however, it is not essential that the composition be known with greater precision.

Temperature. The temperature designated for a datum is the nominal temperature at 639° or 710° C. In practice measurements were accepted over a 2° range of alloy temperature. A separate heater over each end section of the cross arm was regulated to keep that end of the cross arm roughly 20° hotter than the metal below; however, at the time data were taken the temperature differences between cross arm and metal were not more than $\pm 2°$. It was assumed that the temperature difference between the alloy and the cadmium condensate necessary to form the observed alloy would be insignificant between the experimental and nominal alloy temperatures. Since the temperature varied over very limited ranges, the change of activity with temperature is slight, and the drifts of alloy temperature took place over weeks, the assumption introduces no identifiable error. Vapor pressures are again based on the cadmium vapor pressure equation of Kelley as described earlier (4). Corrections applied for air buoyancy and the weight of cadmium vapor have a maximum value of about 4 mg. between the extreme cadmium temperatures at the lower alloy temperature. The corrections do not influence the interpretation of the data.

A platinum–10% rhodium to platinum thermocouple was operated with hot and cold junctions, respectively, in the alloy and condensed cadmium regions. Reference tables (16) were used to convert e.m.f. to absolute temperature. However, in the tables, temperatures are rounded to the nearest 0.1° C., which is too rough for our temperature differences. The tables are based on earlier work (13) with the values adjusted to the 1948 international temperature scale. To evaluate the difference between alloy and cadmium condensate temperatures, we have used without adjustment two equations from the earlier work

$$E = -309.17 + 8.29558\, t + 0.00144103\, t^2 + 0.0000001634\, t^3$$

$$E = -333.29 + 8.29175t + 0.00161080\, t^2$$

for alloys at 639° and 710° C., respectively, where E is in microvolts and t is in degrees centigrade. The use of a single equation for each alloy temperature extends the equations slightly beyond the ranges for which they were intended but avoids spurious breaks in our curves. [For the temperature ranges of interest in the previous paper (4), smoothly varying temperature differences consistent with NBS values (16) could be obtained by dividing the millivolt difference in e.m.f. between the alloy and cadmium condensate by 0.010274 or 0.010041.]

Improvements. Minor changes have significantly improved the equipment, and with experience has come better operating technique. Vibrations have been damped and stray breeze effects reduced. The balance beam and the horizontal arm of the isopiestic equilibrator now remain parallel as they pivot; consequently, the sensitivity of the balance remains constant during the pivoting. The change in weight indicated by the balance is now sixfold larger than the actual cadmium transfer. The copper heat distributors are nickel plated.

The balance calibration technique was changed. At the end of the run while the system was in equilibrium, the alloy and cadmium legs were isolated from each other by collapsing the horizontal arm. The balance calibration was calculated from initial and final balance readings corresponding to having the original known total of metal all in the alloy leg (cadmium leg hotter), and to having a determinable amount of cadmium in the other leg (as sealed off).

Experimental Results

Initial measurements on $CeCd_{\sim 4.5}$, as expected, indicated a continuous variation of cadmium vapor pressure with composition as is shown in the upper curve of Figure 1. However, the system soon demonstrated distinct, discontinuous vapor pressure–composition relationships, as illustrated by the remaining curves of Figure 1 and as shown in greater detail and with additional data in the remaining figures. We have designated these secondary structures as "microphases."

The point numbers are consistent with the order in which measurements were taken; however, approximately one year elapsed between points 234 and 235. During this period other systems were studied with the same equipment but without the appearance of microphases. The point sizes indicate the approximate

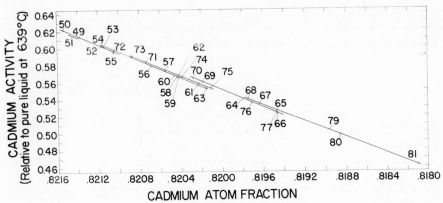

Figure 4.   Enlargement of microphase family observed in points 49 to 81

precision of the data.   (In Figure 1 the points are difficult to distinguish.)   Theory and calculation techniques were presented earlier (4).

In run I (Figures 1 and 4, points 1 to 128) the first five points fell on a smooth curve.   By the time point 5 was taken, the alloy had been at temperature and in the $CeCd_{\sim 4.5}$ region for over 2 weeks.   Point 6 fell off the curve, yet appeared to be experimentally valid.   Points 7 and 8, taken at a higher cadmium pressure, again fell on the smooth curve; points 9 to 11 formed a new curve; point 12 returned to the old curve for the last time in run I.   The alloy had then been in the $CeCd_{\sim 4.5}$ region for 3 weeks.

All further measurements in run I led to a lower cadmium activity at any composition than would be predicted by the initial curve.   As the cadmium pressure increased, new curves of activity *vs.* composition developed.   Curves of similar slopes and spacings tended to define families.   After point 39 the cadmium pressure was again generally decreased.   Finally at activity β the $CeCd_{\sim 4.5}$ went into equilibrium with the next classical phase, presumably $CeCd_3$ as reported by Iandelli and Ferro (8).   [The technique of measurement, which is based on finding the pressure at which the two phases can be in equilibrium at this temperature, is described by Elliott and Lemons (4).]

Run II (Figures 1, 3, and 4, points 129 to 234), with a new charge of cerium and cadmium in a new equilibrator, gave only one point initially which was attributable to the upper curve before the measurements departed from the curve. Successively lower pressures disclosed a number of curves similar and in some cases identical to those observed in part of run I.

From points 149 to 198 (Figure 3) a distinctly different family of curves was measured.   Each microphase occurred over an extremely narrow composition range with intervening two-phase regions whose widths showed an eight-member cyclic relationship.   Within experimental error the widths in mole fraction of the two-phase regions are described by 0.00000343 times the recurring ratios . . . 11, 7, 7, 7, 10, 8, 7, 8, . . .—i.e., 0.000024 was the smallest difference in mole fraction.   The low cadmium member of this family went into equilibrium with the phase presumed to be $CeCd_3$, at a cadmium activity, γ, slightly higher than β. The family disappeared as the pressure increased; more new curves were observed which bore marked similarity to earlier measurements.   Points 211 to 216 fell on the original upper curve.

Points 217 to 230 were taken with the alloy at 710° C. (see Figure 5) and again showed discontinuous curves. Finally, points 231 to 234 were taken at 639° C. and the run was ended.

For runs I and II curves A, C, I, J, K, and S in Figure 1 and the upper curve of Figure 5 show consecutive observations with reversal of direction with respect to composition during the series. The occurrence of nonconsecutive points on the curve for a single microphase occurred among others in Figure 1, points 94, 93, and 97; Figure 4, points 73, 71, 57, 62, 74, 61, and 75; and Figure 3, points 159, 163, 182, and 180. The initial random structure (Figure 1) repeated: Figure 1, points 1 to 5, 7 to 8, and 12 in run I and points 129 and 211 to 215 of the second sample.

In most cases for runs I and II the evidence for significant and distinct curves, and the assignment of points to these curves, were unequivocal. Even in Figure 4, with its closely spaced microphases, a calculation with random statistical assumptions indicates $\ll 1/1000$ likelihood that the least clearly separated lines (N and O, Figure 1) are really a single line. In a few cases, such as points 29 to 48 of Figure 1, the decision was somewhat arbitrary as to how the points were related; however, the extensive investigation of this region shown in Figure 2 and described below suggests that the assigned slopes for these lines are entirely reasonable.

The alloy for run III (Figure 2, points 235 to 291) was maintained in the $CeCd_{\sim 6}$ composition range until it was demonstrated to be at equilibrium, as indicated by behavior consistent with previous observations (4). It was maintained at temperature for 4 days, during which time the equilibrium temperature was established. Cadmium was then transferred from the alloy (by increasing the temperature differential on the vessel) until a composition corresponding approximately to 10% $CeCd_{\sim 6}$ and 90% $CeCd_{\sim 4.5}$ was present. On the sixth day of heating a two-phase equilibrium pressure of about 0.1361 atm. was observed for several hours. The next day the pressure was about 0.1384 atm. [These two pressures were obtained by extrapolating to zero rate the rate of transfer of cadmium as a function of temperature difference between alloy and cadmium condensate. The extrapolation was 1.1° (0.00220 atm.) in the first case and 0.1° (0.00020 atm.) in the second case.] Finally, on the eighth day, an equilibrium pressure of 0.14036 ± 0.00004 atm. was measured by approaching equilibrium from the condition of excess as well as insufficient cadmium pressure. The observed equilibria between $CeCd_{\sim 4.5}$ structures and other phases are summarized in Table I.

Table I. Cadmium Vapor Pressures for CeCd$_{\sim 4.5}$ Structures in Equilibrium with Other Phases at 639° C.

Phases in Equilibrium	Cadmium Pressure[a], Atm.
$CeCd_{\sim 6} + CeCd_{\sim 4.5}$ (run III 1st)	0.13611 ± 0.00041
$CeCd_{\sim 6} + CeCd_{\sim 4.5}$ (run III 2nd)	0.13839 ± 0.00020
$CeCd_{\sim 6} + CeCd_{\sim 4.5}$ (run III 3rd)	0.14036 ± 0.00004
$CeCd_{\sim 6} + CeCd_{\sim 4.5}$ (4)	0.14070 ± 0.00015
$CeCd_3 + CeCd_{\sim 4.5}$ (run I)	0.033116 ± 0.000189
$CeCd_3 + CeCd_{\sim 4.5}$ (run II)	0.034504 ± 0.000019

[a] Based on Kelley equation (4).

The alloy was converted completely to $CeCd_{\sim 4.5}$ and measurements were continued for 2 weeks. The data define two distinct families of curves or microphases. Most of the data fell on a family of 11 equally spaced parallel lines. The separation corresponds to a difference in cadmium mole fraction of 0.000021.

The remaining data could be fitted to two additional parallel lines of different slope but with a mole fraction separation essentially twice that observed for the primary family. Indeed, point 280 may well lie on a "missing line" between these latter lines. The slope of the lines for the primary family is similar to that for lines A and B in Figure 1, and the slope for the secondary family is close to that for lines C and D.

Data points were observed for each of the 11 lines of the primary family, and in six cases points obtained nonconsecutively occur on a given line. Line **V** was observed five separate times and seven equilibrium points were obtained; however, between points 254 and 255 no equilibrium data point was recorded. The primary family disappeared and the secondary family appeared in its place three times—before points 255, 279, and 287. In each case a reconversion to the primary family occurred at a higher cadmium pressure. An effort was made to confine the system to the primary family where possible, since the object of this particular run was to demonstrate unequivocally the reversible nature of a particular family.

In Figure 2 arrows have been drawn where transitions between curves were witnessed and also for some cases where it was known only that a transition had occurred between consecutive points. In these cases the arrow indicates only the extreme limit of composition-activity difference at which transition could have occurred. The transitions which occurred between consecutive points 278 and 279, 279 and 280, 282 and 283, and 286 and 287 have not been indicated. However, following (and very close to) point 278, during a period of less than an hour, the system was observed to undergo an excursion at nearly constant activity which is interpreted to be an attempt at a transition possibly to line **Q,** but it then returned to line **P.** This attempt at transition was doubtless prevented by temperature fluctuation, but it seems definite that the system was very close to the two-phase equilibrium region between two microphases. Also between points 278 and 279 the system was observed to be in the region of mole fraction 0.8220 and line **U,** but the next equilibrium point was 279 in the secondary family. Where the interfamily transitions have been indicated, dashed arrows have been used.

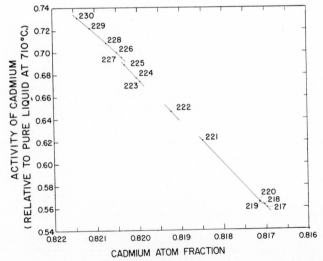

Figure 5.   Microphases observed in CeCd$_{\sim 4.5}$ region at 710° C.

All data except for the upper curves of Figures 1 and 5 are described by straight lines, the equations for which are listed in Tables II, III, and IV. Their identification is consistent with that used in the figures. Figure 3 lines are listed as a single composition in Table III, since the precision of measurements did not permit the demonstration of the variation of composition with vapor pressure which

Table II.   Equation Parameters for Activity-Composition Curves Drawn on Figures 1, 4, and 5

Symbol	Mole Fraction Range Observed At 639° C.	A^a	B^a
A	0.818583–0.818996	39.2074	48.5470
B	0.819260–0.820029	37.1539	46.0340
C	0.819816–0.819960	58.4253	71.9720
D	0.820274–0.820455	71.1216	87.4250
E	0.820610–0.820681	88.0913	108.0850
F	0.820768–0.821146	40.3686	49.9313
G	0.821355–0.821373	198.7760	242.7780
H	0.821566–0.821589	143.6642	175.6520
I	0.821599–0.822547	35.6162	44.1350
J	0.822410–0.822649	50.9748	62.8033
K	0.821821–0.822239	30.5494	37.9545
L	0.821907–0.822054	57.2314	70.4082
51	$(0.821444, 0.61513)^b$		
M	0.821048–0.821540	43.1264	53.2520
N	0.820154–0.821153	41.6841	51.4980
O	0.820111–0.820876	40.4073	49.9445
P	0.819459–0.820280	41.2054	50.9224
Q	0.818108–0.819750	38.4304	47.5396
82	(0.817617, 0.44159)		
R	0.817385–0.817528	80.7053	99.2547
S	0.817185–0.817414	68.6854	84.5560
T	0.817049–0.817244	72.9168	89.7436
U	0.816998–0.817057	89.8773	110.5080
V	0.816732–0.816878	98.5142	121.0960
W	0.816690–0.816702	145.9441	179.1670
X	0.816499–0.816552	104.6804	128.6790
Y	0.816224–0.816511	63.7896	78.6063
108	(0.816206, 0.37257)		
Z	0.815210–0.815726	49.5395	61.1821
A	0.815417–0.815725	44.8889	55.4870
B	0.815572–0.815852	47.1113	58.2143
C	0.814383–0.814936	64.5371	110.0540
D	0.814086–0.814294	160.4660	197.3560
E	0.813996–0.814115	200.5108	246.5550
F	0.818152–0.818867	40.7026	50.3776
G	0.817709–0.817846	45.2143	55.9124
H	0.815742–0.817828	40.9153	50.6632
I	0.815241–0.817718	39.9342	49.4660
J	0.814629–0.815148	51.9902	64.2389
K	0.814408–0.814534	81.4433	100.3970
204	(0.814451, 0.33327)		
146	(0.814408, 0.29581)		
L	0.814160–0.814388	101.8802	125.5040
199	(0.814132, 0.29374)		
M	0.813765–0.814030	104.3436	128.4910
N	0.812791–0.812903	64.0604	79.0278
	At 710° C.		
223	0.819952–0.920313	33.7826	42.0222
222	(0.819225, 0.64674)		
221	0.817146–0.818489	33.2283	41.3552
218	0.816989–0.817046	35.7029	44.3860

^{a} Cadmium activity $= -A + B$ (mole fraction of cadmium).
^{b} Numbers in parenthesis are, respectively, mole fraction and corresponding activity where only one point within phase was observed.

Table III.   Allowed Compositions in a Family of Ordered $CeCd_{\sim 4.5}$ Microphases in Figure 3

Composition[a]	Relative Separation[b]	Observed Activity Range
0.813886		0.26521–0.26606
	8	
0.813859		0.26357–0.26394
	11	
0.813821		0.25975–0.26105
	7	
0.813797		0.25189–0.25841
	7	
0.813773		0.25184–
	7	
0.813749		0.24986–0.25252
	10	
0.813715		0.24026–0.24524
	8	
0.813687		0.23486–0.23875
	7	
0.813663		0.22753–0.23524
	8	
0.813636		0.23161–0.23524
	11	
0.813598		0.22778–0.23132
	7	
0.813574		0.21291–0.22782
	7	
0.813550		0.22522
	7	
0.813526		0.21046
	10	
0.813492		0.20732
	8	
0.813464		0.18605–0.20697
	8	
(0.813437)[c]		
	8	
(0.813409)		
	11	
0.813372		0.18243
	7	
0.813348		0.18029
	7	
(0.813324)		
	7	
0.813300		0.17423–0.17874
	10	
0.813265		0.18136
	8	
0.813238		0.17055–0.18046
	7	
0.813214		0.16969

[a] As mole fraction cadmium.   Accurate relative values; because of analytical uncertainty and unknown effects of impurities on cerium availability, fourth figure may be incorrect by several units.
[b] Composition gap divided by 0.00000343.
[c] Phases in parentheses predicted; no experimental evidence, pro or con.

is thermodynamically required. The upper curve of Figure 1 may be calculated as described elsewhere (3).

In addition to the data described above, room temperature single-crystal x-ray patterns of slowly cooled $CeCd_{\sim 4.5}$ samples (each composition near $CeCd_{\sim 4.3}$) have been taken by C. E. Olsen and D. T. Cromer of this laboratory. Work by Olsen showed that there was probably a complex lattice superimposed upon the

Table IV.   Equation Parameters for Activity-Composition Curves Drawn on Figure 2

Symbol	Activity Range Observed	A^a	B^a
O	0.66949–0.67985	52.94725	65.21739
P	0.67591–0.69025	52.94587	65.21739
Q	0.67346–0.67897	52.94449	65.21739
R	0.69348–0.69431	52.94310	65.21739
S	0.67182–0.68052	52.94172	65.21739
T	0.68439–0.69442	52.94034	65.21739
U	0.68703–0.69014	52.93896	65.21739
V	0.67203–0.69066	52.93757	65.21739
W	0.67264–0.67888	52.93619	65.21739
X	0.67375–0.68000	52.93481	65.21739
Y	0.67774–0.67856	52.93343	65.21739
Z	0.67519–0.68402	31.02044	38.56041
A'	0.68237–0.69077	31.01890	38.56041

a Cadmium activity $= -A + B$ (moles fraction of cadmium).

basic $CeCd_{\sim 4.5}$ pattern.   Cromer's patterns clearly demonstrate that the structure of $CeCd_{\sim 4.5}$ is isomorphous with that of $PuZn_{\sim 4.5}$ and that both patterns are hexagonal with faint spots which double the hexagonal axis.   Analysis of the $PuZn_{\sim 4.5}$ pattern is in progress.

J. A. Jackson, also of this laboratory, has made room temperature nuclear magnetic resonance studies of the Knight shift of cadmium in slowly cooled $CeCd_{\sim 4.5}$ alloys with different compositions and different histories.   All $CeCd_{\sim 4.5}$ samples tested showed a major peak at almost the same position and shifted from that of metallic cadmium.   One sample showed only this peak, while others clearly showed satellite peaks either at larger or at smaller shift.   Possibly some samples had small amounts of both satellite peaks, and there was apparently some further difference in the shapes of satellite peaks and of the major peak; these latter observations are tenuous, however, since they were near the resolution limit of the apparatus.   The differences apparently do not correlate simply with composition; however, they may correlate with differences in microphase structures.

Discussion

A metastable broad single-phase region and many additional phases, termed microphases, are indicated by the measurements.   The consecutively numbered data are plotted in the figures.   Each curve must represent a different structure and its continuous variation of composition with pressure.   In interpreting these results it is assumed, on the basis of experimental evidence, that we are dealing with homogeneous samples and that the system is thermodynamically at equilibrium with respect to a particular microphase structure when each datum point is taken.   In addition, a particular microphase structure may be, and frequently is, metastable relative to other closely related structures in the same family or to other structures in different families.

Reversibility has been demonstrated by the repeated appearance on a single curve of points obtained nonconsecutively, the appearance of consecutive points attributable to a single curve in which there is reversal of direction with respect to composition during the series, the fact that the system can be maintained within a given activity-composition relationship for days and then moved rapidly to a new relationship in which it is equally stable, the fact that the same family of activity-composition relationships can be rediscovered repeatedly as shown in Figure 2, and the fact that the system has returned repeatedly to the upper structure of Figure 1 with its broad solid solubility range.

That the behavior of the system is inconsistent with a model in which successive domain reactions are assumed is indicated as follows:

Any single, condensed-phase reaction at a given temperature in which a component is removed from or added to the equilibrium gas phase will have a single key pressure for the gas phase, above which the reaction can only proceed in one direction and below which it can only reverse. We have observed very many such key pressures; therefore, any reaction to form a single product, even though it involves the transformation of successive domains, cannot explain the data.

Transformation of successive domains involving the structure shown in the upper curve of Figure 1, and a single product, would result in a series of curves of successively steeper slope which, when extrapolated, intersect the upper curve at the same point. Thus a different product phase is required for each different point of intersection, within experimental error.

Transformation of successive domains cannot give parallel curves such as those in Figure 2. In addition, domains of random size could not give the precise periodicity of structure shown in Figures 2 and 3.

The evidence is inconsistent with characteristic surface or diffusion-controlled reactions for many of the same reasons.

Upper Curve in Figure 1. In the previous paper (3) the curve was associated with defects dissolved randomly in an ordered $CeCd_{\sim 4.5}$ parent.

The Microphases. Each line below the upper curve on Figure 1 indicates a distinct true phase, called a microphase. The straight lines are consistent with Henry's law behavior of the nonstoichiometric atoms which cause the total composition of any microphase to vary from that corresponding to the crystallographically ideal microphase structure. [There would be a negligible but theoretically predictable curvature, because the ratio of changes in the species fractions ($\Delta \mathfrak{N}_{Cd\,\Delta}$) to changes in atom fractions ($\Delta N_{Cd\,\Delta}$) is not precisely constant.]

Essentially all the microphases exhibit metastable composition extensions. The significance of these extensions is twofold: They show that nucleation of phases is difficult. They prove that the phase composition limits for stable equilibrium are usually determined by competition between microphases for the available atoms rather than by composition limits inherent in the structure of the microphases.

If two vapor pressures are indicated for a single composition, the structures must be different. Any total composition is made up of parent structure plus defects. If the lines cross, the total compositions and cadmium vapor pressures have become equal, but the cerium vapor pressures, total free energies, and structures in the two microphases are different.

A more stable structure will tend to produce a lower lying curve for the cadmium partial pressure; however, one cannot generalize, since this cannot be true for pressures extending much below that corresponding to the unique pressure for two-solid equilibrium. The thermodynamically required characteristic stair-step nature of the activity mole fraction diagram across the typical family at family equilibrium shown in Figure 2 can be readily visualized. There is a tendency toward conversion at lower cadmium activity across the diagram from left to right and, more clearly, toward reconversion at ever-increasing activity across the diagram from right to left.

Stable phase limits may be determined from the pressure-composition relationships within a phase coupled with a determination of the unique activity at which two phases may be in equilibrium (4). Unfortunately, experimental difficulties were too great to obtain well defined equilibrium data for two-microphase regions. As an example of how this unique activity may be established approximately, consider microphases **W** and **X** in Figure 2. Between points 245 and 246 the first microphase had transformed to the second; at point 247 the process had reversed, giving point 248. Then to continue, between points 249 and 250 microphase **W** transformed to **Y** and between 252 and 253 it transferred back again. After point 253 for a second time **W** transformed to **X** and after 254 back to **V**. Since transformations always lead to a more stable product, the cadmium activity corresponding to the two-phase equilibrium between **W** and **X** must lie between points 248 and 253. It is definitely above point 246. Similarly, the transformation between microphases **X** and **Y** must be above point 249 and below point 248, even though these transformations are not directly between the microphases involved.

A rougher but useful estimate of the unique activities may be made by assuming that each lies half-way along the cadmium activity overlap observed between two microphases. Since the transformations appear to become more probable with greater defect concentrations, the estimates have some kinetic basis.

Thermodynamics. Although we have very accurate relative data for the cadmium vapor pressures, we cannot present equally accurate thermodynamics values for the commonly used standard formation reactions. There are four main sources of difficulty:

So many reactions are observed that we cannot always associate an observed equilibrium pressure with a corresponding reaction.

Between the microphases the two-phase equilibrium pressures are not known accurately.

The absolute vapor pressure of cadmium is not as well known as the relative values.

Since we do not have cadmium vapor pressure across the whole cerium-cadmium system, some standard state other than the pure metal would have to be used for cerium.

The changes of total free energy with composition are very small in both $CeCd_{\sim 6}$ and $CeCd_{\sim 4.5}$. For example, based on a Duhem integration at 912° K. of the upper curve in Figure 1 from $CeCd_{4.5000}$ to $CeCd_{4.6155}$, we find a change in total free energy only 6.4 cal. per mole. The corresponding changes of partial molar free energies for cadmium and cerium are 458.6 and -2081.0 cal. per mole. (The composition $CeCd_{4.6155}$ has been chosen because we guess that the corresponding cadmium activity, 0.676727, is that for equilibrium between $CeCd_{\sim 6}$ and the upper random defect structure.)

Similarly, although there is a maximum difference in cadmium partial molal free energy of a little less than 2 kcal. per mole between the extrapolated upper structure, α, of Figure 1 and the most stable observed microphases, the difference in total molal free energy is less than 10 cal. per mole. (The calculation is based on the path 133 to 209 with assumed two-phase equilibrium pressures of cadmium. This path closes on microphase **H**.) The difference in these two values emphasizes that the vapor pressure measurements have reflected the concentration and bonding of cadmium species which are minor fractions of the total cadmium present and which did not much alter the average bonding of the system.

A generalized free energy of 998 ± 42 cal. is calculated for the observed reactions involving a mole of any $CeCd_{4.5000}$ structure with 1.5000 moles of liquid cadmium to give $CeCd_{6.000}$. Specific free energies may be calculated from the data in Table I. Since an error in the assigned reaction would so strongly change the apparent temperature dependence, no heats or entropies are presented.

Since most microphase limits are not clearly established, most or possibly all of the observed microphases are unstable, and equilibrium between all microphase families has not been established, there is not enough information to present a worthwhile phase diagram.

Why Do Microphases Form? The most simple quantum mechanical model of a metal is a box with only one finite dimension. The walls are infinite barriers, so an electron inside has no chance to escape. This model accepts only those electron energies which correspond to electronhalf-wavelengths which are simple fractions of the box size. Metal electrons may fill part of these energy levels with two electrons per level. The upper level of energy reached is called the Fermi level. A smooth U-shaped curve of energy $vs.$ wave number includes all acceptable energies in this model.

However, in a real lattice the electrons cannot assume the same energies as correspond to Bragg lattice reflections. The energy levels just below these reflections are considered to have been forced down in energy, while those just above are raised. The gaps break the curve into a series of S-shaped curves each corresponding to a Brillouin zone.

If there is a superlattice, there is an additional group of forbidden energies similar to those connected with the main lattice reflections. Slater (17) has pointed out that the depression of the energy levels from the forbidden energies could be the source of energy for the formation of a superlattice if the Fermi level fell at a superlattice forbidden electron energy. He anticipated that order from this cause could be widespread.

The very formation of microphases implies the existence of some long-range signal between the widely separated ordering defects. Therefore two other observations seem pertinent in understanding the microphases: Friedel and his coworkers ($1, 11$) have shown that an impurity atom in a lattice can produce long distance oscillations in the charge density. Seeger has concluded that older calculations of the strains and the electronic redistribution associated with lattice dislocations had given answers which were much too small. Particularly if the dislocations are "piled up," they create large electron barriers, as evidenced by their large effect on electrical resistivity (15).

We like much of the Slater view to explain microphases. However, if possible, we prefer to think of specific defects at specific sites; this is not possible in the reciprocal lattice in k space.

First consider the specific ordering of a group of defects. From the microphases in Figure 3 we know that the addition of only one atom of cadmium per 8000 atoms already present can lead to a new structure rather than a solid solution range. For a number to work with let us assume that the entropy loss on ordering corresponds to restricting to one position an atom which could have occupied any of 8000 positions in a random solution. At our temperatures this leads to a temperature-entropy loss of 4.575 (912/1000) log 8000 = 16 kcal. per mole of defects. In other words, to get a favorable free energy change we must find a heat of reaction per mole of defects of around 16 kcal. If this heat is spread over all cadmium atoms, it need be only 2 cal. per mole of total cadmium. It seems likely to us that the ordering heat evolution comes from replacing a general scattering of all electron levels by a large effect on only a few levels.

As a supplement to the Slater view we have arrived at a working model of microphases. We are unable to express it mathematically and we recognize it as tentative. However, it has been very useful to us, so we pass it on. As we present the model we are also pointing out experimental facts which any corollary or competitive view must explain.

Let us reconsider the electron in a box but now reverse the variable. Let us hold the electron at a single energy and allow the box walls to move. Now the acceptable boxes are quantized in units of the selected half-wavelength.

We consider that in $CeCd_{\sim 4.5}$ the parent lattice periodicity sets the general chemical character and most properties of the Bloch wave for the electrons. When microphases form, the very long wavelength electrons still see effectively a perfect lattice periodicity. The very short wavelengths see slightly different end effects, but they were seeing much thermal agitation anyway. But for wavelengths near the distance between ordered defects the lattice periodicity is severely altered.

When the defects were random, their presence made all the electron waves less than perfect—i.e., of higher energy and less ideal bonding than in the absence of the defects. When the defects ordered, many of the waves became little different from perfect, while other waves were strongly affected. Presumably, the over-all result was a general stabilization of most of the electron energies at the cost of a serious alteration of only a few. Considering the probable large distances over which defects order, the most affected energy levels would lie well below the region of thermal agitation; for this reason, the ordering could be possible, even though at first glance the widely separated defects might appear to be a minor energy factor compared to thermal vibrations at the high temperatures at which microphases are found.

An important question which needs a mathematical answer is whether these ordered defects and their associated perturbations (which are cumulatively very large) must lead to a balance of the increases and decreases in the electron energies caused by the gaps at the Brillouin subzone boundaries: Is there a net change of zero in the total electron energy excluding both the effects such as Slater describes at the Fermi surface and second-order perturbations of the unoccupied levels on the occupied levels? The extreme case of cutting an infinite-walled electron box into two equal parts effectively changes only half the possible energies, all changes being in the same direction. Therefore, it is not obvious to us that the energy differences created at the subzone gaps need cancel.

We assume that for some electron energies the ordered defects may be approximated as the walls of an electron box. A complex energy level spacing is associated with the real parent lattice. If, as discussed in the previous paragraph, the ordering can lead to a nonzero change of electron energy at the lower subzone gaps, different ordering patterns will not be equivalent even though they may each lead to almost equal gap depressions of the topmost energy levels.

We think of the different microphase families as being connected with distinctly different types of order. The microphases within a family can be associated with opening out a parent, boxlike structure in half-wave units. The differences can be similar, as in Figure 2, where the composition gaps are uniform; they can be different in different directions, leading to a complex periodicity as in Figure 3. (Incidentally the superstructure can be very complex, since the defects do not have to fill space in the usual crystallographic sense: The parent lattice provides a supporting structure.)

Finally, the different microphase families show considerable difference in the ability of their microphases to dissolve defects. We associate the tolerant structures (Figure 4) with a $CeCd_4$ parent lattice cut by strongly distorted defective planes in which cadmium atoms can be added or removed easily without disturbing the basic nature of the structure. Ordered isolated point defects would lead to fixed compositions (Figure 3), because atoms could not be removed or added without locally destroying the lattice periodicity.

Conclusions

A single continuously varying solid solution range, analogous to that of $CeCd_{\sim 6}$, has been demonstrated for $CeCd_{\sim 4.5}$.

This solid solution is metastable with respect to various ordered phases (microphases observed in narrower composition ranges.

The microphases group themselves on the pressure composition diagrams into families with related slopes and two-phase regions.

The microphases are, at least in some cases, metastable with respect to other microphases.

In terms of the limited region covered by the experiments (approximate cadmium mole fraction range 0.813 to 0.823) some of the microphases exhibit broad solid solubility ranges. In contrast, for the family shown in Figure 3, the microphase solubility ranges were so narrow that they were not detectable within the precision of the experiments.

The primary family of curves in Figure 2 shows a series of structures having the same cadmium activity-mole fraction relationships and separated by two-phase regions of equal width. Similar relationships are suggested for the secondary family also.

The family of curves in Figure 3 shows a series of structures whose compositions are separated by two-phase regions with widths related by recurring ratios, 11, 7, 7, 7, 10, 8, 7, 8, . . . as described above.

The two-phase regions may have very similar widths in different families. The minimum two-phase gap for the Figure 3 family is very close to that observed for the Figure 2 primary family. A similarity is also apparent for the Figure 3 family and that in Figure 4. The most closely spaced microphases differ in composition by the addition of only one cadmium atom in 8000.

The microphases are reproducible, as is so clearly shown by the repeated appearance of the same structure in Figure 2; however, this reproduction is by chance nucleation in these experiments.

Families of microphases are also reproducible, as illustrated by the repeated appearance and disappearance of the two families in Figure 2.

Besides these microphases at least four other types of precise long-range order of widely separated defects have been observed in systems with metallic character to some bonds:

The homologous oxide series studied by G. Hägg, A. Magneli, and coworkers (10). In these series regular absences of oxygen atoms alter the structures from those of the simple oxide parent. In all cases known to the writers these structures exhibit electronic conduction.

The transition element chalcogenides studied by Haraldsen and coworkers (5) and by Jellinek (9). The former have shown that very many phases exist. Jellinek has pointed out that: in the range CrS to Cr_2S_3 the chromium atoms fit into vacancies in a hexagonal close-packed sulfur frame; and in many compounds, the vacancy distribution can be ordered, disordered, or partially ordered.

Out-of-steps in intermetallic compounds, especially as studied by Watanabe, Ogawa, and coworkers (12) and discussed in this symposium (3).

An ordering of dissolved oxygen atoms in solution in α-zirconium and α-titanium (both metallic phases) has been reported by Dagerhamn and Holmberg (2, 7). Dissolved nitrogen atoms in tantalum also can order (14, 18).

Herasymenko (6) has observed sharply varying partial molal heats and entropies of solution of cadmium in gold or in silver. Although he calculated continuous partial molal quantities, he noted that his changes appeared "almost discontinuous."

Acknowledgment

The authors acknowledge with thanks their particularly helpful discussions with L. Brewer, L. S. Darken, C. C. Herrick, C. E. Holley, H. Taube, and P. D. Waldstein on the chemistry involved, and with J. W. Evans on associated mathematics.

They much appreciate the background information on metal theory pointed out to them by C. C. Herrick, R. N. R. Mulford, W. P. Ellis, S. H. Koenig, K. S. Pitzer, G. H. Vineyard, and especially P. D. Waldstein.

Literature Cited

(1) Blandin, A., *J. Phys. Radium.* **22**, 507 (1961).
(2) Dagerhamn, T., *Acta Chem. Scand.* **15**, 214 (1961).
(3) Elliott, G. R. B., Lemons, J. F., Advan. Chem. Ser. No. **39**, 144 (1963).
(4) Elliott, G. R. B., Lemons, J. F., *J. Phys. Chem.* **64**, 137 (1960).
(5) Haraldsen, H., "Papers Presented to Inorganic Section of 16th International Congress of Pure and Applied Chemistry, Paris, 1957," p. 9, Butterworth Scientific Publications, London, 1958.
(6) Herasymenko, P., *Acta Met.* **4**, 1 (1956); "Vapor Pressure of Cadmium over Alpha Ag-Cd Alloys and Alpha and Beta Au-Cd Alloys," Office of Ordnance Research Project No. 568, Final Report submitted to Box CM, Duke Station, Durham, N. C.
(7) Holmberg, G., Dagerhamn, T., *Acta Chem. Scand.* **15**, 919 (1961).
(8) Iandelli, A., Ferro, R., *Gazz. Chim. Ital.* **84**, 463 (1954).
(9) Jellinek, F., "Papers Presented to Inorganic Section of 16th International Congress of Pure and Applied Chemistry, Paris, 1957," p. 187, Butterworth Scientific Publications, London, 1958.
(10) Kihlborg, L., Andersson, S., *Ibid.*, p. 59.
(11) Leman, G., *J. Phys. Chem. Solids* **13**, 221 (1960).
(12) Ogawa, S., Watanabe, H., Komada, T., *Acta Cryst.* **11**, 872 (1958).
(13) Roeser, W. F., Wenzel, H. T., *Bur. Stds. J. Res.* **10**, 275 (1933).
(14) Schoenberg, N., *Acta Chem. Scand.* **8**, 199 (1954).
(15) Seeger, A., *Physica Status Solidi* **1**, 690 (1961).
(16) Shenker, H., Lauritzen, J. I., Jr., Corruccini, R. J., Lonberger, S. T., "Reference Tables for Thermocouples," Nat. Bur. Stds., Cir. **561**, (April 27, 1955).
(17) Slater, J. C., *Phys. Rev.* **84**, 179 (1951).
(18) Stemple, N. R. Novick, D. T., *J. Appl. Phys.* **33**, 136 (1962).

RECEIVED September 6, 1962. Presented in part at the 141st Meeting, American Chemical Society, Washington, D. C., March 1962, and in part at the Montreal Meeting, International Union of Pure and Applied Chemistry, September 1961. Work performed under the auspices of the U. S. Atomic Energy Commission. Material supplementary to this article has been deposited as Document No. 7435 with the ADI Auxiliary Publications Project, Photoduplication Service, Library of Congress, Washington 25, D. C. A copy may be secured by citing the document number and by remitting $2.25 for photoprints of $1.75 for 35-mm. microfilm. Advance payment is required. Make checks or money orders payable to Chief, Photoduplication Service, Library of Congress.

15

Nonstoichiometry in Chalcogenide Systems

J. S. PRENER

General Electric Research Laboratory, Schenectady, N. Y.

This paper reviews experimental and theoretical studies of nonstoichiometry in metallic chalcogenides exhibiting both small and large deviations from stoichiometry. These deviations result from the presence of lattice disorder arising from the presence of structural defects. The statistical thermodynamic theory is outlined which gives the equilibrium concentration of these defects, and hence the stoichiometry, as a function of the values of the pressure, temperature, and chemical potential of one of the constituents. The experimental methods used to determine the concentration of defects and the limits of stability of the single-phase region are presented. For compounds having extended ranges of homogeneity, Anderson's statistical thermodynamic treatment is presented, in which defect interaction is included. Finally, some structural studies of nonstoichiometric transition metal chalcogenides are reviewed.

In principle, at any temperature above absolute zero every crystalline compound can exist as a single phase over a range of composition. Among the metallic chalcogenides are two broad classes of compounds: (1) that group of chalcogenides, particularly those of the transition elements, which from chemical analysis and structure determinations by x-ray diffraction have been found to exist as stable homogeneous phases over a considerable range of composition (these are the compounds which exhibit large stoichiometric deviations), and (2) chalcogenides such as the II to VI compounds—e.g., ZnS, CdTe—and the compounds of Pb whose deviations from a 1:1 stoichiometry are extremely small. These two classes are discussed separately, since the experimental and theoretical methods used in studying them have been different.

Chalcogenide Compounds with Small Stoichiometric Deviations

In compounds such as CdTe (*26*), CdS (*23*), PbS (*5*), or PbTe (*7*), the very small deviations from 1 to 1 stoichiometry result from lattice disorder arising from the presence, in small concentrations, of vacancies or interstitials. Thus, in CdTe it is believed that the predominant structural defects are Cd interstitials

(Cd_i) and Cd vacancies (V_{Cd}), and an excess of one over the other gives Cd-rich or Te-rich CdTe. In CdS it was presumed that Cd vacancies and sulfur vacancies (V_s) are the predominant defects and here again nonstoichiometric compositions arise from an excess of one type of defect over the other. Other combinations of interstitials and vacancies are possible and in Bi_2Te_3 (*15*) indications are that stoichiometric deviations arise from the presence of one type or atom upon the sublattice of the other (Bi_{Te} and Te_{Bi}).

The maximum deviations from stoichiometry in CdTe have been found to be about 10^{17} excess Te or Cd atoms per cc., and in PbTe about 4×10^{18} excess Pb and 10^{19} excess Te atoms per cc. Because these deviations from a 1 to 1 stoichiometry are so small (5×10^{-4} or less), they cannot be studied by chemical analysis, x-ray diffraction, or density measurements. Rather the extent of nonstoichiometry and the nature of the defects must be inferred from such quantities as obtained from electrical, optical, magnetic, and self-diffusion studies.

To make the connection between the observed electrical, optical, etc., behavior and the type and concentration of point defects in a solid compound, one must first have some qualitative ideas as to the expected properties of a solid arising from the presence of a particular type of defect. A simple example is discussed. Further details are given by Kroger and Vink (*20, 22*). Secondly, some theory must be available which relates the concentration of the various defects to the independent intensive variables of the solid phase and the parameters which characterize the particular compound under study. This theory and some of its applications are discussed below.

Properties of Point Defects

The qualitative properties of a defect such as a sulfur vacancy in ZnS are fortunately independent of the type of bonding in the compound. If we consider first that ZnS is an ionic compound composed of Zn^{+2} and S^{-2} ions, the removal of a neutral S atom to the gas phase to form S_2 molecules leaves behind a neutral sulfur vacancy, V_s^0, since charge neutrality must be preserved in the crystal. The two electrons left behind can be considered as being trapped in the vicinity of the vacancy and can be removed one at a time into the conduction band of the solid by thermal ionization. These processes can be written as ordinary chemical equations:

$$V_s^0 \rightarrow V_s^+ + e^- - \text{energy}$$
$$V_s^+ \rightarrow V_s^{+2} + e^- - \text{energy}$$

It is therefore possible, in a compound like ZnS, to have not only neutral but also singly and doubly positively charged S vacancies and conduction electrons. The binding energy of the electrons to V_s^+ and V_s^0 arises, in the simplest model due to Bethe (*3*), from the electrostatic attraction between the positively charged defects V_s^{+2} and V_s^+ and the negatively charged electrons moving in a solid characterized by its static dielectric constant. If we now consider the other extreme of covalent bonding, ZnS is made of Zn^{-2} (. . . $3d^{10} \ 4s4p^3$) and S^{+2} (. . . $3s3p^3$), each with the tetrahedral sp^3 configuration which gives rise to the 4 covalent bonds of the zinc blende structure (*9*). The removal of a neutral S (. . . $3s^23p^4$) to the gas phase removes six of the eight bonding electrons, leaving, as before, two electrons bound to the V_s^0 which is formed.

The above description of a sulfur vacancy is summarized by the statement that such a defect may behave as a doubly ionizable donor. Evidence for such behavior in ZnS was observed by adding to the solid a small amount of Cu which acts as a singly ionizable acceptor (2). A transfer of two S atoms from the solid phase to the gas phase (to give S_2 gas), leaves two V_s^0 defects, which, since there are Cu acceptor impurities present, can transfer a total of four electrons to these impurity atoms. The concentration of Cu acceptors empty of electrons, as measured by the intensity of the infrared fluorescence from these defects, should then vary as the $+1/4$ power of the sulfur pressure, when ZnS:Cu is equilibrated at some high temperature under various sulfur pressures. The data presented by Apple and Prener (2) show this quarter-power dependence measured over four decades of sulfur pressure. In a similar fashion, a Cd_i in CdTe can act as a double donor (Cd_i^0, Cd_i^+, Cd_i^{+2}) and a V_{Cd} as a double acceptor (V_{Cd}^0, V_{Cd}^-, V_{Cd}^{-2}). The change from n to p type conductivity with changes in stoichiometry has been observed in the II–VI compounds (5, 7, 23, 26). However, since both a Cd_i and V_{Te} can act as doubly ionizable donors, a decision as to the type of defect present cannot be made on the basis of electrical or optical measurements but must rather be inferred from other evidence, such as self-diffusion data or consideration of atomic sizes. For the chalcogenide compounds exhibiting small deviations from stoichiometry, the identification of the predominant structural defects is by no means certain at the present time and remains as a challenging problem. No doubt the application of such techniques as electron paramagnetic resonance will contribute much toward a solution of this problem.

Statistical Thermodynamics of Nonstoichiometric Chalcogenides

It can be shown generally that for a binary compound the number of degrees of freedom are three, independent of the nature and number of defects (21, 27). The concentration of all defects, and therefore the stoichiometry of the compound, are determined when any three independent intensive variables of the solid phase are fixed. Conveniently these are the temperature, pressure, and chemical potential of one of the constituents of the compound. The problem of determining the quantitative relationships between the concentrations of defects (where these are small compared to the number of lattice sites) and the values of the three variables was essentially solved some 30 years ago by Wagner and Schottky (31). Since that time, their work has been extended by including within the framework of the original theory present-day concepts of the donor and acceptor properties of defects and the band theory of solids (6, 28), and by the introduction of graphical methods for obtaining solutions to the resulting equations (22). Using CdTe as an example, we can obtain a set of eight equations from which the concentrations of the defects (in number per cc.) Cd_i^0, Cd_i^+, Cd_i^{+2}, V_{Cd}^0, V_{Cd}^-, and V_{Cd}^{-2} as well as the free charge carrier electrons, e^-, and holes, h^+, can be determined as functions of the three independent intensive variables T, P, and μ_{Cd}. The last equation gives the condition for charge neutrality in the solid.

$$kT \ln a(V_{Cd}^0) = -\mu_{Cd} + C_1$$

$$kT \ln a(Cd_i^0) = \mu_{Cd} + C_2$$

$$kT [\ln a(V_{Cd}^-) + \ln a(h^+)] = -\mu_{Cd} + C_1 + C_3$$

$$kT [\ln a(V_{Cd}^{-2}) + 2 \ln a(h^+)] = -\mu_{Cd} + C_1 + C_3 + C_5$$

$$kT [\ln a(Cd_i^+) + \ln a(e^-)] = \mu_{Cd} + C_2 + C_4$$

$$kT [\ln a(Cd_i^{+2}) + 2 \ln a(e^-)] = \mu_{Cd} + C_2 + C_4 + C_6$$

$$kT [\ln a(h^+) + \ln a (e^-)] = C_7$$

$$2[Cd_i^{+2}] + [Cd_i^+] + [h^+] = 2[V_{Cd}^{-2}] + [V_{Cd}^-] + [e^-]$$

At low defect concentrations:

$$a(V_{Cd}^0) = [V_{Cd}^0]/N_2, \; a(Cd_i^0) = [Cd_i^0]/N_i$$

$$a(e^-) = [e^-]/N_c, \; a(h^+) = [h^+]/N_v, \text{ etc.}$$

If μ_{Te} rather than μ_{Cd} is chosen as the third independent variable, the Gibbs-Duhem equation for small defect concentrations gives:

$$\mu_{Cd} + \mu_{Te} = C_8$$

The various constants, C_1 . . . . C_8, are functions of the temperature and pressure of the solid phase only and contain the various parameters characteristic of CdTe—namely, the thermal band gap, the thermal ionization energies of the donor and acceptor levels, the cohesive energy of CdTe relative to a reference state of infinite dispersion of Cd and Te in their lowest quantum states, and the energies required to remove a Cd atom from the solid to the reference state and that required to introduce an interstitial Cd atom. They also contain the pressure-volume work terms associated with the various processes and the vibrational entropy terms. Since the pressure-volume terms are very small for condensed phases, the dependence of the C's on pressure can generally be neglected. The quantities N_s, N_i, N_v, and N_c are, respectively, the number of lattice sites per cubic centimeter, the number of interstitial sites per cubic centimeter, and the effective density of states near the valence and conduction band edges of CdTe. The specific forms of the C's are not given here, since they can be found in many of the references already cited. In experimental work it is most convenient to fix the values of μ_{Cd} or μ_{Te} by allowing the solid to reach equilibrium with a gaseous phase containing Cd or Te at a given partial pressure. The relationships are:

$$\mu_{Cd} = \mu^0(Cd) + kT \ln p_{Cd}$$

$$\mu_{Te} = \mu^0(Te_2) + kT \ln p_{Te_2}^{1/2}$$

The μ^0's can be found in standard texts (10).

Experimentally, the quantities that can be determined are $[e^-]$ and $[h^+]$ as obtained from suitable electrical measurements as the Hall effect; these measurements are made on crystals which have been equilibrated at some high temperature and quenched. Details as to how such measurements can lead to estimates of the quantities C and thus to the concentration of defects obtained by solving graphically the set of equations are given by de Nobel (26). The stoichiometry of the solid at a given T, P, and μ_{Cd} is given by:

$$x_{Cd} = [Cd]/[Cd] + [Te]$$

where

$$[Cd] = N_s - \{[V_{Cd}^0] + [V_{Cd}^-] + [V_{Cd}^{-2}]\} + [Cd_i^0] + [Cd_i^+] + [Cd_i^{+2}]$$

$$[Te] = N_s$$

Stability Limits of a Nonstoichiometric Compound

The group of nonstoichiometric metallic chalcogenides discussed here have very narrow limits of stability. On either side of the solid phase region in the T-x diagram above the eutectic temperatures there coexists a liquid phase (Cd + Te, Pb + S, etc.). The limits of stability of the nonstoichiometric compound can be determined experimentally by the procedure given above, if the solid phase is now equilibrated with the coexisting phase, contact between the two condensed phases being made by way of the vapor phase. Such a three-phase, two-component system has only one degree of freedom, the temperature. The equilibrium concentration of defects found corresponds to that at the stability limit of the solid phase at the particular temperature. This is the method used to determine the composition limits of PbTe (7). Alternatively, if the liquidus P-T phase diagram is determined, then the concentration of defects at the stability limits of the solid phase can be evaluated from the set of equations given above. This is the method used to determine the composition limits of CdTe (26).

Maximum Melting Point

The available data on a number of chalcogenides show that the maximum melting point (the temperature at which solid and liquid phases have the same composition) does not occur at the stoichiometric composition (5, 7, 8, 26). Any theoretical analysis of the solid composition at the maximum melting point must involve some model for the liquid phase, since the condition for equilibrium between two phases is given by the equality of the chemical potentials of each component in the two phases. The analysis of Hodgkinson (16), which was based on the properties of the solid phase alone, cannot therefore be completely valid. In the case of the Pb compounds, the defects present in the solid at high temperatures have been taken to be V_{Pb}^-, Pb_i^+, e^-, and h^+. From the set of equations given, we find that the chemical potential of lead at the stoichiometric composition $(x_{Pb}^S = 1/2)$ of the solid as a function of temperature is given by:

$$\mu^S = \frac{kT}{2} \ln (N_v N_s / N_c N_i) + 1/2 (C_1 + C_3 - C_2 - C_4)$$

For the liquid phase the chemical potential of Pb can be written as:

$$\mu^L = C_9(T,P) + kT \ln \gamma^L x^L$$

The quantities C_9 and γ^L are properties of the liquid phase alone. When the two phases are in equilibrium, $\mu^S = \mu^L$. Therefore, the composition of the liquid phase can in principle be found and it is not difficult to see that the value $x_{Pb}^L = 1/2$ would be an exception rather than the rule. The temperature at which the liquid phase is in equilibrium with the stoichiometric solid may be a great many degrees below the maximum melting point and x_{Pb}^L may be very far from $1/2$.

Chalcogenides with Large Stoichiometric Deviations

Many of the chalcogenide compounds of the transition elements can exist as homogeneous phases over rather large composition ranges. This range usually, but not always, encompasses some simple stoichiometric composition. As with the compounds discussed above, the composition range is made possible by the presence of native structural defects built into the crystalline lattice. A theoretical analysis of the dependence of the concentration of defects and hence the stoichiometry upon the independent intensive variables must take into account additional energy terms arising out of interaction between the defects. These interactions have been taken into account in a simple model of a nonstoichiometric solid and are discussed below.

From a chemical viewpoint one frequently speaks of the presence of metal atoms in two valence states in these transition metal chalcogenides. For example, a composition such as $Fe_{0.9}S$ can be considered to be $Fe_{0.7}{}^{+2}Fe_{0.2}{}^{+3}S$. This ionic picture may be too simple, for in the NiAs structure of this solid there are short metal-metal distances along the trigonal axis. It is therefore possible that the positive hole instead of being localized about the Fe^{+2} moves in a partially filled $3d$ band arising from the overlap of the $3d$ orbitals of the metal atoms along the trigonal axis. Morin (25) has discussed the electrical properties of the transition metal oxides from this point of view. Unfortunately, as practically nothing is known about the energy band structures or the electrical transport properties of the transition metal chalcogenides, there obviously exists a tremendous gap in our knowledge of these compounds and of the solid state. On the other hand, the very fact that we are dealing here with compounds having large single-phase composition ranges has made it possible to study stoichiometric deviations by the combined measurements of density and lattice parameter. These have resulted in the determination of the predominant structural defects responsible for the deviations from stoichiometry. Thus, in $Fe_{1-\delta}S$ it has been shown that there are metal vacancies in the NiAs structure rather than excess interstitial sulfur.

Statistical Thermodynamics of Chalcogenides with Large Stoichiometric Deviations

The statistical treatment assumed that the defect concentration was so small that the interaction energy between defects could be neglected. However, with increasing concentrations of defects in compounds exhibiting large stoichiometric deviations this interaction energy must be taken into account. Anderson (1) used the approximation that the total interaction energy among defects could be represented as a sum of the contributions of those pairs of like defects that occur as nearest neighbors in a completely random distribution. This assumption of a random distribution of defects cannot, of course, be completely accurate, since the number of nearest neighbor defects in a given lattice depends on the concentration of defects and also on the value of E_i/kT, where E_i is the interaction energy. The approximation is nevertheless sufficiently good at the present time in view of the scarcity of good experimental data, with which the theory may be tested.

When the defect interaction energy is much larger than the thermal energy, it can lead to an ordering of defects into superlattice structures and to the appearance of phases having ordered arrays of defects. Other interactions may also become important as the spin-dependent interactions between the d electrons in the $F_{1-\delta}S$ system (24). We shall not consider these order-disorder phenomena, since they are discussed by Wadsley (30). Some of the structural consequences of ordering are considered below.

In Anderson's treatment, no account is taken of changes in the electronic disorder of the compound arising from changes in the stoichiometry. In the sense of the notation used previously this is equivalent to considering the presence of only neutral defects. For a binary compound exhibiting only Frenkel disorder in the metal lattice, the defects are therefore $V_m{}^0$ and $M_i{}^0$, with no defects in chalcogenide lattice. The presentation given here is equivalent to that of Anderson, since we can write:

$$(-\mu_m + C_1)/kT = \ln a(V_m{}^0)$$

$$(\mu_m + C_2)kT = \ln a(M_i{}^0)$$

In this case of large stoichiometric deviations and interaction between like pairs of defects, $a(V_m^0)$ is not $[V_m^0]/N_s$, but is given by:

$$a(V_m^0) = \gamma(V_m^0)[V_m^0]/(N_s - [V_m^0])$$

$$a(M_i^0) = \gamma(M_i^0)[M_i^0]/(N_i - [M_i^0])$$

For the assumed random distribution of defects, the activity coefficients, γ, are given by the temperature and concentration dependent expressions:

$$kT \ln \gamma(V_m^0) = dE(V_m^0 - V_m^0)/d[V_m^0] = Z_s[V_m^0]\epsilon(V_m^0 - V_m^0)/N_s$$

$$kT \ln \gamma(M_i^0) = dE(M_i^0 - M_i^0)/d[M_i^0] = Z_i[M_i^0]\epsilon(M_i^0 - M_i^0)/N_i$$

where E is the total interaction energy per unit volume, ϵ is the interaction per pair, and Z_s, Z_i are the number of nearest neighbor metal and interstitial sites. Finally defining $\theta_v = [V_m^0]/N_s$ and $\theta_i = [M_i^0]/N_i$ we get:

$$\ln \left(\frac{\theta_v}{1 - \theta_v} \right) = [-\mu_m + C_1 - Z_s\theta_v\epsilon(V_m^0 - V_m^0)]/kT$$

$$\ln \left(\frac{\theta_i}{1 - \theta_i} \right) = [\mu_m + C_2 - Z_i\theta_i\epsilon(M_i^0 - M_i^0)]/kT$$

These are the results given by Anderson, with the difference that he used μ_x as the independent variable and took:

$$\mu_m + \mu_x = C_s(T,P)$$

As can easily be confirmed by the application of the Gibbs-Duhem equation, this again is only approximately true when θ is not negligible with respect to unity. It was shown that for temperatures greater than $-Z\epsilon/4k$ (ϵ is negative for attractive forces between defects), there is one value of θ for each value of μ but at lower temperature there are two physically significant values. This represents physically two solid phases in equilibrium with the defect concentration given by $(\theta_v)_1$, $(\theta_i)_1$, and $(\theta_v)_2$ and $(\theta_i)_2$, but with the same structure and a random distribution of defects. This theory then gives the dependence of the defect concentrations on the intensive variables μ_m (or μ_x), T and P in the nonstoichiometric single-phase region, and predicts the range of stability of the phase. It also predicts a complete single phase region between two adjacent compounds, AB_p and AB_r, above a certain critical temperature which depends on the defect interaction energy. The equations were applied by Anderson to the Pt-PtS-PtS$_2$ system, among others, based on the isothermal pressure measurements of Biltz and Juza (4). In spite of the approximations of the theory the experimental data are reproduced with critical temperatures of about 690° C. for PtS$_2$-PtS and 1427° C. for Pt-PtS. Chalcogenide systems are known in which complete miscibility has been found experimentally between MX and MX$_2$.

Structural Studies of Nonstoichiometric Chalcogenides

Studies of the structures of the phases appearing in transition metal chalcogenides have been very numerous and cannot all be reviewed here. There are, however, a number of transition metal chalcogenides with compositions near MX which exhibit, in certain temperature ranges, the nickel arsenide structure. Among these are FeS (11), VSe (17), CoTe (29), NiTe (19), and CrS, CrSe, and CrTe (14). On the other hand, there are a number of compounds with compositions near MX$_2$ which crystallize in the cadmium iodide structure. Among these are VSe$_2$ (17), CoTe$_2$ (29), and NiTe$_2$ (19). Both of these lattices are of the hexagonal class. In the NiAs structure there are metal atoms at $(0, 0, 0)$, $(1, 0, 0)$, $(0, 1, 0)$, $(1, 1, 0)$, and another similar layer at $c = \frac{1}{2}$ and 1. The two chalcogenide atoms are located at $(\frac{2}{3}, \frac{2}{3}, \frac{1}{4})$ and $(\frac{1}{3}, \frac{1}{3}, \frac{3}{4})$. The CdI_2 lattice is derived from the NiAs lattice by removal of the layer of metal atoms at $c = \frac{1}{2}$. In the nonstoichiometric compounds $M_{1-\delta}X$ having excess chalcogenide, x-ray and density studies have shown that vacancies appear in the metal lattice of the Ni-As structure, and in the nonstoichiometric compounds $MX_{2-\delta}$ having a metal excess, interstitial metal atoms (at $c = \frac{1}{2}$) appear in the CdI_2 structure. These systems are therefore structurally equivalent to the case treated above, except that with respect to MX, the metal vacancies in MX_2 are not randomly distributed over all the metal sites but are confined to every second layer.

It is possible to pass continuously from the NiAs to the CdI_2 lattice by first forming metal vacancies in the MX compound randomly distributed over all the metal sites. As the concentration of these defects becomes larger, the increasing interaction energy leads to an ordering of these defects. They tend to segregate into every second metal layer, leading finally to the CdI_2 lattice at the composition MX_2 (*29*). This process allows one to pass from one phase to another of a different structure without a first-order phase transition, and is equivalent to a continuous change in composition above the critical temperature as discussed above. Behavior of this type has been found in the systems $CoTe$-$CoTe_2$ (*29*) and $NiTe$-$NiTe_2$ (*19*) prepared at elevated temperatures. The VSe-VSe_2 (*17*) system behaves similarly, except that between $VSe_{1.2}$ and $VSe_{1.6}$ an ordering of defects into a phase of lower symmetry occurs. Beyond $VSe_{1.6}$ a further ordering into the CdI_2 lattice sets in.

An x-ray study of the Cr-S system at room temperature shows the type of behavior expected below the critical temperature in which small regions of homogeneity exist near ideal stoichiometric compositions with two-phase regions in between (*18*). The compounds found were Cr_2S_3, Cr_3S_4, Cr_5S_6, Cr_7S_8, and CrS and at least three of these (Cr_2S_3, Cr_3S_4, and Cr_7S_8) exist over a range of composition as homogeneous phases. All these compounds (except CrS) have structures intermediate between those of NiAs and CdI_2. Cr_7S_8, having the lowest metal vacancy concentration, has a random distribution of vacancies in every second layer of the NiAs structure. At higher temperatures the range of homogeneity about the composition Cr_7S_8 is much broader and the defects apparently become completely disordered over both metal layers of the NiAs lattice (*12, 13, 14*). In Cr_5S_6, Cr_3S_4, and Cr_2S_3, which have higher defect concentrations, the lattices are supercells derived from the NiAs lattice by confining the vacancies to every second metal layer and ordering these within the layers as well. This leads to phases of lower symmetry but still related structurally to the NiAs and CdI_2 lattices. Nonstoichiometry in these lower symmetry phases arises from adding or removing metal atoms randomly from the ordered array in every second metal layer; these layers are incompletely filled when referred to the NiAs lattice. These observations and many more in the literature on the range of homogeneity of binary compounds and order-disorder phenomena, are at least qualitatively in accord with the discussion in the previous section. More quantitative studies are needed on the changes in the limits of homogeneity with temperature and of the partial pressures of the chalcogenide (and therefore its chemical potential) over the nonstoichiometric solid over its entire range of stability. More data are also needed on the dependence of order-disorder phenomena on the temperature and composition of nonstoichiometric chalcogenides. Finally, knowledge of the electronic structure of these materials must be gained by studies of various electro-magneto-thermo-optical effects upon single crystals of nonstoichiometric chalcogenides.

Literature Cited

(1) Anderson, J. S., *Proc. Roy. Soc.* **A185**, 69 (1946).
(2) Apple, E. F., Prener, J. S., *J. Phys. Chem. Solids* **13**, 81 (1960).
(3) Bethe, H., MIT Radiation Laboratory, Rept. **43-12** (1942).
(4) Blitz, W., Juza, R., *Z. anorg. u. allgem. Chem.* **190**, 161 (1930).
(5) Bloem, J., Kroger, F. A., *Z. physik. Chem. (Frankfurt)* **7**, 1 (1956).
(6) Brebrick, R. F., *J. Phys. Chem. Solids* **4**, 190 (1958).
(7) Brebrick, R. F., Allgaier, R. S., *J. Chem. Phys.* **32**, 1826 (1960).
(8) Brebrick, R. F., Gubner, E., *Ibid.*, **36**, 170 (1962).
(9) Coulson, C. A., "Valence" p. 263, Oxford University Press, London, 1952.
(10) Fowler, R. H., Guggenheim, E. A., "Statistical Thermodynamics," p. 170, Cambridge University Press, London, 1939.
(11) Haraldsen, H., *Z. anorg. u. allgem. Chem.* **231**, 78 (1937); **246**, 169 (1941).
(12) *Ibid.*, **234**, 372 (1937).
(13) Haraldsen, H., Mehmed, F., *Ibid.*, **239**, 369 (1938).
(14) Haraldsen, H., Neuber, A., *Ibid.*, **234**, 353 (1937).
(15) Harman, T. C., Paris, P., Miller, S. E., Goering, H. L., *J. Phys. Chem. Solids* **2**, 181 (1957).
(16) Hodgkinson, R. J., *J. Electronics and Control* **1**, 612 (1956).
(17) Hoschek, E., Klemm, W., *Z. anorg. u. allgem. Chem.* **242**, 49 (1939).
(18) Jellinek, F., *Acta Cryst.* **10**, 620 (1957).
(19) Klemm, W., Fratini, N., *Z. anorg. u. allgem. Chem.* **251**, 222 (1943).
(20) Kroger, F. A., *J. Phys. Chem. Solids* **7**, 277 (1958).
(21) Kroger, F. A., Stieltjes, F. H., Vink, H. J., *Philips Res. Repts.* **14**, 557 (1959).
(22) Kroger, F. A., Vink, H. J., "Solid State Physics," F. Seitz and R. Turnbull, eds., Vol. 3, pp. 307–435, Academic Press, New York, 1956.
(23) Kroger, F. A., Vink, H. J., van den Boomgaard, J., *Z. physik. Chem.* **203**, 1 (1954).
(24) Lotgering, F. K., *Philips Res. Repts.* **11**, 190 (1956).
(25) Morin, F. J., "Semiconductors," N. B. Hannay, ed., pp. 600–33, Reinhold, New York, 1959.
(26) Nobel, D. de, *Philips Res. Repts.* **14**, 430 (1959).
(27) Prener, J. S., *J. Appl. Phys.* **33**, 434 (1962).
(28) Schottky, W., "Halbleiterprobleme," W. Schottky, ed., Vol. 4, pp. 235–81, Friedrich Vieweg und Sohn, Braunschweig, Germany, 1958.
(29) Tengner, S., *Z. anorg. u. allgem. Chem.* **239**, 127 (1938).
(30) Wadsley A. D., ADVAN. CHEM. SER., No **39**, 23 (1962).
(31) Wagner, C., Schottky, W., *Z. physik. Chem.* **B11**, 163 (1931).

RECEIVED September 6, 1962.

Nonstoichiometric Phases in the MS-M$_2$S$_3$ Sulfide Systems

JEAN FLAHAUT, LOUIS DOMANGE, MADELEINE PATRIE, ANNE-MARIE BOSTSARRON, and MICHELINE GUITTARD

Faculty of Pharmacy, University of Paris, Paris, France

Nonstoichiometric phases are observed in the systems formed by the sulfides of the divalent metals and the sulfides of the trivalent elements of the third column of the periodic table. The solid solutions may be found between sulfides of the same structural types: Of the Th$_3$P$_4$ type in the systems La$_2$S$_3$-CaLa$_2$S$_3$, La$_2$S$_3$-SrLa$_2$S$_4$, and La$_2$S$_3$-BaLa$_2$S$_4$: With MnS only a narrow range of homogeneity is observed; MnLa$_2$S$_4$ has another structural type. Of the spinel type between In$_2$S$_3$ and some spinels M^{II} In$_2$S$_4$. The solid solutions can exist between sulfides which have closely related structural types. This happens with Al$_2$S$_3$ and Ga$_2$S$_3$, which have tetrahedral structures and form with ZnS some wide regions of homogeneity. In rare cases, solid solutions exist between sulfides of different structural types, such as those of the rock salt type obtained by adding Y$_2$S$_3$ to MgS, MnS, CaS, and Pbs.

Only fragmentary information was available to us two years ago when this investigation of mixed metal sulfides was started. For a study of nonstoichiometric phases, the systems involving the sesquisulfides of the Group III metals with the sulfides of divalent metals seemed to be most suitable. The former frequently have crystal structures exhibiting vacant cation sites, while the latter offer a wide variety of chemical bond types.

Systems Formed with Divalent Metal Sulfides

Boron Sulfide. Boron sulfide has essentially covalent bonds. The covalent radius of the boron atom is small; so the formation of solid solutions does not appear to be compatible with B$_2$S$_3$. Experimentally we did not observe any solid solution with BeS, ZnS, CdS, and MgS.

Aluminum and Gallium Sulfides. The crystal structures of the various forms of Al$_2$S$_3$ were studied by Flahaut (*2*) and those of Ga$_2$S$_3$ by Hahn and his coworkers (*13, 15*). These crystal structures are similar, and closely related to the wurtzite and zinc blende types.

In all these structures, the sulfur atoms have a regular close packing. The metal atoms lie in the tetrahedral interstitial positions which are occupied by zinc in the wurtzite or blende structure. However, a third of the positions remain unoccupied. Two possibilities may occur in the distribution of the metal on these positions.

The atoms and the gaps can be distributed at random among the positions of the metal lattice. β-Al_2S_3 and β-Ga_2S_3 are of the wurtzite type, and γ-Ga_2S_3 is of the blende type.

The atoms and the gaps lie regularly on the positions of the metal lattice, and form a superlattice of the blende or wurtzite type. Two examples are α-Al_2S_3 and α-Ga_2S_3, which have the same structure. The description of this structure, given by Hahn and Frank (*12*), does not seem to be corroborated by the recent work of Goodyear, Duffin, and Steigmann (*11*), but these authors were not able to obtain a full description of the structure.

Al_2S_3-ZnS SYSTEM. One intermediate compound, $ZnAl_2S_4$, and two regions of homogeneity are observed on the equilibrium diagram of Figure 1. The compound $ZnAl_2S_4$ has two polymorphic forms (*12*), with a reversible change at about 980° C. The low temperature modification has the spinel structure (*2*), with a regular distribution of the cations. The aluminum atoms lie in the tetrahedral spaces (*12*). This spinel phase gives a wide region of homogeneity, toward the Al_2S-₃rich side. At 800° C., it extends beyond $ZnAl_2S_4$ as far as the atomic ratio Zn/Zn + Al = 0.08 or Al_2S_3.0.17 ZnS. But it is not possible to give a detailed picture of the upper part of this region, because the products which are quenched at elevated temperature (> 900°) are amorphous to the x-ray when the aluminum content is large.

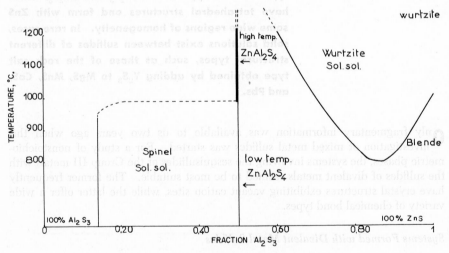

Figure 1.   Phase diagram of Al_2S_3–ZnS system

The high temperature modification of $ZnAl_2S_4$ was described by Hahn and Frank (*12*) as being of the wurtzite type, with a disordered distribution of the three metal atoms and one gap on the four sites of the metal lattice. Recently, it has been shown (*5*) that this compound has a superstructure of wurtzite with an orthorhombic unit cell. The unit cell of $ZnAl_2S_4$ is actually monoclinic with a β angle of 90°. Its space group is $Pm-C^1_s$. The parameters of the unit cell have a simple relation with those of the wurtzite structure (indicated by a' and c'):

$$a = 2 a' \qquad b = a'\sqrt{3} \qquad c = c'$$

We think that this ordered superstructure is the stable modification at moderately high temperature and that the disordered wurtzite type is the stable modification at higher temperatures, but since we are not able to obtain the disordered form by heating at 1250° C., it is not possible to confirm this point.

A second argument against the conception of Hahn and Frank is our observation that the wurtzite ZnS yields an extended solid solution when Al_2S_3 is added to it. At 1200° C. the homogeneity range extends from 0 to 49.9 atomic % of aluminum (as from ZnS to about $Al_2S_3 \cdot 2ZnS$). If the compound $ZnAl_2S_4$ were disordered, we would expect the solid solution to extend to the composition $Al_2S_3 \cdot ZnS$.

Al_2S_3-CdS-MgS-MnS SYSTEMS. Aluminum sulfide with CdS, MgS (2), and MnS (2) gives MAl_2S_4 as definite compounds, but their structures have not been completely investigated. We did not observe any solid solution in the MS-rich region of the systems, on adding Al_2S_3 to these three MS sulfides. In the Al_2S_3-rich region, the products are always amorphous to the x-ray when they have been quenched.

Ga_2S_3-ZnS SYSTEM. The phase diagram of Figure 2 (3) shows many similarities to that of the Al_2S_3-ZnS system.

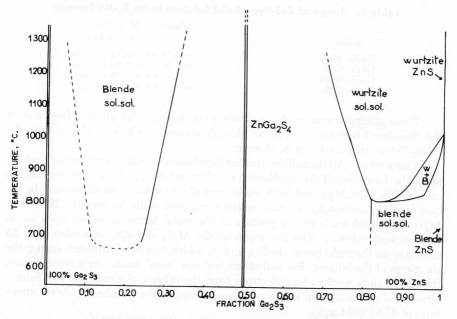

Figure 2. Phase diagram of Ga_2S_3–ZnS system

The compound $ZnGa_2S_4$ has a crystal structure which is closely related to the blende type (14). There is no appreciable range of composition for this compound. Two extensive homogeneity regions are observed, at elevated temperatures, one of the wurzite type near ZnS and the other of the blende type near Ga_2S_3.

We think there is another phase of the blende type near ZnS, under the region of the wurtzite solid solution, with a two-phase region between them. Nevertheless, some observations permit us to consider the possibility of this blende phase as being not a continuous solid solution, but a discontinuous series of definite compounds of similar compositions, each having a narrow homogeneity range. We are continuing this study.

Ga_2S_3-CdS-MgS-MnS Systems. The Ga_2S_3-CdS and Ga_2S_3-MgS systems are closely related. They give the definite compounds $CdGa_2S_4$ and $MgGa_2S_4$. The structure of the first is a superstructure of the blende (*14*). The structure of the second is not yet known.

In the Ga_2S_3-MnS system, we observed several definite compounds between the compositions $2Ga_2S_3$-MnS and Ga_2S_3-MnS. The compound $MnGa_2S_4$ has three polymorphic modifications. We are still studying this region.

In these three systems, no solid solution can be obtained by adding Ga_2S_3 to the MS sulfides or to the definite compounds. We observed only a very narrow homogeneity region of the wurtzite type near Ga_2S_3. At 1200° C. we estimated the limits given in Table I. (The compositions are in atoms per cent of metal.) This wurtzite-type phase is still observed at 1000° C. in the last two systems, but it disappears at about 1100° C. in the Ga_2S_3-MgS system. So the solid solution seems more extensive in the Ga_2S_3-CdS and Ga_2S_3-MnS systems than in the Ga_2S_3-MgS system.

Table 1.   Range of ZnS-Type Solid Solution in Ga_2S_3-MS Systems

System	Limits $\dfrac{M \ Atoms}{M + Ga \ Atoms}$	
Ga_2S_3–MgS	$\approx 0.08 \leftrightarrow \approx 0.12$	wurtzite
Ga_2S_3–CdS	$\approx 0.04 \leftrightarrow \approx 0.16$	wurtzite
Ga_2S_3–MnS	$\approx 0.08 \leftrightarrow \approx 0.16$	wurtzite
Ga_2S_3–ZnS	$\approx 0 \leftrightarrow \approx 0.30$	blende

Some attempts were made to obtain a continuous solid solution from one of the disordered forms of Ga_2S_3, but this phenomenon, which is observed in the Ga_2S_3-ZnS system, could not be observed.

Discussion. All the sulfides studied here have electronic configurations which allow the formation of the tetrahedral covalent sp^3 bond. This is obvious in the case of ZnS, CdS, MgS, and MnS, each atom of which has eight electrons. In the case of Al_2S_3 and Ga_2S_3, we can use the suggestion made by Suchet (*22*) about In_2Te_3, in which each vacant position of the metal lattice is looked upon as an atom of zero valence. The five atoms of the Al_2S_3 or Ga_2S_3 molecules have 24 electrons on their electronic shells s and p, which can be distributed among the six spaces of the lattice: five real atoms and one "zero" atom. As a consequence, the "zero" atom receives four electrons from the other real atoms and can form a tetrahedral sp^3 bond. In this way we can visualize the tetrahedral defect structures of Al_2S_3 and Ga_2S_3.

From the values of the covalent radii of the metals (Table II) we can expect the formation of solid solutions between Al_2S_3 (or Ga_2S_3) and ZnS, since the difference of the atomic radii is not very large (about 7%). With the other sulfides (MnS, MgS, and CdS) the existence of solid solutions seems unlikely because of the large differences in the atomic radii (about 12% for MnS, 13% for MgS, and 18% for CdS). In fact, we cannot obtain them experimentally by adding Al_2S_3 (or Ga_2S_3) to MnS, MgS, and CdS. But, on the other side of the diagrams, the very narrow solid solutions observed by adding MnS, MgS, or CdS to Ga_2S_3 can be explained by the presence of many gaps in the metal lattice of Ga_2S_3, which allow the introduction of other atoms more easily than in the full structures of MgS, MnS, and CdS.

Table II.   Covalent Radii of Metals in MS Sulfides

$(R_s = 1.040$ A.$)$

Al	1.222 A. in α-Al_2S_3
Ga	1.230 A. in α-Ga_2S_3
	1.215 A. in blende-type Ga_2S_3
Zn	1.306 A. in two forms of ZnS
Mn	1.390 A. in pink MnS sulfides
Mg	1.38 A. (from tables)
Cd	1.490 A. in two forms of CdS

We can observe a connection between the fact that MgS, when added to Ga_2S_3, gives a narrower solid solution range than does MnS (or CdS), and the fact that pure MgS is the only sulfide of this group known to have an NaCl rather than a tetrahedral structure. So the possibility that the magnesium will enter a tetrahedral structure is limited.

The M-S distances observed in the blende or wurtzite-type solid solutions are given in Table III. From the radii of the metals measured in their pure sulfides (Table II) it is possible to evaluate the M-S distance for each composition of these solid solutions. The calculated values are always a little larger than the observed values, and the difference increases with the quantity of sulfide added. So, in these solid solutions, we observed a small contraction of the radius of the metal added. In the Ga_2S_3-ZnS system, for instance, we obtained good agreement between the calculations and the experiments with $R_{Ga} = 1.196$ A. (instead of $R_{Ga} = 1.215$ A.) in the ZnS-rich solid solutions, and with $R_{Zn} = 1.290$ (instead of $R_{Zn} = 1.306$ A.) in the Ga_2S_3-rich solid solution.

Table III.   M-S Distances Observed and Calculated in Wurtzite and Blende Solid Solutions

(With Al $-$ S $= 2.262$ A., Ga $-$ S $= 2.54$ A.)

Al_2S_3-ZnS System.   Wurtzite Solid Solution

$n = \dfrac{\text{Zn atoms}}{\text{(Zn + Al) atoms}}$	1	0.882	0.750	
Observed M-S, A.	2.346	2.332	2.315	
Calculated M-S, A.	2.346	2.336	2.325	

Ga_2S_3–ZnS System.   Wurtzite and Blende-Solid Solutions in ZnS-Rich Region

$n = \dfrac{\text{Zn atoms}}{\text{(Zn + Ga) atoms}}$	1	0.882	0.750	0.670
Observed M-S, A.	2.346	2.334	2.319	2.308
Calculated M-S, A.	2.346	2.335	2.323	2.316

Blende-Solid Solution in Ga_2S_3-Rich Region

$n = \dfrac{\text{Zn atoms}}{\text{(Zn + Ga) atoms}}$	0	0.0323	0.0833	0.143
Observed M-S, A.	2.254	2.257	2.260	2.263
Calculated M-S, A.	2.254	2.257	2.261	2.267

Indium Sulfide. The indium sulfide (In_2S_3) possesses a high temperature modification which has a defect spinel structure, and a low temperature modification which is a superstructure of the spinel structure (*16, 18, 19, 21*). Several MIn_2S_4 compounds have the spinel structure (*17*) and we observed the existence of regular solid solutions of the spinel type in In_2S_3-$MgIn_2S_4$, In_2S_3-$MnIn_2S_4$, In_2S_3-$CrIn_2S_4$, and In_2S_3-$CdIn_2S_4$; but only partial solid solution in the In_2S_3-$CaIn_2S_4$ system. This work is not yet finished, and we cannot draw significant conclusions from our actual results.

Rare Earth Sulfides. In Group IIIa of the periodic classification, there are scandium, yttrium, and the rare earths. We have not yet studied the scandium sulfides, but we have studied the yttrium sulfides and the rare earth sulfides for the last six years (4, 9, 10, 20). We now turn to the research on these last sulfides done in our laboratory (6, 7, 8).

It is possible to include yttrium among the rare earths, because of its properties, which are rather like those of some of the rare earths. For instance, when we express a physical property of the sulfides as a function of the ionic radii of the metals, the yttrium sulfide normally lies among the rare earth series, without any discontinuity, between dysprosium and erbium sulfides.

From a structural standpoint, the rare earth sulfides have several polymorphic forms (20), whose stability regions are represented in Figure 3. The high temperature form (γ) exists from lanthanum to dysprosium. It is cubic and is of the Th_3P_4 type, with a defect structure. In each unit cell, there are $10^2/_3$ metal atoms which are distributed at random among the 12 sites of the metal lattice. The structures of the low temperature α and β forms are not yet known. The structure of the δ form, which is peculiar to dysprosium, yttrium, and erbium, is monoclinic (20). The three last forms have low crystal symmetry, and certainly have no vacant lattices.

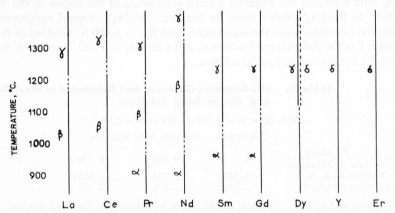

Figure 3. Polymorphic varieties of rare earth sulfides, L_2S_3

The rare earth elements which have a L_2S_3 sulfide of the Th_3P_4 type generally have another sulfide which has the L_3S_4 formula and the same structural type. In the structure of these last compounds, all the sites of the metal lattice are occupied. In all cases, there is a continuous regular solid solution between the two sulfides L_2S_3 and L_3S_4 of a same rare earth element. This phenomenon was experimentally proved for Ce_2S_3-Ce_3S_4 (25) and Sm_2S_3-Sm_3S_4 (20).

We first experimented with the systems formed by yttrium sulfide (Y_2S_3) with the following divalent metal sulfides: MgS, CaS, SrS, BaS, CrS, MnS, FeS, PbS, ZnS, and CdS (7, 8). From this preliminary study, we concluded that solid solutions can be observed only with the MS sulfides of the NaCl structural type: MgS, CaS, SrS, BaS, MnS, and PbS. So we have continued our researches on the diagrams formed by the rare earth sulfides, studying only the case of the NaCl-type divalent sulfides.

SOLID SOLUTIONS OF Th_3P_4 TYPE. By heating at appropriate temperatures equimolecular mixtures of the rare earth sulfides and the MS sulfides, we generally obtained compounds having the ML_2S_4 formula (Table IV). These compounds have five different crystal structures, but the most frequent is the Th_3P_4-like structure. We always observe a regular solid solution between L_2S_3 and ML_2S_4 when they are of the Th_3P_4 structural type.

Table IV.   Crystal Structures of ML_2S_4 Compounds

	La_2S_3	Ce_2S_3	Pr_2S_3	Nd_2S_3	Sm_2S_3	Gd_2S_3	Dy_2S_3	Y_2S_3	Er_2S_3	Yb_2S_3
MgS	O	O	O	O	O	O	A	A	A	C
MnS	E	O	O	O	O	O	A	A	A	C
CaS	T	T	T	T	T	T	T	A	A	A
SrS	T	T	T	T	T	T	B	B	B	B
BaS	T	T	T	T	B	B	B	B	B	B

T.   Cubic Th_3P_4 type
A.   Orthorhombic
B, E, C.   Unknown structures
O.   No compounds

In some cases, chiefly in the systems containing MgS and MnS, the ML_2S_4 compounds do not exist. However, we always observed solid solutions having the Th_3P_4-like structure very close to the rare earth sulfides (L_2S_3).

We were not able to observe solid solutions with the other structural forms of the L_2S_3 sulfides, so we present only compounds having the Th_3P_4 type in this paper.

To observe a solid solution from the L_2S_3 sulfides it is necessary to prepare the products at high enough temperatures (about 1300° C. for lanthanum and cerium products) and to quench them quickly. At the lower temperatures, the solid solution does not begin at L_2S_3, but further on, because the rare earth sulfides have other polymorphic forms in the equilibrium conditions, and because these other forms, α and β, do not dissolve the MS sulfides.

It may be seen from Table IV, where the rare earth elements, L, and the divalent metals, M, are listed in order of their ionic radii, that the incidence of the Th_3P_4-type structure is related to the ionic sizes of the elements. [The radii of the rare earth cations, L^{+3}, were calculated from the sulfides, LS, which have NaCl-like structures. These sulfides do not have purely ionic bonds, but the values of the radii calculated by this way are in good accord with those published by Templeton and Dauben (23).] Table IV seems to indicate two necessary conditions:

The percentage differences in the radius of the M^{+2} cation from the lanthanide cation $\left(\dfrac{\text{difference in radius}}{\text{radius of lanthanide ion}}\right) \times 100$ are listed in Table V, in which the different structures are also indicated. It appears that solid solutions are formed when the percentage difference in cation radius is less than 28. The exceptions ($BaS\text{-}Pr_2S_3$ and $BaS\text{-}Nd_2S_3$) lie near the border between two types of structures.

The Th_3P_4 structure is found in all lanthanon sulfides when the radius of the lanthanon ion is 0.93 A. or greater. The existence of a solid solution ($MS\text{-}L_2S_3$) with this structure may be assumed to depend on the weighted average radius (R_a) of the cation derived from the expression $R_a = \dfrac{R_L\,2 + n\,R_M}{2 + n}$, where n is the number of moles of MS added to one mole of L_2S_3 and R_L and R_M are the radii of the two cations. When R_a is greater than 0.93 A., the Th_3P_4 structure should be obtained.

Table V.　Solid

MS	r_M^{+2}	L_2S_3 r_L^{+3}	La_2S_3 1.10	Ce_2S_3 1.07	Pr_2S_3 1.05	Nd_2S_3 1.03
MgS	0.775		B 29.5	27.6	26.2	24.8
MnS	0.79		. . . . . 28.2	26.2	24.8	23.3
CaS	1.02		. . . . . 7.3	4.7	2.9	1.0
SrS	1.185		7.7	10.7	12.9	15.0
BaS	1.36		23.6	27.1	29.5	32.0

——— Continuous solid solution from L_2S_3 to ML_2S_4
– – – Partial solid solution
. . . . . Very narrow range of homogeneity close to L_2S_3

With the small cations Mg^{+2} and Mn^{+2}, Dy_2S_3 does not give any phase with the thorium phosphide structure. Calcium sulfide, on the other hand, yields phases with this structure with Dy_2S_3 and Y_2S_3 but not with Er_2S_3 (maximum value of $R_a = 0.94$).

Table VI.　Predictions and Experimental Determinations of Range of Solid Solutions of Th_3P_4 Type

Systems	n Calculated	n Observed
Sm_2S_3–MgS	0–0.77	0–0.33 (1200° C.)
Sm_2S_3–MnS	0–0.86	0–0.60 (1200° C.)
Gd_2S_3–MgS	0–0.52	0–0.25 (1200° C.)
Gd_2S_3–MnS	0–0.57	0–0.25 (1200° C.)
Y_2S_3–CaS	0.22–1	0.25–0.61 (1200° C.)
Er_2S_3–CaS	0.67–1	No Th_3P_4 phase (from 800° to 1300° C.)

n = number of MS molecules added to one molecule of L_2S_3.

On the basis of the average cation ratio, it should be possible to predict the range of solid solution in these systems, by calculating the value of n when $R_a = 0.93$. Some of the systems which have been considered in this way are listed in Table VI. Temperature has a profound influence. This is well illustrated by Figure 4, which gives the phase diagram of the $CaS-Y_2S_3$ system. The phase with the thorium phosphide structure has a eutectoid at 980° C. at $n = 0.47$. At higher temperatures the lowest value of n approaches the calculated value of 0.22. Thus we see that the two factors—the average and the relative size of the cations—give a rational explanation of the existence of most of the phases with the thorium phosphide structure. There remain, however, some anomalies. The Th_3P_4 structure in the $CaS-Y_2S_3$ and $MgS-Nd_2S_3$ systems does not extend to the composition $n = 1$. No phase with the Th_3P_4 structure has been found in the $CaS-Er_2S_3$ system.

Solid Solutions of NaCl Type. On the other side of the L_2S_3-MS diagrams, we observed the formation of extended solid solutions of the NaCl type.

In our research, appropriate mixtures of a rare earth sulfide and an MS sulfide were prepared by grinding in an agate mortar. The mixtures were compressed in little tablets, which were placed in a sealed quartz tube, and heated at a constant temperature—for instance, 2 days at 1000° C., 3 hours at 1200° C., or 1 hour at 1300° C. Then the tubes were quenched in water.

Solutions of Th_3P_4 Type

Sm_2S_3	Gd_2S_3	Dy_2S_3	Y_2S_3	Er_2S_3	Yb_2S_3
0.99	0.97	0.93	0.92	0.90	0.88
			A		
21.7	20.1	16.7	15.8	13.9	11.9
---	---				
20.2	18.6	15.1	14.1	12.2	10.2
---	---				
3.0	5.2	9.7	10.9	13.3	15.9

19.7	22.2	27.4	28.8	31.7	34.7
37.4	40.2	46.2	47.8	51.1	54.5
			B		

For areas A and B, theoretical conditions show that the Th_3P_4 phase cannot form.

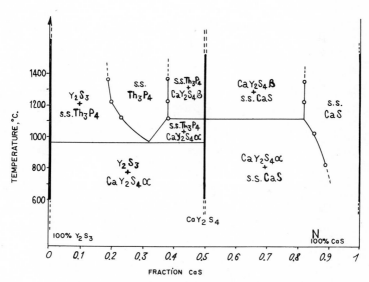

Figure 4.   Phase diagram of system Y_2S_3–CaS

S.S. *Solid solution*

The results of our experiments are given in Table VII. Extended solid solutions are observed only with the last rare earth sulfides—Dy_2S_3, Y_2S_3, Er_2S_3, and Yb_2S_3—when added to MgS, MnS, or CaS. Extremely limited solid solutions are observed when one of these rare earth sulfides is added to SrS. We never observed solid solutions of the NaCl type with other rare earth sulfides, nor with BaS.

The variations of the unit cell parameter, a, according to the compositions were established for five systems at one temperature, 1200° C. The limits of these solid solutions are given in Table VIII, by the ratio n,

$$n = \frac{\text{number of M atoms}}{\text{number of M atoms} + \text{number of L atoms}}$$

In the case of the Y_2S_3-CaS and Y_2S_3-MnS systems the compositions of the solid solutions were determined at several temperatures (Figure 4).

Table VII.   NaCl-Type Solid Solutions

$r_L{}^{+3}$ $r_M{}^+$	La_2S_3 1.10	Ce_2S_3 1.07	Pr_2S_3 1.05	Nd_2S_3 1.03	Sm_2S_3 0.99	Gd_2S_3 0.97	Dy_2S_3 0.93	Y_2S_3 0.92	Er_2S_3 0.90	Yb_2S_3 0.88
MgS 0.775	41.9	38.1	35.5	32.9	27.7	25.2	20.0	18.7	16.1	13.5
MnS 0.79	39.2	35.4	32.9	30.4	25.3	22.8	17.7	16.5	13.9	11.4
CaS 1.02	7.8	4.9	2.9	1.0	2.9	4.9	9.7	9.8	11.8	13.7
SrS 1.185	7.2	5.7	11.4	13.1	16.5	18.1	21.5	22.4	24.1	25.7
BaS 1.36	19.1	21.3	22.8	24.3	27.2	28.7	31.6	32.4	33.8	35.3

——— Extended solid solutions
– – – Extremely narrow solid solutions

Table VIII.   Range of NaCl-Type Solid Solutions at 1200° C. in System L_2S_3-MS

L_2S_3–MS	n
Y_2S_3–MgS	0.61 – 1
Y_2S_3–MnS	0.64 – 1
Y_2S_3–CaS	0.70 – 1
Dy_2S_3–CaS	0.66 – 1
Er_2S_3–CaS	0.64 – 1

In order to decide whether the nonstoichiometric phases contain interstitial anions, or vacant cation sites, we compared the pycnometric density with the calculated density for each type of defect. The experimental values agree with the last type of defects, and these solid solutions are represented using Rees's notation by

$$(S^{-2}/-)(L_x{}^{+3} M_{1-1.5x}^{+2}/+)$$

The following limit values of x were found: MnS-Y_2S_3 (0 to 0.31), MgS-Y_2S_3 (0 to 0.33), CaS-Y_2S_3 (0 to 0.27), CaS-Dy_2S_3 (0 to 0.29), and CaS-Er_2S_3 (0 to 0.31).

We were not able to find a basis for the prediction of the extent of these solid solutions. For instance, if we consider only the relative ionic radii of the two cations L^{+3} and M^+, the solid solution should be more extended in the Y_2S_3-CaS than in the Y_2S_3-MnS and Y_2S_3-MgS systems, because the ionic radii are closer in the first system.

The interionic distances (M-S) observed in the solid solutions are given in Table IX for each mixture studied. In the same table, we have calculated the theoretical M-S distances for the same compositions, taking the radii of the cations as measured in their pure sulfides (with $R_s = 1.82$ A.). In each case the calculated value is much smaller than the observed value, and the difference increases with the content of the L^{+3} cation. So, in these solid solutions, we observed an increase of the radius of the ion added. This behavior is opposite to that of the blende or wurtzite solid solutions in the Al_2S_3-ZnS and Ga_2S_3-ZnS systems.

We obtained agreement between the experimental and the calculated M-S distances with the following radii of the L^{+3} cations:

R_Y = 1.02 A. in Y_2S_3-MgS solid solution
R_Y = 1.01 A. in Y_2S_3-MnS solid solution
R_Y = 0.96 A. in Y_2S_3-CaS solid solution
R_{Dy} = 0.98 A. in Dy_2S_3-CaS solid solution
R_{Er} = 0.94 A. in Er_2S_3-CaS soild solution

The radii of these cations in their sulfides are, respectively, $R_y = 0.92$ A.; $R_{Dy} = 0.93$ A.; and $R_{Er} = 0.90$ A.

The precentage differences in the radii of the M and L cations with respect to the radius of the M cation are given in Table VII. For the systems which give solid solutions, these numbers are underlined.

Table IX.   M-S Distances Observed and Calculated in NaCl-Type Solid Solutions
(Dy − S = 2.75 A., Y-S = 2.74 A., Er-S = 2.72 A.)

CaS–Dy$_2$S$_3$ System

$n = \dfrac{\text{Ca atoms}}{\text{(Ca + Dy) atoms}}$

	1	0.923	0.846	0.750	0.637
M-S, A.					
Observed	2.847	2.847	2.840	2.836	2.832
Calculated	2.847	2.840	2.832	2.822	2.811

CaS–Y$_2$S$_3$ System

$n = \dfrac{\text{Ca atoms}}{\text{(Ca + Y) atoms}}$

	1	0.938	0.875	0.750	0.667
M-S, A.					
Observed	2.847	2.843	2.834	2.827	2.825
Calculated	2.847	2.834	2.823	2.804	2.793

CaS–Er$_2$S$_3$ System

$n = \dfrac{\text{Ca atoms}}{\text{(Ca + Er) atoms}}$

	1	...	0.882	0.750	0.667
M-S, A.					
Observed	2.847	...	2.838	2.826	2.820
Calculated	2.847	...	2.832	2.817	2.805

As with the Th$_3$P$_4$-type solid solutions, we can see that the NaCl-type solid solutions are not possible when the ionic radii differ by more than 20%. This condition explains why on the right side of Table VII the strontium sulfide does not give extended solid solutions with the rare earth sulfides, but has an extremely narrow homogeneity range, and why BaS never gives solid solutions.

The NaCl-type solid solutions are observed only from dysprosium to the last element of the rare earth series, but we were unable to find a valid reason.

Our results are in contradiction with those of Banks, Ward, and Yakel (1, 24). These authors described solid solutions between SrS and the rare earth sulfides of the first elements of the series—La$_2$S$_3$, Ce$_2$S$_3$, Pr$_2$S$_3$, Nd$_2$S$_3$, and Sm$_2$S$_3$—but their results were obtained under different conditions. They always added about 6 to 12% by weight of LiF flux to the sulfides. These mixtures were heated for an hour in an atmosphere of purified hydrogen sulfide at 1000° C., after which they were allowed to cool in the furnace. We think that lithium fluoride is transformed into lithium sulfide under these conditions, and so could favor the formation of the solid solutions. This view is backed up by the observation of the authors, who were not able to obtain extended solid solutions when the mixtures were heated in a nitrogen atmosphere.

We studied the action of lithium sulfide on the formation of the NaCl-type solid solution. First of all, we observed that Li$_2$S does not give a solid solution with pure SrS or pure Nd$_2$S$_3$. Then we used a mixture in the constant proportions of one molecule of Nd$_2$S$_3$ and six molecules of SrS, to which we added increasing proportions of Li$_2$S. The a parameter of the NaCl-like structure decreases with the atomic content of lithium, but becomes constant at about two lithium atoms for the Nd$_2$S$_3$-6SrS mixture.

We think that the solid solution is produced by the simultaneous substitution of neodymium and lithium atoms for the strontium atoms of the cation lattice of

SrS. So it should be theoretically impossible to add more than one Li_2S molecule to the $(Nd_2S_3\text{-}6SrS)$ mixture, because all the sites of the cation lattice are occupied for this proportion of the cations.

Banks and Ward always used large quantities of lithium fluoride and thus had the best conditions for obtaining extended and reproducible solid solutions.

Literature Cited

(1) Banks, E., Ward, R., J. Electrochem. 96, 301 (1949).
(2) Flahaut, J., Ann. Chim. 7 (12), 632 (1952).
(3) Flahaut, J., Domange, L., Bostsarron, A.-M., Guittard, M., to be published.
(4) Flahaut, J., Domange, L., Guittard, M., Patrie, M., Bull. Soc. Chim. (France) 1960, 221.
(5) Flahaut, J., Domange, L., Guittard, to be published.
(6) Flahaut, J., Domange, L., Patrie, M., Bull. Soc. Chim. (France) 1961, 105, 1887; 1962, 157, 159.
(7) Flahaut, J., Domange, L., Patrie, M., Compt. Rend. 253, 1454 (1961).
(8) Ibid., to be published.
(9) Flahaut, J., Guittard, M., Patrie, M., Bull. Soc. Chim. (France) 1958, 990.
(10) Ibid., 1959, 1917.
(11) Goodyear, J., Duffin, W. J., Steigmann, A., Acta Cryst. 14, 1168 (1961).
(12) Hahn, H., Frank, G., Z. anorg. Chem. 269, 227 (1952).
(13) Ibid., 278, 333 (1955).
(14) Hahn, H., Frank, G., Klingler, W., Storger, A. D., Storger, G., Ibid., 279, 241 (1955).
(15) Hahn, H., Klingler W., Ibid., 259, 135 (1949).
(16) Ibid., 260, 97 (1949).
(17) Ibid., 263, 177 (1950).
(18) Hatwell, H., Offergeld, G., Herinckx, C., Van Cakenberghe, J., Compt. Rend. 252, 3586 (1961).
(19) Huber, M., Ibid., 253, 471 (1961).
(20) Picon, M., Domange, L., Flahaut, J., Guittard, M., Patrie, M., Bull. Soc. Chim. (France) 1960, 221.
(21) Rooymans, C. J., J. Inorg. Nucl. Chem. 11, 78 (1959).
(22) Suchet, J. P., "Chimie Physique des Semiconducteurs," Dunod, Paris, 1962.
(23) Templeton, D. H., Dauben, C. H., J. Am. Chem. Soc. 76, 5237 (1954).
(24) Yakel, H. L., Banks, E., Ward, R., J. Electrochem. Soc. 96, 304 (1949).
(25) Zachariasen, W. N., Acta Cryst. 2, 57 (1949).

RECEIVED September 6, 1962.

17

Investigations of Nonstoichiometric Sulfides

I. Titanium Sulfides, TiS$_2$ and Ti$_2$S$_3$

JACQUES BENARD and YVES JEANNIN

Ecole Nationale Supérieure de Chimie, Paris, France

The nonstoichiometric phases TiS$_2$ and Ti$_2$S$_3$ have been studied in sulfides prepared by direct synthesis at 1000° and 800° C. Lattice constants and densities have been measured as functions of composition. Characteristics of the transition from the TiS$_2$ crystal structure to the Ti$_2$S$_3$ structure have been investigated.

Compounds with layer lattices constitute a family characterized by special crystallo-chemical properties which have been the object of comparative studies (*10*). It is customary to relate the chemical behavior of these compounds to their crystallographic structure composed of more or less complex layers, or sheets.

An example of a layer structure is offered by cadmium iodide. It is an important example, since many sulfides, selenides, and tellurides of the transition metals are of this same crystal type. The crystal lattice is composed of planar sheets, $(CdI_2)_n$, consisting of CdI_6 octahedra joined at their edges (Figure 1) (*7*); the different sheets are held together by Van der Waals forces. It is possible to insert metal atoms between these sheets; thus, cases are known in which a continuous transition has been observed between MX_2 and MX—that is, between the CdI_2 structure and that of NiAs. The plane situated between two $(MX_2)_n$ sheets is completely filled with metal atoms, becoming identical to the M plane of one of the $(MX_2)_n$ sheets. A classic example is furnished by the system CoTe-CoTe$_2$ (*8*).

The sulfides of titanium are, in this connection, of particular interest. Inasmuch as TiS crystallizes with the NiAs structure and TiS$_2$ with the CdI$_2$ structure, the existence of an intermediate compound of the sesquisulfide type has long been the object of speculation (*1, 3*), until the last few years when its existence has been definitely established (*4, 5, 9*). For our part, we have concentrated our attention on titanium disulfide, titanium sesquisulfide, and the manner of transition from one to the other.

Experimental Methods

Preparation. The sulfides were prepared by mixing weighed amounts of titanium and sulfur in the required proportions; the S/Ti ratio was known with a precision of 0.2%. The titanium, in spongy form, was made available through the courtesy of E. I. du Pont de Nemours & Co. The impurity content is:

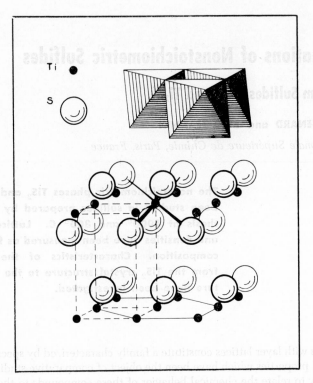

*Figure 1. The structure of titanium bisulfide, show-
ing nature of layers*

O₂ 0.043%	N₂ 0.004%	H₂ 0.014%
Fe 0.045%	Cr 0.005%	
C 0.025%	Si 0.007%	

The titanium-sulfur mixture was placed in a transparent silica tube which
was evacuated, then sealed under a vacuum estimated at 10^{-4} mm. of Hg. Although silica can, according to theory, be reduced by titanium, our experience has
shown such attack to be exceptional, at least in the case of the particular sulfur-rich
sulfides that we have studied.

The reaction tube and its contents were then brought to the desired
temperature. The heat treatment was extended over 2 to 3 weeks. In certain
cases, particularly when single crystals were grown, an intermediate grinding was
carried out. The silica tube was cooled by dipping it in water.

The homogeneity of the sulfide obtained was verified by examination with an
optical microscope and with x-rays (sharpness of the back-reflections).

Analysis. To confirm the value of the S/Ti ratio, the sulfides were chemically
analyzed by roasting in air at 900° C. The weighings, made with a balance
sensitive to 0.01 mg., gave the ratio with a precision of 0.2% for a quantity of
oxidized sulfide on the order of 0.1 gram. In the great majority of cases, experiment showed the discrepancy between the values of the S/Ti ratio determined in
the preparation and in the analysis to be less than 0.5%.

X-Ray Methods. A camera with a curved quartz crystal monochromator
served to identify the crystal type of the sulfide under study and to verify that it
belonged to a single-phase system. To reduce the effect of the titanium fluorescence excited by the copper radiation used, an aluminum filter 0.03 mm. thick was
placed over the photographic film. Under these conditions, well-focused weak
lines stood out clearly against a continuous background reduced as much as
possible.

The lattice constants were measured by a back-reflection method with an internal standard of sodium chloride. The sulfides studied possess hexagonal symmetry. Thus two diffraction lines are needed for a determination of the two constants. The two lines were chosen in such a way as not to increase unduly the experimental error, which was of the order of 0.15%.

Only diffraction lines whose Bragg angles exceeded 73° were photographed. Therefore it was not possible to perform an extrapolation that would have permitted reducing the error due to absorption. However, since the mean Bragg angle of the lines used was 78°, the residual systematic error should be relatively slight.

X-ray intensities were measured photometrically. To reduce the effect of absorption as much as possible, the sulfide was diluted with magnesium oxide. The value of the coefficient μR was experimentally determined. Moreover, to eliminate the effect of preferred orientation, which arises when the sample assumes the form of a cylindrical rod, we adopted a spherical sample shape of 0.3-mm. diameter.

Density Measurements. The measurements were made according to the method of Archimedes. As the amount of sulfide was limited to 0.2 or 0.3 gram, the resulting loss of precision was offset by choosing a liquid whose density was as close as possible to those of the sulfides studied. The density of 1,1,2,2-tetrabromoethane, the liquid chosen, was determined in advance as a function of temperature. The sulfides, placed in a special weighing boat, were immersed under vacuum in the apparatus shown in Figure 2. Under these conditions, the densities of the sulfides were determined with a precision of 0.2%.

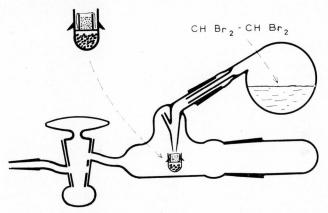

CH Br$_2$ - CH Br$_2$

Figure 2. Apparatus for measurement of density by immersion of sulfide under vacuum

Nonstoichiometric Phase, TiS$_2$

Crystals of titanium disulfide occur in the form of golden hexagonal plates with an extremely marked metallic luster. If the reaction tube does not contain enough sulfur to give a S/Ti ratio of 2, a powdery compound will be formed which has the same unit cell as the stoichiometric sulfide, but which maintains a S/Ti ratio of less than 2.

Two series of sulfides obtained in this manner were prepared; they are differentiated only by the temperatures of preparation, 1000° and 800° C. The experimental results are collected in Table I. Lattice constants and density increase linearly with a decreasing S/Ti ratio (Figures 3 and 4). Calculating the mass of the unit cell and studying its variation as a function of composition indicate the nature of the lattice defects responsible for the variations from stoichiometry:

They correspond to the insertion of titanium between layers (Figures 5 and 6) (6).

Table I.   TiS₂ Phase

Preparation	S/Ti Analysis	a, A.	c, A.	ρ, G./Cc.
		Series Prepared at 1000° C.		
Ti₃S₅	1.667		Outside of phase	
	1.804	1.823	3.4138	5.7170	3.355
	1.821	1.816	3.4131	5.7176	3.358
	1.812	1.819	3.4123	5.7166	3.345
	1.814	1.816	3.4134	5.6166	3.344
	1.820	1.825	3.4132	5.7153	3.357
	1.865	1.841	3.4125	5.7138	3.328
	1.850	1.856	3.4123	5.7119	3.326
	1.874	1.869	3.4109	5.7089	3.313
	1.900	1.875	3.4109	5.7077	3.296
	1.952	1.903	3.4095	5.7040	3.298
	1.900	1.904	3.4089	5.7060	3.306
	1.905	1.919	3.4091	5.7019	3.293
	1.915	1.919	3.4085	5.7028	3.294
TiS₂	2	Cannot be isolated at this temperature		
		Series Prepared at 800° C.		
Ti₃S₅	1.667		Outside of phase	
	1.817	1.818	3.4127	5.7142	3.362
	1.821	1.818	3.4127	5.7140	3.352
	1.818	1.819	3.4125	5.7139	3.345
	1.824	1.825	3.4124	5.7129	3.354
	1.851	1.854	3.4108	5.7090	3.311
	1.873	1.870	3.4098	5.7053	3.327
	1.883	1.897	3.4090	5.7025	3.291
	1.917	1.898	3.4092	5.7027	3.309
	1.904	1.908	3.4094	5.7013	3.315
	1.920	1.922	3.4079	5.7002	3.289
	1.943	1.928	3.4075	5.6977	3.285
	1.982	1.943	3.4075	5.6976	3.266
TiS₂	2	Cannot be isolated at this temperature		

Stoichiometric TiS_2 cannot be isolated at 1000° or at 800° C. Indeed, at these temperatures it decomposes to give sulfur vapor and a nonstoichiometric sulfide with the TiS_2 structure:

Sulfide (S/Ti = 2) → sulfide (S/Ti = 2 − α) + sulfur vapor

The value of α is less in proportion as the temperature is lower. One may expect an excess of sulfur vapor to affect the value of α. This is the reason for finding the sulfur-rich limit in analyzing the solid sulfide from a reaction tube containing just a slight excess of sulfur. Washing the sulfide with carbon disulfide assures that this excess does not lead to a false analytical result.

The lattice constants of the stoichiometric disulfide may be obtained by extrapolating the curves of Figures 3 and 4. The values found agree within experimental error. We accept the following values for the lattice constants of the stoichiometric disulfide:

$$a = 3.4048 \pm 0.0004 \text{ A.}$$

$$c = 5.6904 \pm 0.0007 \text{ A.}$$

On the low-sulfur side the phase limit is less clearly defined. Indeed, if this limit was deduced from lattice constants variation curves, it should be located at

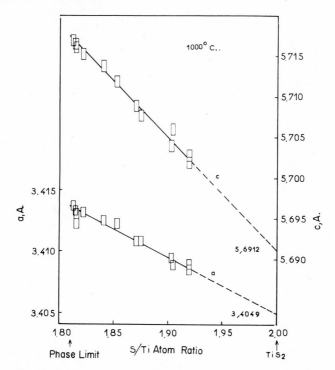

*Figure 3.   Variation of parameters as a function of com-
position*

Sulfides prepared at 1000 C.

S/Ti ~ 1.7; then a discontinuity in the c parameter appears at this composition. This value agrees precisely with the phase limit reported by Ehrlich (2); yet careful examination of the patterns obtained with the monochromator reveals that, beyond a value of about 1.8 in the S/Ti ratio, additional sharp lines appear alongside those of the TiS_2 phase, whose lattice constants, however, do not stop changing (6). For sulfides prepared at 1000° C. these additional lines first appear at S/Ti = 1.810, and for 800° C. at S/Ti = 1.818. The limits determined in this way are known with a precision estimated at ±0.005.

For most substances crystallizing with the CdI_2 structure, the value of the z coordinate of iodine, hence of sulfur in the case of TiS_2, is generally taken to be 1/4 (11). We sought to determine this value more precisely and to follow its variation, if any, as a function of the S/Ti ratio (Table II). We tried to restrict the comparison of intensities to lines whose Bragg angles are not too far apart, in order that temperature and absorption effects may be neglected. The error in z has a value of ± 0.01.

Table II.   Determination of z Value

Preparation Temp., ° C.	S/Ti	Formula	z
1000	1.918	$Ti_{1.042}S_2$	0.23
	1.813	$Ti_{1.103}S_2$	0.25
800	1.934	$Ti_{1.034}S_2$	0.23
	1.824	$Ti_{1.096}S_2$	0.25

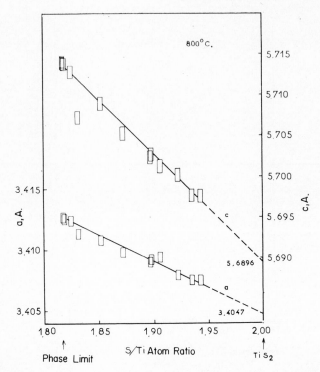

Figure 4. Variation of parameters as a function of composition

Sulfides prepared at 800° C.

The two sulfur planes adjacent to a plane of titanium draw closer to it, the nearer the sulfide is to the stoichiometric composition. The latter corresponds to a Ti-S distance of 2.32 A. The S-S distance between two $(TiS_2)_n$ sheets is 3.62 A. This value is in exact agreement with the Van der Waals radius of sulfur. When titanium is inserted between these sulfur atoms, the sulfur planes tend toward positions at a height of $1/4$. And, whether the sulfides are prepared at 1000° or 800° C., the phase limit corresponds to $z = 1/4$. The octahedra formed by sulfur atoms are all identical in this case, whether or not they contain titanium atoms. We consider this criterion as decisive in the transition from the TiS_2 structure to another structure characterizing the next phase.

If one tries to prepare sulfides having S/Ti ratios less than 1.8, a peculiar change in the x-ray diffraction pattern is observed. Additional lines appear, although the lattice constants do not stop changing. These weak lines are easily interpreted if the sixfold axis, c, of TiS_2 is multiplied by an integer. The value of this integer is rather hard to determine. In fact, the number and the intensities of these surplus lines, as well as the intensities of a majority of lines characteristic of TiS_2, gradually change in a continuous fashion as S/Ti decreases from 1.8 to 1.6. These experimental facts might be explained qualitatively by considering a variation in the order of stacking planes of sulfur and planes of titanium, filled, or with random vacancies. This is only a hypothesis, as work has not been pursued in this direction. It seems, nonetheless, that the transition from the TiS_2 structure

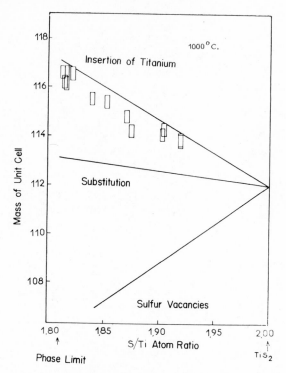

Figure 5.   Density variation as a function of composition for determination of nature of defects

Sulfides prepared at 1000° C.

to the Ti_2S_3 structure is not as simple as Wadsley has reported (*10*), but that it requires a whole series of intermediate stages.

Nonstoichiometric Phase, Ti_2S_3

If the S/Ti ratio becomes less than 1.594, the diffraction pattern becomes simpler; indeed, the integer which multiplies the sixfold axis, *c*, is then equal to 2. S/Ti = 1.594, determined in the same way as the sulfur-deficient limit of the TiS_2 phase, marks the sulfur-rich limit of a new nonstoichiometric phase. The latter, characterized by a hexagonal unit cell and lattice parameters (*5, 9*),

$$a = 3.42 \text{ A.}$$

$$c = 11.44 \text{ A.}$$

is referred to as Ti_2S_3; it includes all sulfides prepared at 1000° C. whose compositions correspond to a S/Ti ratio between 1.594 and 1.377.

Hahn and Harder found this same unit cell in studying a single crystal taken from a sample corresponding in over-all composition to Ti_3S_4 (*4*). We assign this particular sulfide a position outside the homogeneous range of Ti_2S_3 if its temperature of preparation is 1000° C.

The titanium-rich limit of the Ti_2S_3 phase, corresponding to S/Ti = 1.377, was determined by careful inspection of the x-ray diffraction patterns obtained with the monochromator. Around the value S/Ti = 1.37, certain lines broaden

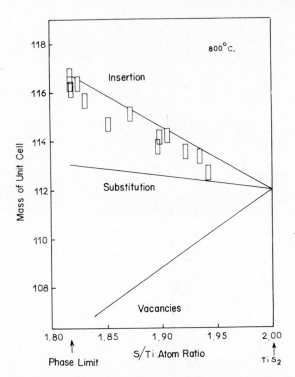

Figure 6.   Density variation as a function of composition for determination of nature of defects

Sulfides prepared at 800° C.

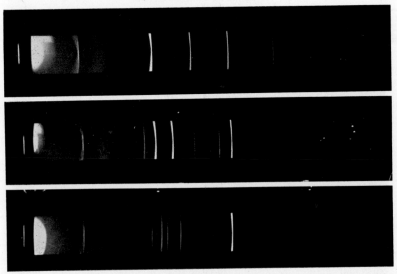

Figure 7.   X-ray powder diffraction patterns characteristic of TiS_2, Ti_2S_3, and Ti_8S_{12}

Upper, TiS_2
Center, Ti_2S_3
Lower, Ti_8S_{12}

before being resolved each into several separate, closely spaced lines when S/Ti has reached the value 1.36.   Such a development, indicating very probably the appearance of a superlattice of lower symmetry, makes it impracticable to measure lattice constants by means of back-reflections, and forces us to observe the monochromator photographs carefully in determining the limit, whose precision we estimate at ± 0.005.

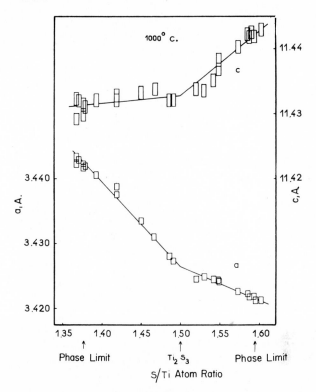

Figure 8.   Variation of parameters of phase Ti_2S_3 as a function of composition

Sulfides prepared at 1000° C.

Results of the lattice constants and density measurements are given in Table III; their variations as a function of composition are shown in Figures 8 and 9.   At the present time, two crystal structures only slightly different from one another have been proposed (*4, 9*).   They differ only in the origin of *z*, the distances between planes of titanium and of sulfur, and in the distribution of titanium among the available sites (Figure 10).   In the present case, density measurements do not permit making a decision; they simply show that lattice defects are related to the variable number of titanium atoms per unit cell, and that the number of sulfur atoms per unit cell is constant and equal to 4.

The curves showing the lattice constants as functions of composition reveal the existence of a discontinuity in the immediate vicinity of S/Ti = 1.5.   If the monochromator photograph of a sulfide with this composition, Ti_2S_3, is examined closely, the detection of several extra lines, weak and diffuse, suggests the appearance of a superlattice.   If this sulfide, Ti_2S_3, is then prepared at 800° C., the

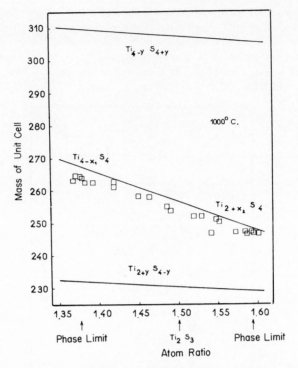

Figure 9.   Variation of density of phase Ti_2S_3 as a function of composition

Sulfides prepared at 1000° C.

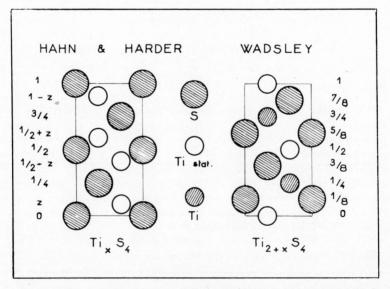

Figure 10.   Diagrams representing the two structures proposed for Ti_2S_3

Table III. Ti$_2$S$_3$ Phase

(Sulfides that comprise this phase were prepared at 1000° C.; they correspond
to the general formula Ti$_x$S$_4$)

Preparation	Analysis	a, A.	c, A.	Density
Ti$_3$S$_4$	1.333		Outside of phase	
1.387	1.377	3.4422	11.4298	3.743
1.374	1.378	3.4416	11.4314	3.737
1.379	1.379	3.4417	11.4310	3.747
1.393	1.393	3.4405	11.4322	3.718
1.400	1.419	3.4388	11.4327	3 701
1.451	1.450	3.4335	11.4333	3.673
1.461	1.466	3.4310	11.4339	3.676
1.483	1.486	3.4279	11.4318	3.640
1.490	1.491	3.4272	11.4320	3.622
Ti$_2$S$_3$	1.500			
1.513	1.520	3.4245	11.4338	3.602
1.528	1.533	3.4249	11.4334	3.600
1.521	1.542	3.4245	11.4352	3.528
1.550	1.548	3.4244	11.4383	3.587
1.549	1.549	3.4243	11.4368	3.585
1.575	1.573	3.4226	11.4402	3.532
1.583	1.585	3.4222	11.4422	3.537
1.588	1.587	3.4218	11.4418	3.529
1.590	1.593	3.4219	11.4419	3.538
1.594	1.595	3.4213	11.4400	3.532
Ti$_3$S$_5$	1.667		Outside of phase	

The columns *S/Ti* (Preparation, Analysis) and *Parameters* (a, A., c, A.) with *Density*.

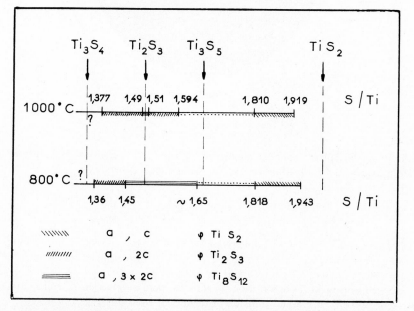

Figure 11. Schematic representation of various phases in Ti-S system

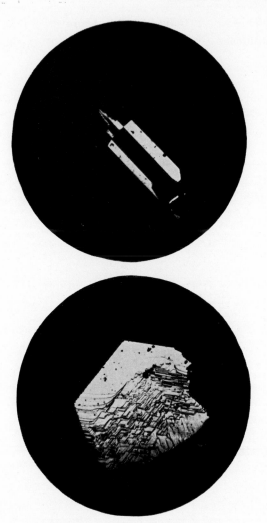

Figure 12. Single crystals of Ti$_2$S$_3$
phase ($\times$ 20)

Upper. Atom ratio S/Ti = 1.574
Lower. Atom ration S/Ti = 1.393

validity of this observation is confirmed: It is only necessary to multiply the
sixfold axis by 3 (5), leading to the following lattice constants,

$$a = 3.43 \text{ A.}$$

$$c = 34.3 \text{ A.}$$

(Figure 7)

The factor 3 is easy to interpret; indeed, from the results of the density determinations, Ti$_2$S$_3$ should be written Ti$_8$ $_3$S$_4$.   In this case, the factor of 3 yields
a unit cell containing 8 titaniums and 12 sulfurs.

Starting from this composition, if sulfides increasingly rich in sulfur are prepared at 800° C., a gradual transition is observed from the Ti$_8$S$_{12}$ unit cell to that
of TiS$_2$ by way of intermediate cells of varying complexity, as occurs with sulfides

prepared at 1000° C. The only difference lies in the fact that at 800° C. the Ti_2S_3 (Figure 11) unit cell is no longer found between S/Ti = 1.5 and S/Ti = 2.

We have observed, as did Hahn and Harder (4), the formation of single crystals, sometimes as large as 0.5 cm. in their longest dimension. However, such crystals do not form at all S/Ti values. Two composition regions, situated around S/Ti = 1.4 and S/Ti = 1.55, are especially favorable. The direction of rapid crystal growth is not the same in the two cases: Near S/Ti = 1.40 it is perpendicular to the sixfold axis, and near S/Ti = 1.55 it is parallel to this axis (Figure 12).

Conclusions

The mean systematic deviation between the observed and the calculated values of the unit cell's mass—or, what amounts to the same thing, the density—increases as S/Ti decreases. Now, the sulfides belonging to the TiS_2 and Ti_2S_3 phases are always well crystallized, and the errors in measuring lattice parameters and densities are of the same order. It is thus not unreasonable that the increase of this deviation should be due to the creation of sulfur vacancies, which proceeds simultaneously with the insertion of titanium. The observation has been previously made in connection with other analogous systems in which there is a transition from the compound MX_2 to MX.

We have not studied sulfides of higher titanium content than those constituting the Ti_2S_3 phase. We concentrated on determining the nature of the defects responsible for the deviations from stoichiometry that can occur in titanium disulfide. Next, we inquired into the alteration of the structure of this system as titanium is inserted. This led us to encounter a whole series of complex forms, in the nature of superlattices, which account for the transition between TiS_2 and Ti_2S_3. To make the study complete, it would be necessary also to determine the conditions required for the transition from Ti_2S_3 to TiS, and to elucidate in particular the structure of the compound which occurs between these two phases.

Literature Cited

(1) Biltz, W., Ehrlich, P., Meisel, K., *Z. anorg. allgem. Chem.* **234**, 97 (1937).
(2) Ehrlich, P., *Z. anorg. Chem.* **260**, 1 (1949).
(3) Hägg, G., Schönberg, N., *Arkiv Kemi* **7**, 371 (1954).
(4) Hahn, H., Harder, B., *Z. anorg. allgem. Chem.* **288**, 241 (1957).
(5) Jeannin, Y., *Compt. Rend.* **251**, 246 (1960).
(6) Jeannin, Y., Benard, J., *Ibid.*, **248**, 2475 (1959).
(7) Oftedal, I., *Z. phys. Chem.* **134**, 301 (1928); **135**, 291 (1928).
(8) Tengner, S., *Z. anorg. allgem. Chem.* **239**, 127 (1938).
(9) Wadsley, A. D., *Acta Cryst.* **10**, 715 (1957).
(10) Wadsley, A. D., *Rev. Pure. Appl. Chem.* **5**, 165 (1955).
(11) Wyckoff, R., "Crystal Structures," Chap. IV, p. 9, Interscience, New York, 1948.

RECEIVED September 6, 1962.

18

Investigations of Nonstoichiometric Sulfides

II. The System In₂S₃.MgS

JACQUES BENARD, GÉRARD DUCHEFDELAVILLE, and MICHEL HUBER

Ecole Nationale Supérieure de Chimie, Paris, France

The stoichiometric compound $MgIn_2S_4$, as well as the terms of the nonstoichiometric phase $In_2S_3.xMgS$, has the spinel structure. X-ray diffraction on this series and extrapolation for $x = 0$ present a simpler approach to the problem of the position of the vacancies in the lattice than direct investigation of the pure In_2S_3, which has a superstructure of the spinel structure. A careful study of the diffraction intensities of $MgIn_2S_4$, of several members of the $In_2S_3.xMgS$ series, and of disordered In_2S_3 indicates the tetrahedral nature of the vacancies for members of the series that are low in magnesium and for In_2S_3 itself. A concise comparative study of the patterns of ordered and disordered forms of In_2S_3 suggests a mechanism for the order-disorder transition.

At the present time, the structures of In_2S_3 are rather poorly understood; two forms have been reported, and it appears that impurities have an influence on the crystallographic structure. Only the so-called "β" form is well established.

Ordered Form, β-In₂S₃

The structure of β-In₂S₃ is not yet known with certainty. To a first approximation its structure is identical with that of the spinels, but additional lines in the x-ray pattern imply the existence of a superlattice whose origin must be sought in the ordering of existing vacancies. This superlattice is tetragonal, and results from the stacking of three spinel unit cells (7).

The assumed arrangement of vacancies deduced from the determination of the space group by powder x-ray diffraction (7) requires for its confirmation a comparison of the observed and calculated intensities. This is difficult to accomplish directly on the powdery ordered product for two reasons:

1. In the powder method, except at very small angles, there is considerable overlapping of superlattice lines with each other, or with primary lines, as is shown by single-crystal spectra, and this renders unreliable an interpretation of intensity measurements.

2. The displacement of atoms in passing from the spinel structure to the superlattice structure may introduce a considerable error into any calculation based on the atomic coordinates of the spinel structure. The determination of these displacements, considering the large number of position parameters, is out of the question except by Fourier analysis of measurements made on a single crystal.

Disordered Forms

α-In$_2$S$_3$, a form reported by Hahn and Klinger (3) as having a cubic structure, and in which the vacancies should be disordered, would be suitable for x-ray study, but we have not succeeded in reproducing it; its existence, moreover, is debatable. But we have obtained, by quenching liquid In$_2$S$_3$, a product with a strict spinel structure. The interpretation of its pattern leads to a clear rejection of the hypothesis of octahedral vacancies.

The Phase In$_2$S$_3$.xMgS

The trial and error method used for disordered In$_2$S$_3$ cannot account quantitatively for observed intensities, since it offers no way to correct the systematic deviations that tend to restrict considerably the significance of precise measurements.

A comparative study of the variations of intensities in the In$_2$S$_3$.xMgS system makes it possible to evaluate these corrections and to draw conclusions about pure In$_2$S$_3$ by extrapolation to $x = 0$. Our study has therefore centered primarily on this nonstoichiometric phase, In$_2$S$_3$.xMgS.

Preparation of Samples. All samples in the series were prepared between 950° and 1000° C. by direct combination of the constituents in a silica tube sealed under vacuum.

The disordered form of In$_2$S$_3$ was prepared by heating to 1200° C. and very fast quenching to room temperature.

X-Ray Patterns and Calculations. We used, under the same conditions, the apparatus previously employed in studying MgGa$_2$O$_4$ and CdGa$_2$O$_4$ (6), and our calculations were carried out in the same manner. Intensity measurements were made with a Geiger-Müller counter. The wavelength used was that of CuKα.

Lattice parameters were measured with a relative precision of $\pm 5 \times 10^{-4}$ A.

We have referred all measurements to the series limit, MgIn$_2$S$_4$, as a standard. The structure of the latter was precisely determined, with the following results: The degree of inversion (percentage of indium atoms in tetrahedral positions), β, is $78 \pm 3\%$; the sulfur position parameter, u ($=2\pi x$), has a value of 93° $\pm$ 0.5°, rather far from the ideal value, $u = 90°$. The criterion for the convergence is the continuity of the curve of log (I_c/I_0) as a function of sin$^2\theta$. The refinement showed the need for a correction in the f factor for indium given in the tables. This correction allows the factor $R = \Sigma|\Delta F|/\Sigma|F|$ to be reduced from 8% to 3.5%. This corrected value of f was used in all remaining calculations.

The Series In$_2$S$_3$.xMgS

The fundamental assumption about this type of structure is the existence of a single kind of defect: metal vacancies.

We set out, first, to determine qualitatively the nature of the metal vacancies. The results are shown schematically in Figure 1, where two triangles, $F_1F_NF_C$, represent the domain of F_0 values that could be observed in one case with tetra-

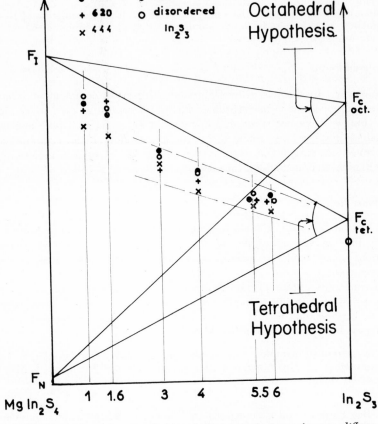

Figure 1. Comparison of measured structure factors of x-ray diffraction lines with those calculated on basis of octahedral and tetrahedral vacancies

Values of F vs. number of vacancies

hedral vacancies, and in the other with octahedral vacancies. Subscripts I and N refer to the inverse and normal structures.

The occurrence of vacancies requires the adoption of two definitions of the degree of inversion, depending on the hypothesis made about the vacancies. Tetrahedral hypothesis: β measures the concentration of indium in tetrahedral positions with respect to the maximum possible concentration. Octahedral hypothesis: β measures the concentration of magnesium in octahedral positions with respect to the maximum possible concentration.

The average of the experimental points corresponding to four lines among those most sensitive to the distribution of cations and vacancies indicates uniformly a tendency, at all compositions, toward a very marked inversion, and for phases lowest in magnesium, shows the tetrahedral nature of the vacancies. The experimental point representing disordered In_2S_3 is located almost on the extension of the straight portion of the average curve, near the corner of the triangle which is theoretically its only possible position.

The quantitative study was made with the aid of the function

$$Z = \left[\frac{F'(hkl)}{F'(440)}\right] \Big/ \left[\frac{F(hkl)}{F(440)}\right]_{standard}$$

used previously in the study of nonstoichiometric $CdGa_2O_4$. This function has the considerable advantage of eliminating the systematic corrections that are necessary in direct comparisons—for example, in the previous diagram. Its graphical representation consists of two families of straight lines corresponding to each hypothesis and to every composition. To each observed value of Z, there corresponds a value of β for each of the hypotheses, both on the same horizontal level. A graphical solution is very easy; it leads to a single possible solution for phases low in magnesium, that of the tetrahedral hypothesis (Figure 2). The results of these graphical solutions are shown in Figure 3.

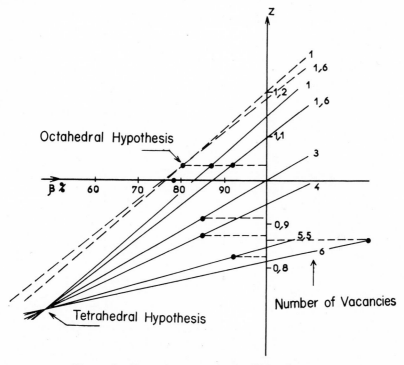

Figure 2. Z as a function of β for 620 reflection

Deviations from Vegard's law are also shown in Figure 3.

Beyond six vacancies (for a tripled cell) only the tetrahedral hypothesis is possible and Vegard's law is sensibly followed. With a single vacancy, both hypotheses are possible, and the two types of vacancies conceivably could co-exist. In the intermediate region, it is not possible to proceed with certainty. However, considering the results of Verwey (8) on the series $M^{II}M_{2III}O_4$ (where M^{II} is Fe, Ni, Co, etc.), relating the cell edge to the degree of inversion, and those of Baffier and Huber (1) on the strict correspondence between the curves of lattice dimension and the distribution, it can be supposed with some confidence that the degree of inversion increases or at least varies little. The product

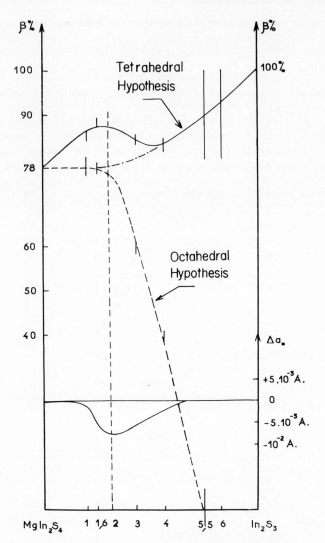

*Figure 3.   Comparison of hypotheses of octahedral vs.
tetrahedral vacancies in the system $MgS.In_2S_3$*

Deviations from Vegard's law

thus remains inverse in the intermediate range, as the qualitative graph (Figure 1)
suggests, and the tetrahedral hypothesis will be equally valid.

Compounds Low in Magnesium Content

These compounds are spinels up to very low concentrations or can be
obtained as such by quenching. The existence of the α form is perhaps due to the
presence of impurities.

Discussion

The tetrahedral nature of the vacancies predicted by Rooymans (7) for
In_2S_3 is thus confirmed by our study. In addition, this suggests a physical ex-

planation for the residual difference between the characteristics of the structures of β-In$_2$S$_3$, of disordered In$_2$S$_3$, and of the idealized extrapolated structure, agreeing with the crystallographic data and the irreversible nature of the order-disorder transformation at low temperature. Indeed the disordered compound becomes ordered rapidly and irreversibly at temperatures as low as 250° C., which leads one to suppose that the ordering occurs without much movement of the metal atoms through the sulfur lattice.

On the other hand the pattern of disordered In$_2$S$_3$ is between the idealized structure and β-In$_2$S$_3$ so far as the intensities are concerned, which means that the majority of the vacancies are already at the sites they occupy when the structure is ordered. The nonappearance of the superstructure lines would be due in this case to the rather small size of the zones in which the vacancies are in phase, and to a statistical distribution of the metal atoms among their positions in the superstructure. The appearance of the latter would require only small displacements of the metal atoms within the sulfur polyhedra, whereas the domains in phase generate homogeneous superstructure zones, those out of phase generate twins which have been observed both by microscopy (*2, 4*) and by diffraction from crystals and from whiskers (*5*). This multiply-twinned state of crystals of β-In$_2$S$_3$ is probably very stable and is an example of antiphase domains (*2, 4*). This equilibrium state justified in a certain measure the ratio $c/a = 3.0000$ between the axes of the β-In$_2$S$_3$ lattice which the structural data appeared to forbid.

Literature Cited

(1) Baffier, N., Huber, M., *Compt. Rend.* **252**, 3586 (1961).
(2) Goodyear, J., Steigman, G. A., *Proc. Phys. Soc.* **78**, 491–5 (1941).
(3) Hahn, H., Klinger, W., *Z. anorg. allgem. Chem.* **260**, 97 (1949).
(4) Hatwell, H., Offerfeld, G., Herinckx, C., Van Cakenberghe, J., *Compt. Rend.* **252**. 3586 (1961).
(5) Huber, M., *Ibid.*, **253**, 471–3 (1961).
(6) Huber, M., *J. Chim. Phys. France* **57** (3), 203–27 (1960).
(7) Rooymans, C. J. M., *J. Inorg. Nucl. Chem.* **2**, 78 (1959).
(8) Verwey, E. J. W., Heilmann, E. L., *J. Chem. Phys.* **15**, 174–87 (1947).

RECEIVED September 6, 1962.

19

Nonstoichiometry in Some Group IV Tellurides

ROBERT MAZELSKY and M. S. LUBELL

Westinghouse Research Laboratories, Pittsburgh 35, Pa.

Germanium telluride is a nonstoichiometric semiconductor with a narrow phase field. Changes in crystallographic rhombohedral angle, Seebeck coefficient, and Hall constant have been studied for the nominal compositions GeTe and $GeTe_{1.025}$ with additions of $TlSbTe_2$, $TlBiTe_2$, and Bi_2Te_3. The solubility of germanium in $GeTe_{1.025}$ is shown to be dependent on total vacancy concentration. A dependence of the lattice parameter on vacancy concentration was observed for tin telluride. However, no simple relationship of either carrier concentration or Seebeck coefficient to vacancy concentration was found.

A major portion of the effort on semiconductors has been expended on the binary compounds having the zinc blende or wurtzite structure. These are commonly classified by the A group numbers such as III–V (InAs) and II–VI (CdTe) and have what may loosely be described as a 1 to 1 cation-anion ratio. However, another series of compounds that has become of increased interest can be generally classified as the IV–VI compounds. Specifically, these are the chalcogenides of germanium, tin, and lead. In this discussion, we present some experimental observations on the tellurides of these group IV A elements.

The series of germanium, tin, and lead tellurides is found to have the rocksalt structure, SnTe and PbTe being cubic and GeTe being rhombohedrally distorted from the cube. In the series, PbTe appears to be the only material that can be prepared with nearly a 1 to 1 ratio of the metal to tellurium. GeTe has recently been investigated by McHugh and Tiller (4) and shown to be congruently melting at a composition corresponding to $GeTe_{1.025}$. Phase diagram data on SnTe are not available, but indications are that it too is a nonstoichiometric material. This discussion is confined to the germanium and tin tellurides. For clarity the experimental results and discussions of these materials are treated separately.

Experimental

All the samples under discussion were prepared by a modified powder metallurgical technique. The elements (99.999% pure with respect to metallic impurities) were weighed in the proper proportions and placed in a Vycor tube, which was then evacuated and sealed. The elements were melted and manually mixed while molten. The samples were air-quenched and the resulting ingot was ground into powder, pressed, and sintered at around 500° C. for 16 hours.

Three analytical tools were used to characterize the compounds. The first is powder x-ray diffraction methods using a 114.6-mm. diameter camera. The photographs were in general poor for germanium telluride and, as a result, the parameters were determined from low-angle reflections only. The second procedure involved room temperature Seebeck coefficient data (taken versus copper and converted to absolute values) which qualitatively vary inversely as the log of the carrier concentration. Finally, Hall measurements were taken on $1.6 \times 0.5 \times 0.1$ cm. plates in a manner already described (6).

Carrier concentrations were calculated from the Hall measurements on the basis of a degenerate, single-band model using the expression $p = \dfrac{1}{R_H |e|}$, where $|e|$ is the absolute value of the electric charge. Because some of the Hall measurements showed an anomalous rise with temperature (presumably due to two-phase material), all the calculations used Hall measurements taken at liquid nitrogen temperature. In this way, we obtain a self-consistent set of values for carrier concentrations, although not necessarily the absolute values. All the samples discussed in this paper are p-type.

Germanium Telluride Results

The nominal compositions GeTe and GeTe$_{1.025}$ were prepared in the manner described. The composition GeTe by itself and in solid solutions is not a single-phase material, about 2 atom % germanium metal being present. Small amounts of other components were added to both GeTe and GeTe$_{1.025}$ in order to investigate the changes in rhombohedral angle, Seebeck coefficient, and Hall constant. The materials used were TlBiTe$_2$, TlSbTe$_2$, and Bi$_2$Te$_3$.

The first two materials were reported by Hockings and White (3), who characterized them as having a rhombohedral structure with the cations ordered in layers perpendicular to the c direction of the hexagonal cell. The space group was reported to be $R\bar{3}m$-D^5_{3d} for both materials. Bi$_2$Te$_3$ is reported to have the same space group.

The solid solutions prepared with GeTe were of the following general type:

$$(1 - x)\text{GeTe} + \frac{x}{2}\,\text{Tl (Sb, Bi) Te}_2 \rightarrow \text{Ge}_{1-x}\text{Tl}_{\frac{x}{2}}\,(\text{Sb, Bi})_{\frac{x}{2}}\text{Te}$$

$$(1 - x)\text{GeTe} + x\text{Bi}_2\text{Te}_3 \qquad \rightarrow \text{Ge}_{1-x}\text{Bi}_{2x}\text{Te}_{1+2x}$$

For simplicity in comparing the systems, the atom per cent of the cations was recalculated on the basis of one tellurium atom per molecule—i.e., Ge$_{\frac{1-x}{1+2x}}$ Bi$_{\frac{2x}{1+2x}}$ Te. Therefore, the solid solution of GeTe with Bi$_2$Te$_3$ was considered to result in vacancies on the cation sites. These are introduced via an essentially stoichiometric material and do not in themselves affect the carrier concentrations. (Bi$_2$Te$_3$ is nearly stoichiometric, the deviation from 2 to 3 ratio being so small that its carrier concentration is negligible compared to that of GeTe$_{1.025}$.) Similar solutions were prepared using GeTe$_{1.025}$ as a base material.

Figure 1 shows the variation of the rhombohedral angle of GeTe and GeTe$_{1.025}$ with varying concentrations of the solute materials. Up to around 4 atomic % bismuth, the rhombohedral angle with GeTe and GeTe$_{1.025}$ is the same. Beyond this amount, the rhombohedral angle for GeTe continues to increase whereas that for GeTe$_{1.025}$ does not. TlSbTe$_2$ and TlBiTe$_2$, on the other hand, seem to affect the germanium telluride distortion to the same extent, whether GeTe or GeTe$_{1.025}$ is used as the host. At 8% TlSbTe$_2$ or TlBiTe$_2$, the distortion seems to be less for GeTe than for GeTe$_{1.025}$. Beyond 8% the x-rays indicate that the materials are no longer single phase.

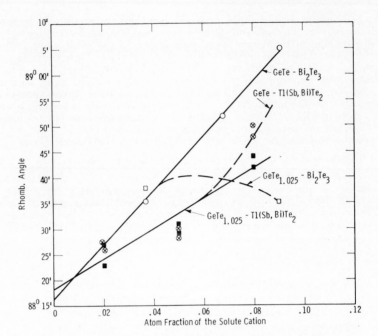

Figure 1. Effect of solute concentration on rhombohedral angle

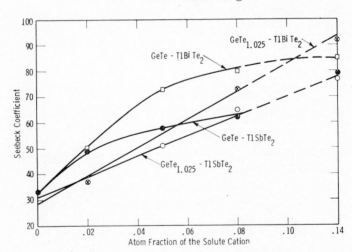

Figure 2.   Effect of solute concentration on Seebeck coefficient

μv. per degree

On Figure 2, the Seebeck coefficients of GeTe and GeTe$_{1.025}$ with TlSbTe$_2$ and TlBiTe$_2$ are drawn versus composition of the solute compound. With both TlSbTe$_2$ and TlBiTe$_2$, the Seebeck coefficient increases significantly when GeTe rather than GeTe$_{1.025}$ is used as the solvent, and a maximum Seebeck voltage of +80 to 90 μv. per degree is obtained. On Figure 3, the Seebeck coefficients of Bi$_2$Te$_3$ dissolved in GeTe and GeTe$_{1.025}$ are shown. The difference between the

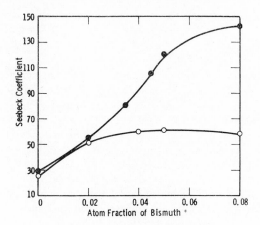

Figure 3. *Effect of bismuth concentration on Seebeck coefficient*

◉ *GeTe*
o *GeTe₁.₀₂₅*

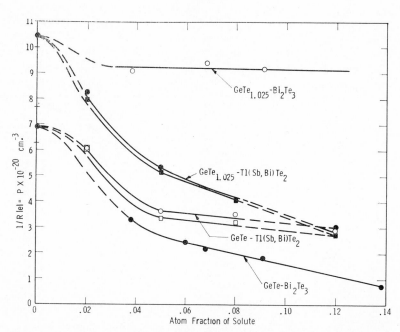

Figure 4. *Relation of solute concentrations to hole carrier concentration*

two is appreciable and the maximum Seebeck value is $+140$ μv. per degree—higher than that observed with TlBiTe$_2$ or TlSbTe$_2$.

On Figure 4, carrier concentrations calculated from Hall data are plotted against solute concentration. The difference in carrier concentrations between GeTe and GeTe$_{1.025}$ with TlSbTe$_2$ and TlBiTe$_2$ seems to be fairly constant over the single-phase range—i.e., to $x = 0.08$—and is small. The difference in carrier concentrations seems to be of the same order of magnitude as that between GeTe and $GeTe_{1.025}$. In accord with the Seebeck coefficient, the carrier concentration with Bi_2Te_3 doping in GeTe shows a marked difference from that in $GeTe_{1.025}$.

Germanium Telluride Discussion

The Hall measurements show that there is a significant difference in carrier concentration between the nominal compositions of GeTe and $GeTe_{1.025}$. Assuming two carriers per vacancy and the composition $GeTe_{1.025}$ (equivalent to $Ge_{0.976}Te$), a carrier concentration of 9.0×10^{20} cm.$^{-3}$ is expected. A value of 10 to 11×10^{20} cm.$^{-3}$ was measured. The material with a nominal composition GeTe has a measured carrier concentration of 7.0×10^{20} cm.$^{-3}$, indicating a composition $Ge_{0.980}Te$, resulting in 1.97 atomic % vacancies (and an equal amount of germanium metal present as a second phase). We have interpreted the difference in the carrier concentration of the two compositions to mean that there is a small width in the phase field at the sintering temperature. There is, then, a reasonable dependence between the vacancies in the $Ge_{1-x}Te$ lattice (hereafter referred to as "empty Ge sites") and the carrier concentrations calculated from Hall measurements. It is, on the other hand, possible to change the vacancy concentration without changing carrier concentration. Bi_2Te_3 serves as an example. If it is dissolved in GeTe, it is convenient to assume no change in the tellurium sublattice. (Other models assuming Ge^{+2}, Bi^{+3}, and Te^{-2} yield analogous results.) However, for every three tellurium ions introduced only two cations are placed in the cation sites, resulting in a single vacancy in the cation sublattice. Although these may be physically indistinguishable from the empty germanium sites already present in the lattice, they do not contribute any charge imbalance upon their introduction, and therefore do not affect the carrier concentration. For convenience, the vacancies introduced in such a manner are called "neutral vacancies."

We can see from Figure 4 that there is little change in carrier concentration as greater amounts of Bi_2Te_3 are dissolved in $GeTe_{1.025}$—that is, no antidoping

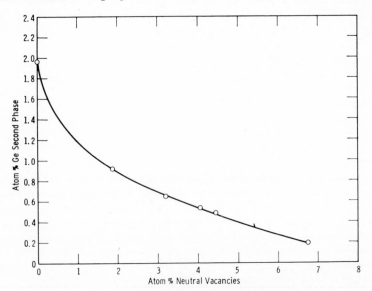

*Figure 5. Effect of neutral vacancies introduced via Bi_2Te_3
on germanium second phase*

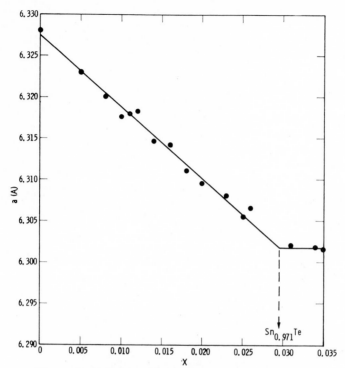

Figure 6. Relation of lattice parameter to vacancy concentration in Sn$_{(1-x)}$ Te

effect is observed as with TlSbTe$_2$ or TlBiTe$_2$. When Bi$_2$Te$_3$ is dissolved in GeTe[Ge$_{1-x}$Te + Ge(m)], there is a decided diminution in the number of carriers as calculated from Hall measurements. Since the only difference in the two preparations is the presence of excess germanium via GeTe, it seems probable that when bismuth telluride dissolves in germanium telluride, the germanium present as a second phase dissolves into the lattice, thereby filling up vacancies and reducing the carrier concentration.

The amount of solution of germanium appears to be governed by the number of "neutral vacancies" introduced by Bi$_2$Te$_3$. Figure 5 is a plot of the atom per cent of neutral vacancies introduced by Bi$_2$Te$_3$ versus the atomic per cent of germanium second phase. Since germanium telluride was prepared as GeTe, the amount of germanium left as a second phase is equivalent to the empty germanium sites, which we have assumed yields two carriers per vacancy. The calculations of both the neutral vacancies and the germanium second phase (empty germanium sites) are based on one formula weight of the congruently melting composition, Ge$_{0.976}$Te. When no neutral vacancies are added, about 0.47 atom % germanium in the second phase dissolves. This leaves 1.97 atom % germanium as a second phase. The amount of germanium second phase decreases as the vacancies increase. Since the shape of the curve appears exponential, it does not seem that stoichiometry can be reached.

Tin Telluride Results

A somewhat different situation exists for SnTe. From the x-ray data the phase field of SnTe appears to be wide, at least at the 500° C. sintering tempera-

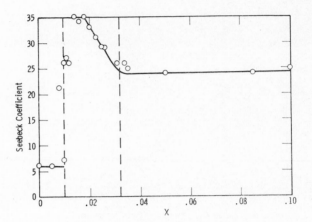

Figure 7. Effect of vacancy concentration in
Sn_{1-x} *Te on Seebeck coefficient*

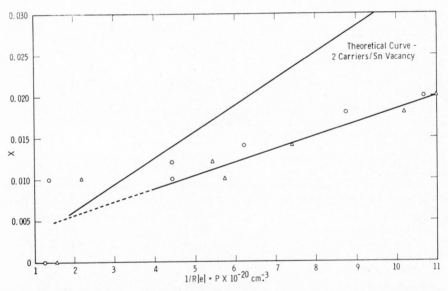

Figure 8. Relation of vacancy concentration in $Sn_{1-x}TE$ *to experimental*
hole carrier concentration

△ *Liquid nitrogen*
● *Room temperature*

ture. It can be seen on Figure 6 that the lattice parameter of $Sn_{1-x}Te$ varies monotonically from $x = 0.0$ to approximately $x = 0.03$. As the defect concentration increases, the lattice contracts. On the other hand, the Seebeck coefficient does not show a smooth trend. On Figure 7 it can be seen that the Seebeck coefficient remains constant at about +24 μv. per degree in the two-phase region. until the single-phase region, as indicated by the change in slope of the lattice parameter, is reached. Then the Seebeck coefficient begins to increase as expected, since the number of vacancies and consequently charge carriers are decreasing. However, at near $Sn_{0.99}Te$, the Seebeck coefficient shows a sharp decrease, although the vacancy concentration must still be decreasing, since the lattice parameter keeps increasing.

Tin Telluride Discussion

On Figure 8 the hole concentration is plotted against vacancy concentration. A theoretical curve calculated on the basis of two carriers per vacancy is also shown. There is a very poor agreement between the two curves. To get the theoretical curve to fit the experimental points, it is necessary to assume more than two carriers per vacancy. This is difficult to reconcile. It is apparent that SnTe is not a simple semiconductor like GeTe. At present single crystals of SnTe are being investigated at our laboratory, at the U. S. Naval Ordnance Laboratory, and at Lincoln Laboratory. Preliminary results indicate a complex band structure for this compound (1, 2, 5).

Acknowledgment

The authors acknowledge the technical assistance of W. E. Kramer, D. A. Zupon, and R. Jones. They also appreciate the helpful criticism of R. R. Heikes and R. C. Miller.

Literature Cited

(1) Allgaier, R. S., Scheie, P. O., *Bull. Am. Phys. Soc.*, Ser. II, **6**, 436 (1961).
(2) Brebrick, R. F., Strauss, A. J., *Ibid.*, **7**, 203 (1962).
(3) Hockings, E. F., White, J. F., *Acta Cryst.* **14**, 328 (1961).
(4) McHugh, J. R., Tiller, W. A., *Trans AIME* **218**, 187 (1960).
(5) Sagar, A., Miller, R. C., *Bull. Am. Phys. Soc.*, Ser. II, **7**, 203 (1962).
(6) Ure, R. W., Jr., *Rev. Sci. Instr.* **28**, 836 (1957).

RECEIVED September 6, 1962. Work supported by the U. S. Navy, Bureau of Ships, Contract NOBS-84317.

20

Nonstoichiometry in Clathrate Compounds

L. A. K. STAVELEY
The Inorganic Chemistry Laboratory, Oxford University, Oxford, England

van der Waals and Platteeuw have treated theoretically the problem of the extent to which the holes in a clathrate must be filled by guest molecules before it becomes thermodynamically stable. This theory is briefly reviewed, with special reference to hydroquinone clathrates and gas hydrates. Heat capacity studies of hydroquinone clathrates give information about the movement of the trapped guest molecules, and the estimates so obtained of the heights of the energy barriers restricting the rotation of the molecules are compared with those derived from spectroscopy and susceptibility studies.

Clathrate compounds are systems, usually solid, in which guest molecules are enclosed within the cavities of a host lattice. The best known examples are probably those in which hydroquinone forms the host lattice while the guest molecules may be argon, krypton, xenon, diatomic molecules, and even molecules as large as methanol and acetonitrile. The well-known hydrates of the rare gases and of gases like chlorine and hydrogen sulfide are clathrate compounds, as is the solid in which benzene molecules are enclosed in the holes in a host lattice formed from nickel cyanide and ammonia. Since the forces acting between the guest molecules and the host lattice are general intermolecular forces and not specific chemical forces, it is questionable whether such systems should be called compounds, and it is perhaps better to refer to them simply as "clathrates."

Factors Affecting Stability of Clathrates

The lattice of the host in the form it takes in the clathrate is usually thermodynamically unstable by itself—that is, with the holes empty. It is stabilized by inclusion of the guest molecules, and it is of obvious interest in connection with the nonstoichiometry of clathrates to consider the extent to which the cavities in the host lattice must be filled before the system achieves thermodynamic stability. The cavities in the host lattice may all be identical in size and environment, as in the hydroquinone clathrates, or they may be of more than one kind. The gas hydrates, for example, have two possible structures, in each of which there are two sorts of cavity. van der Waals and Platteeuw (*15*) have developed a general statistical theory of clathrates containing more than one type of cavity.

The relations they derive take a simpler form if there is only one kind of hole, and we confine our considerations chiefly to systems of this kind.

van der Waals treatment (*14*) uses classical statistics and further assumes that a cavity can contain only one molecule, that the free energy of the host lattice is not altered by occupation of the cavities, and that the mutual interaction of guest molecules in different cavities can be neglected. We later briefly mention some experimental evidence bearing on the last two assumptions. Since the guest-guest and guest-host relationships are then virtually the same as those in localized monolayer absorption, it is not surprising to find that the relation between P, the partial pressure of the gaseous guest, and y, the fraction of the cavities filled, is similar to a Langmuir isotherm, being

$$y = \frac{KP}{1 + KP} \tag{1}$$

This also follows if the clathrate is regarded as involving the equilibrium:

Empty cavity $+$ gaseous molecule $\rightleftharpoons$ occupied cavity

Substituting $(1 - y)$, P, and y for the concentrations of the three species, respectively, we have

$$K = \frac{y}{P(1 - y)} \tag{2}$$

K being the equilibrium constant.

The stable form of hydroquinone is α-quinol, Q^{α}. The unstable form which gives the clathrate is β-quinol, Q^{β}. The difference, $\Delta\mu = (\mu_Q{}^{\beta} - \mu_Q{}^{\alpha})$, between the chemical potentials of the two forms must therefore be positive. The clathrate formed from a gas, A, will just reach stability with the α form when the pressure, P, and the fraction of the holes filled, y, are such that

$$\mu_A = \mu_A{}^G \tag{3}$$

and

$$\mu_a = \mu_Q{}^\alpha \tag{4}$$

where μ_A and $\mu_A{}^G$ are, respectively, the chemical potentials of the guest in the clathrate and in the gaseous state. The statistical theory leads to the result that for equilibrium between the clathrate, gas, and α-quinol,

$$\frac{1}{3} \ln (1 - y) = -\frac{\Delta\mu}{kT} \tag{5}$$

the factor $\frac{1}{3}$ entering because there is one cavity to three quinol molecules. It follows that the fraction of the holes which must be filled to achieve stability is independent of the nature of the guest molecules. This conclusion is confirmed by experiment, so long as the guest molecules are not large enough to distort the hydroquinone lattice in the way that the molecules of methanol and acetonitrile do, when the assumption that the free energy of the host is unaffected by occupation of the cavities is no longer valid. van der Waals and Platteeuw (*16*) showed that the equilibrium pressure for the system clathrate, gas, and α-quinol could be measured by establishing the equilibrium in the presence of a solvent (1-propanol), and in this way found for the argon clathrate at 25° C. an equilibrium pressure of 3.4 atm. The value of y for the equilibrium clathrate was found to be 0.34 (the same figure was obtained for the krypton clathrate), which gives $\Delta\mu = 0.082$ kcal. per mole. Thus, only a small difference in chemical potential between the α and β forms is involved. For the difference in the molar heat contents of the two forms, Evans and Richards (*4*) obtained a value of 0.13 kcal. per mole. The entropy difference has apparently not yet been directly determined. The energy evolved in the formation of a hydroquinone clathrate from the β form and the gaseous guest is usually between 4 and 8 kcal. per mole of guest.

The situation with the gas hydrates is rather more complicated, since two types of cavity exist, and Equation 5 becomes

$$\nu_1 \ln (1 - y_1) + \nu_2 \ln (1 - y_2) = -\Delta\mu/kT \tag{6}$$

where ν_1 and ν_2 are the number of cavities of types 1 and 2 per molecule of host and y_1 and y_2 are the respective fractions of the cavities occupied. Since an infinite number of pairs of values of y_1 and y_2 satisfy Equation 6, the total concentration of the guest in the solid gas hydrate is no longer a constant at a given temperature but varies with the nature of the guest. However, if the guest molecule is of such a size that while unable to enter the smaller cavities it can still be accommodated in the larger ones—e.g., Br_2, CH_3Br—then Equation 6 reduces to 5, and $\Delta\mu$ can again be estimated. From a study of the bromine hydrate $\Delta\mu$ has been found to be ~ 0.19 kcal. per mole, so here too it is small.

Hydroquinone Clathrates as Examples of Cell Model

Whereas the equilibrium pressures for the gas hydrates are usually greater than 1 atm. (sometimes considerably greater), for some of the hydroquinone clathrates this pressure is much less than 1 atm., and even when it is a few atmospheres (as for the argon and nitrogen clathrates) the crystals can be kept for months at ordinary temperatures without decomposition, since such decomposition would require the breaking of the rather strong hydrogen-bonded host lattice. Moreover, by varying the conditions of preparation, it is possible to prepare a given clathrate with different proportions of the holes filled and even to prepare the unstable form with all the cavities empty. For these reasons, combined with their comparative structural simplicity, the hydroquinone clathrates lend themselves to a number of interesting physiocochemical studies. Thus, the oxygen (3, 9) and nitric oxide (2, 8) clathrates have been used to examine down to very low temperatures the magnetic properties of each of these molecules when virtually uninfluenced by magnetic interaction with others of their own kind. Such clathrates also make it possible to examine the movement of small molecules trapped individually in roughly spherical cells of approximately fixed dimensions. The wall of a cavity is made up of 12 oxygen atoms, 12 carbon atoms, and 18 hydrogen atoms. As the oxygen atoms are grouped near the poles and the carbon atoms near the equator, the environment of the trapped molecule is not strictly spherically symmetrical. But the atoms of the wall are approximately evenly distributed over a sphere (radius 3.95 A.), and the clathrate provides as good an example as one is likely to find of the so-called cell model which has been widely used in developing statistical theories of liquids and solutions. van der Waals (14) has in fact used the well-known Lennard-Jones and Devonshire approach to evaluate the partition function for a molecule in its cavity and hence to calculate some of the thermodynamic properties of the clathrates. The potential energy, ϕ, of a trapped molecule at a distance R from an "element" of the cavity wall is assumed to be the Lennard-Jones potential

$$\phi = 4\epsilon[(\sigma/R)^{12} - (\sigma/R)^6] \tag{7}$$

where the energy and distance parameters, ϵ and σ, are given by the equations

$$\epsilon = (\epsilon_A \ \epsilon_Q)^{1/2} \qquad (8)$$

$$\sigma = {}^1\!/_2(\sigma_A + \sigma_Q) \qquad (9)$$

The intermolecular parameters, ϵ_A and σ_A, are those characteristic of an isolated pair of the guest molecules and can be evaluated by well-known methods, while ϵ_Q and σ_Q are characteristic of the quinol lattice. ϵ is always associated with Z, the effective number of the "elements" in the wall of a cavity, and $Z(\epsilon_Q/_k)^{1/2}$ can be treated as a single parameter, which, together with σ_Q, must be fixed by using a suitable experimentally determinable property. The theory can then be quantitatively tested by calculating other properties and comparing the values obtained with the experimental ones.

Thermodynamic Studies of Movement of the Guest Molecules in Hydroquinone Clathrates

The author and his coworkers have measured the heat capacities of a number of quinol clathrates from $\sim 15°$ K. to room temperature. If C_p is the molar heat capacity of the clathrate, formulated as $3C_6H_4(OH)_2.yA$, where y is the fraction of the cavities filled, then experiments on different samples of a given kind of clathrate show that usually, at any fixed temperature, C_p is a linear function of y, as it should be if the interaction of molecules in different cavities, and the effect of the guest on the host lattice, are both negligible. Thus C_A can be determined as a function of temperature, where C_A is the contribution to the heat capacity of the clathrate per mole of the guest, A. The only motion which monatomic molecules like krypton and argon undergo in the cavities is their vibration or "rattling," and theoretical expressions for the value of C_A to which this motion gives rise can be obtained from van der Waals theory.

It transpires that the values of $X(\epsilon_Q/_k)^{1/2}$ and σ_Q which satisfactorily account for the observed C_A values for the argon (11) and krypton (6) clathrates as a function of temperature also give calculated values for the equilibrium pressures and energies of formation of several different clathrates which are in very reasonable agreement with experiment. We can therefore use with some confidence these values of $Z(\epsilon_Q/_k)^{1/2}$ and σ_Q in conjunction with the theoretical heat capacity expressions to evaluate the contribution C_{vib} made to C_A by the rattling of diatomic and polyatomic guest molecules, at least from $100°$ K. upward. (At lower temperatures, the underlying assumption that classical statistics are valid breaks down.) Whereas for monatomic molecules $C_A = C_{vib}$, for diatomic or polyatomic molecules C_A is a composite quantity. We can write $C_A = C_{vib} + C_{rot} + C_{int}$, where C_{rot} is the contribution made by the rotational movement of the trapped molecules and C_{int} that form the intramolecular vibrations. C_{int} is always small, often negligible, and in any case calculable.

From the experimental values of C_A for the methane (12), oxygen, nitrogen, and carbon monoxide (7) clathrates and the calculated values of C_{vib}, C_{rot} has been estimated for each of these guest molecules as a function of temperature. For freely rotating diatomic molecules C_{rot} would be R; the corresponding value for methane molecules is $3R/2$. For a restricted rotator C_{rot} would rise to a maximum and then decrease toward the limiting value for free rotation. For the methane clathrate from about $150°$ K. upwards C_{rot} is in fact $3R/2$ within experimental error, showing that any restriction on the rotation of this guest molecule is very small. For the oxygen, nitrogen, and carbon monoxide clathrates C_{rot} is decreasing as room temperature is approached, but does not reach the limiting value for free rotation.

Using the well-known tables of Pitzer and Gwinn (13) relating to the thermo-dynamic properties of restricted rotators, estimates can be made of the heights of the energy barrier hindering the rotation of the molecules in the cavities. The figures so obtained are ~250 cal. per mole for the oxygen clathrate, and ~1000 and ~1200 cal. per mole for the nitrogen and carbon monoxide clathrates, respectively. Coulter (1), from an independent analysis of his own heat capacity results, has obtained a value of 820 cal. per mole for the nitrogen clathrate.

Susceptibility and Spectroscopic Studies of Rotational Movement of Guest Molecules

Different methods have also been used to estimate these barrier heights, notably by Meyer and his colleagues. Thus, the course taken by the magnetic susceptibility of oxygen in the oxygen clathrate at very low temperatures (~0.25° to ~2° K.) is best interpreted on the restricted rotation model (9), and a quantitative treatment gave 128 cal. per mole for the barrier height. Meyer and Scott (10) have studied the nuclear quadrupole resonance spectrum of N_2^{14} in the quinol clathrate. Such a spectrum is due to the transitions between the energy levels available to a nucleus with spin $>1/2$ when situated in an inhomogeneous electric field. As the temperature rises from 0° K., the amplitude of the oscillations of the molecules in the cavities increases, and since this reduces the inhomogeneity of the field, the quadrupole resonance frequency drops. From the temperature dependence of this frequency between 1.5° and 25° K. Meyer and Scott estimated the oscillation frequency of the molecule. This quantity can be related to the barrier height, for which a value of 940 cal. per mole was thus obtained.

There is therefore reasonable agreement between the barrier heights for the oxygen and nitrogen molecules obtained by different methods. Actually, perfect agreement is not to be expected, apart from any experimental inaccuracy, since the different methods use observations made over different temperature ranges. For while at very low temperatures the guest molecules will occupy the lowest vibrational level, at higher temperatures some molecules will be promoted to higher energy levels, and in these they will for part of the time be in closer contact with the cavity walls than if they had remained in the ground level. This must naturally affect the average barrier height. The barrier is much lower for oxygen than for nitrogen. This difference does not seem to depend on molecular size, but may arise from the difference in the molecular quadrupole moments. The field within a cavity in the β-quinol lattice does not have spherical symmetry and so the potential energy of a diatomic molecule due to its quadrupole will depend on the orientation of this molecule. The oxygen molecule may therefore be associated with a lower energy barrier to rotation than the nitrogen molecule, because it has the smaller quadrupole moment.

Host-Guest and Guest-Guest Interaction in Hydroquinone Clathrates

There is evidence from Meyer's work that even a diatomic molecule in a quinol clathrate can slightly distort the host lattice. Whereas, for example, pure solid nitrogen gives a single quadrupole resonance line, β-quinol with the holes partially filled with nitrogen gives a spectrum of at least seven closely grouped lines, so there must be slight variations in the electric field gradient from one cavity to another. This is understandable if a nitrogen molecule slightly distorts the lattice around it, for then the electric field gradient acting on the nuclei in any one nitrogen molecule will depend on how many of the neighboring cavities happen to be filled.

Finally, an interesting study by Foner, Meyer, and Kleiner (5) of the paramagnetic resonance spectrum of oxygen in the quinol clathrate at low temperatures has given information on the interaction of the guest molecules in adjacent cavities, small though this interaction is. They found that the spectrum given by crystals containing both nitrogen and oxygen, with nitrogen molecules occupying more than half the holes and oxygen molecules less than 5%, consisted of three lines, the relative intensities of which depended on the nitrogen content. The quinol clathrate is such that any cavity has two nearest neighbors 5.6 A. away; the next cavities are considerably more remote (9.5 A.).

In a clathrate dilute in oxygen and rich in nitrogen, an oxygen molecule will probably have 0, 1, or 2 nitrogen molecules as nearest neighbors. Its interaction with these nitrogen molecules will be due primarily to London dispersion forces and perhaps to quadrupole-quadrupole forces, both of which are anisotropic for diatomic molecules. Effectively, therefore, there will be three possible values for the height of the energy barrier opposing the rotation of an oxygen molecule, according to whether it has 0, 1, or 2 nitrogen molecules near to it. This would account for the observed splitting of the resonance line. Foner *et al.* showed that the splitting was in fact of the order of magnitude to be expected from the anisotropy of the London forces.

Literature Cited

(1) Coulter, L. V., private communication.
(2) Cooke, A. H., Duffus, H. J., *Proc. Phys. Soc. (London)* **67A**, 525 (1954).
(3) Cooke, A. H., Meyer, H., Wolf, W. P., Evans, D. F., Richards, R. E., *Proc. Roy. Soc. (London)* **225A**, 112 (1954).
(4) Evans, D. F., Richards, R. E., *J. Chem. Soc. (London)* **1952**, 3932.
(5) Foner, S., Meyer, H., Kleiner, W. H., *J. Phys. Chem. Solids* **18**, 273 (1961).
(6) Grey, N. R., Parsonage, N. G., Staveley, L. A. K., *Mol. Phys.* **4**, 153 (1961).
(7) Grey, N. R., Staveley, L. A. K., unpublished results.
(8) Meyer, H., *J. Phys. Chem. Solids* **20**, 238 (1961).
(9) Meyer, H., O'Brien, M. C. M., Van Vleck, J. H., *Proc. Roy. Soc. (London)* **243A**, 414 (1957).
(10) Meyer, H., Scott, T. A., *J. Phys. Chem. Solids* **11**, 215 (1959).
(11) Parsonage, N. G., Staveley, L. A. K., *Mol. Phys.* **2**, 212 (1959).
(12) *Ibid.*, **3**, 59 (1960).
(13) Pitzer, K. S., Gwinn, W. S., *J. Chem. Phys.* **10**, 428 (1942).
(14) van der Waals, J. H., *Trans. Faraday Soc.* **52**, 184 (1956).
(15) van der Waals, J. H., Platteeuw, J. C., *Advan. Chem. Phys.* **2**, 1 (1959).
(16) van der Waals, J. H., Platteeuw, J. C., *Rec. trav. chim.* **75**, 912 (1956).

RECEIVED September 6, 1962.

21

Electric and Magnetic Properties of the Tungsten and Vanadium Bronzes

M. J. SIENKO

Baker Laboratory of Chemistry, Cornell University, Ithaca, N. Y.

The metallic properties of the tungsten bronzes, M_xWO_3, are discussed in terms of a band model in which a conduction band resulting from overlap of the $5d(t_{2g})$ orbitals of the tungsten is populated by donor atoms, M. Optical properties and magnetic susceptibilities are consistent with the model. The apparent semiconductivity in Cu_xWO_3 and Ag_xWO_3 is attributed to second-order transitions in the host WO_3 structure. The vanadium bronzes, $M_xV_2O_5$, are more complicated, in that the carriers are more localized, giving rise to higher magnetic moments and a lower conductivity which is anisotropic and not metallic. NMR experiments on $Li_xV_2O_5$ give no Knight shift but a line narrowing which indicates diffusional motion of lithium. Pulse decay experiments suggest an oscillating motion of lithium in the tunnels of the oxyvanadium network at lower temperatures than those at which diffusion along the tunnels is initiated.

The term "tungsten bronze" is used in this paper to represent any one of a series of nonstoichiometric compounds of empirical composition M_xWO_3, in which M is an alkali metal (Cu, Ag, Pb, or Tl) and x has some value between 0 and 1. The term "vanadium bronze" is used to represent materials of composition $M_xV_2O_5$, in which M is an alkali metal (Cu or Ag), and x, though variable, is very close to 0.3. Originally, the designation "wolframbronce" was introduced, apparently by Philipp and Schwebel (28), to describe the yellow, metallic luster of Na_xWO_3 ($x = 0.8$), though the term was also applied to the blue ($x = 0.4$) and purple-red ($x = 0.6$) materials. The term "vanadium bronze" appears to have been introduced by Ozerov (25), who pointed out that the vanadic vanadates of composition $mM_2O.nV_2O_4.pV_2O_5$ could be formulated as $M_xV_2O_5$ in the same way that the "mixed-oxide" tungstates, $mM_2O.nW_2O_5.pWO_3$, can be represented as M_xWO_3.

It was recognized early (38) that the sodium-tungsten bronzes were "vollkommene Leiter für den elektrischen Strom," though the first quantitative measurements of conductivity as a function of temperature indicated semiconducting behavior (14). Such semiconducting behavior continues to be reported (24) whenever the measurements are carried out on powders, though powder work suffers from irreproducibility—for example, after a single increasing-decreasing temperature cycle. The importance of using single crystals to get meaningful values of the conductivity was amply demonstrated by Brown and Banks (3), who gave the first reliable results indicating that Na_xWO_3 ($0.53 < x < 0.85$) is strictly metallic in the sense that its resistivity rises linearly with temperature. Gardner and Danielson, working with single crystals in the range Na_xWO_3 ($0.58 < x < 0.90$), found similar metallic behavior both in the linear rise of resistivity with temperature and in the Hall voltage (10). The fact of metallic behavior seems clearly established for sodium-tungsten bronze, at least for $Na:WO_3$ ratios greater than 0.3. For reasons discussed below, semiconductivity would be predicted at low values of x in Na_xWO_3 and this actually has been found in single crystal measurements by McNeill (20).

The classical model that is used for nonstoichiometric compounds of the transition elements assumes presence of isolated ions in several oxidation states, and the conductivity process is postulated to proceed via an electron transfer from a lower- to a higher-valent ion. With the recognition that antiferromagnetic interactions such as are commonly encountered in transition metal oxides require some overlap of the atomic orbitals, it becomes clear that isolated energy states have to be replaced by delocalized levels such as are postulated in the band theory of solids. Such a band theory, particularly in the hands of Morin (15), has proved qualitatively very useful in accounting for the metal-to-semiconductor discontinuities observed with decreasing temperature for some of the $3d$ metal oxides and for the decreasing carrier mobilities observed from left to right in the conducting oxides of the $3d$ transition sequence. Furthermore, the low, temperature-independent paramagnetism observed for the lithium and sodium-tungsten bronzes argues against isolated spin states such as would be implied for the tungsten bronzes by formulating them as solid solutions of $W(VI)O_3$ in hypothetical $MW(V)O_3$.

The simplest model for a tungsten bronze, M_xWO_3, is to regard it as a host WO_3 structure in which M atoms have been introduced interstitially. For the simplest case, which leads to a perovskite-like structure, the unit cell can be represented as in Figure 1, with a tungsten atom at the center, six oxygen atoms at face centers, and eight "interstitial sites" at the cube corners more or less occupied by alkali atoms. When these sites are completely empty, x in M_xWO_3 is zero and the structure resembles that of WO_3 except that the tungsten atoms

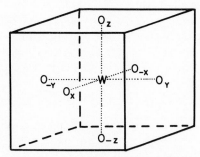

Figure 1.   Structure of idealized tungsten bronze, M_xWO_3

$x = 0$

need to be slightly off-center in adjacent unit cells. The tungsten atom can be considered to be in an octahedral electric field, so its $5d$ orbitals would split into a doublet (e_g or $d\gamma$) and a triplet (t_{2g} or $d\epsilon$). In a completely ionic model ($W^{+6}O_3^{-2}$), the $5d$ tungsten orbitals are completely vacant and there are 18 electrons per unit cell distributed in the p_x, p_y, p_z orbitals of the oxygen atoms. However, it would seem that a covalent model is more appropriate for WO_3, so allowance has to be made for partial transfer of the oxygen electrons to the tungsten e_g orbitals. This can be done by setting up molecular orbitals which extend over the tungsten nucleus and the oxygen atoms. There is a problem of extending the molecular orbitals into adjacent unit cells, but this can be taken care of by counting only half of the set of orbitals obtained for a WO_3 configuration.

There are 12 molecular orbitals which can be written using the two $5d\gamma$, one $6s$, and three $6p$ orbitals of the tungsten and the appropriate p orbital (p_x, p_y, or p_z) that faces the W from each of the face-centered oxygen atoms. Six of these molecular orbitals will be bonding and six antibonding. However, in the idealized WO_3 network, the oxygen atoms would be shared by two unit cells, so that only half of the above orbitals can be counted per unit cell. The three orbitals per unit cell that eventually result are derived by joining the wave functions at the unit cell boundaries and introducing multiplying functions having the period of the lattice. We can designate these three orbitals per unit cell as φ_α, φ_β, and $\varphi\gamma$, noting merely that they concentrate charge along the three Cartesian directions of the cubic structure.

Only one of the three p orbitals of each oxygen atom is used in the above analysis, the assumption being that the other p orbitals remain as localized levels. There are 12 of these atomic orbitals: p_y and p_z on O_x and on O_{-x}, p_x and p_z on O_y and on O_{-y}, and p_x and p_y on O_z and on O_{-z}. Again, half of these must be assigned to adjacent unit cells, so the number of local p levels available per unit cell is six. Taken with φ_α, φ_β, and $\varphi\gamma$, this gives a total of nine orbitals per unit cell—three delocalized molecular orbitals (M.O.) and six atomic orbitals (A.O.). Given, in WO_3, three oxygen atoms per unit cell each contributing six electrons, there are 18 electrons to be accommodated. For the nine available orbitals, this means complete filling of the delocalized M.O.'s and complete filling of the remaining A.O.'s. This set of completely occupied orbitals is what is called the "valence band" of WO_3. As a filled band, it provides no mechanism for net charge transfer in the WO_3 structure.

The conduction band in WO_3 is believed to arise from overlap of the t_{2g} orbitals of the tungsten atoms. Morin (22) has suggested for the $3d$ transition series that a band of energy levels is produced by overlap of the $3d\epsilon$ (t_{2g}) orbitals. There is a finite band width which decreases from scandium to titanium to vanadium, because of increasing z, and reaches zero in chromium oxide. Inasmuch as the $5d$ orbitals have considerably greater radial extension than the $3d$ orbitals, we can surmise that the zero overlap of the $3d(t_{2g})$ orbitals in chromium gives way to finite overlap of the $5d(t_{2g})$ orbitals in tungsten. [Even if $5d(t_{2g})$ orbitals did not overlap, there would still be the possibility of getting delocalized molecular orbital formation through overlay, for example, of $\psi_{d_{xy}}$ of the W with the p_y of O_x and of O_{-x}. Such an orbital would have π character in contrast to the σ character of φ_α, φ_β, and $\varphi\gamma$ above.] Figure 2 shows the relation of the valence and conduction bands in WO_3. The energy separation between the top of the valence bands and the bottom of the conduction band is estimated to be about 2.5 e.v. on the basis of the minimum frequency required to excite the

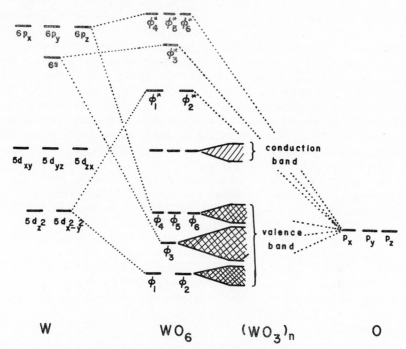

W WO_6 $(WO_3)_n$ O

Figure 2. Correlation diagram for WO_6 configuration and relation to WO_3 band structure

ultraviolet absorption of pure WO_3. In the tungsten bronzes, added metal M is assumed to introduce impurity levels in the forbidden gap of WO_3 just below the conduction band or possibly in the band region itself. Excitation energy for getting carriers from the impurity levels into the conduction band cannot be very large, as is evidenced by the lack of an activation energy for the conduction process.

The supporting evidence for this kind of band model, in which WO_3 has been called an "electronless metal" which is populated by electron donors M, comes from various kinds of measurements, some of which are given below. These include resistivity *vs.* temperature, Hall voltage, thermoelectric power, and magnetic susceptibility measurements.

The broad applicability of the model can be judged from the fact that it can even account for the observed changes in colors of the tungsten bronzes. Brown and Banks (2) in their investigation of the spectral distribution of visible light from Na_xWO_3 samples report that the peak of absorption moves to shorter wavelength as x in Na_xWO_3 increases and the absorption peak narrows appreciably as x increases. Both of these effects are consistent with a $5d\epsilon$-band model. The extent of doping—i.e., the value of x in Na_xWO_3—governs the extent to which the conduction band is filled. The higher the sodium content, the more levels in the $5d\epsilon$ band required. The largest energy gap between the valence band and the first vacant level of the conduction band would occur when the sodium content is largest—namely, for the yellow sodium bronze ($x \cong 0.9$). As the sodium content is decreased, the optical absorption energy would also be expected to decrease, since the first vacant level in the conduction band would then be lower; hence, the optical absorption should shift to lower frequency. The breadth of the absorption band would depend on the density of states in the conduction band.

This density of states is probably a minimum at the bottom of the conduction band and increases to a maximum in the center of the band. When x in Na_xWO_3 is small, optical excitation would be to the bottom of the conduction band, where the energy level density is small. Any finite number of transitions would necessitate use of several adjacent levels, which would be significantly spread out on an energy scale. When x in Na_xWO_3 approaches unity, the band is well populated and the Fermi energy is in a region where there are many states of almost identical energy. Any finite number of transitions would require a smaller spread between the adjacent levels, and hence the optical absorption curve would be narrower.

The structure of the vanadium bronzes is considerably more complicated than that of the tungsten bronzes. For one thing, the local symmetry of the oxygen positions about the vanadium is considerably distorted from the octahedral; for another thing, the vanadium bronze structure is much more anisotropic than that of the tungsten bronzes. As shown by Wadsley (37) and also by Ozerov, God'der, and Zhadanov (27) the crystal structure of $Na_xV_2O_5$ corresponds to two NaV_6O_{15} formula units per unit cell, with the sodium atoms lying in tunnels formed by the characteristic oxygen packing that arises from edge sharing of distorted VO_6 octahedra. This kind of tunnel formation leads to the possibility of cation migration parallel to the b axis, which indeed had been observed for lithium-vanadium bronze (11), and also to considerable anisotropy in the d-orbital overlap.

Tungsten Bronzes

Preparation of Tungsten Bronzes. Three methods have been successfully used by the Cornell group for making single crystals of M_xWO_3:

A vapor phase reaction

$$xM(g) + WO_3(g) \rightarrow M_xWO_3(s)$$

where M is produced by a suitable reaction in one combustion boat alongside another combustion boat serving as a source of WO_3 in a combustion tube containing a cold-finger projecting into the reaction chamber. This method was particularly good for making single crystals of Tl_xWO_3.

A thermal reaction

$$\frac{x}{2} M_2WO_4(s) + \frac{3 - 2x}{3} WO_3(s) + \frac{x}{6} W(s) \rightarrow M_xWO_3(s)$$

in which the reagents are finely ground and heated to give product via solid state reaction. This method has proved most successful for Ag_xWO_3 and Cu_xWO_3.

An electrolytic reaction in which molten mixtures of M_2WO_4 and WO_3 are decomposed with platinum or tungsten electrodes. If the melt is poured off immediately after the electrolysis, rather good single crystals of K_xWO_3 can be prepared in this way. The product forms on the cathode, whereas oxygen is liberated at the anode.

All of the tungsten bronzes, independent of the identity of interstitial M, are inert to chemical attack by most acidic reagents. However, they can be dissolved by basic reagents which can destroy the WO_3 (acidic) matrix. The surprising resistance to oxidizing attack—e.g., of Na_xWO_3—is attributed to the stability of the WO_3 matrix and the self-stopping of the reaction by space charge effects when relatively few electrons have been removed from the bronze. The inability of Na^+ to migrate out of the structure easily favors a residual charge. The greater susceptibility to attack of Li_xWO_3 is attributable to greater mobility of Li^+. Purification of the bronzes and separation of unwanted starting materials can usually be achieved by successive leaches with water, acid, mild alkali, and HF.

Resistivity Measurements. The measurements by the Cornell group have all been made on single crystals by a potential-probe method, the details of which have been reported (*32*). Typical results are presented graphically in Figure 3.

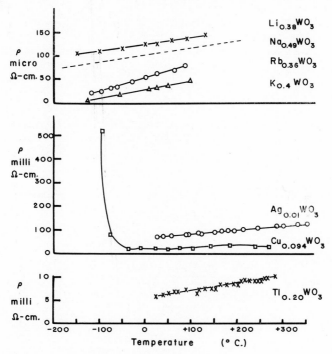

Figure 3.   Resistivity vs. temperature of some tungsten bronzes

Table I identifies the various compositions and gives resistivity values in ohm-centimeters at 25° C., and the temperature coefficient of resistivity, $\frac{1}{\rho}\frac{d\rho}{dT}$, at 25° C.

Considering the thousandfold variation observed in the resistivity values at room temperature, the constancy in the thermal coefficient of resistivity is striking. It suggests that the scattering mechanism for the charge carriers has an identical origin, which would be the case if conduction were proceeding via the same band mechanism and if lattice scattering were the main contributor to the relaxation time.   That this is indeed the case is supported by studies (*7*) of the thermal variation of the carrier mobilities, shown in Figure 4 as a plot of reduced mobility

Table I.   Room Temperature Resistivities and Thermal Coefficients of Tungsten Bronzes

Composition	ρ 25° C.	$\frac{1}{\rho}\frac{d\rho}{dT}$	Reference
$Li_{0.38}WO_3$	1.26×10^{-4}	1.1×10^{-3}	(*35*)
$Na_{0.49}WO_3$	1.05×10^{-4}	1.4×10^{-3}	(*8*)
$K_{0.4}WO_3$	3.82×10^{-5}	4.5×10^{-3}	(*21*)
$Rb_{0.32}WO_3$	6.3×10^{-5}	4.7×10^{-3}	(*21*)
$Cu_{0.094}WO_3$	2.0×10^{-2}	3.9×10^{-3}	(*36*)
$Ag_{0.01}WO_3$	7.2×10^{-2}	2.1×10^{-3}	(*34*)
$Tl_{0.20}WO_3$	6.0×10^{-3}	2.3×10^{-3}	(*32*)

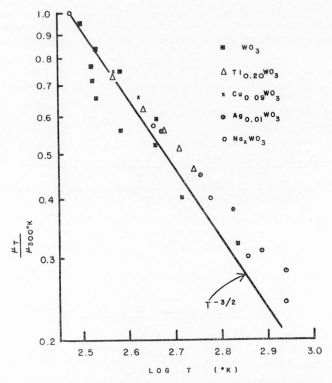

Figure 4.   Log reduced carrier mobility vs. log T of WO₃
and related systems, M_xWO_3

as a function of temperature.   The important comparison here is with the recent
data obtained for single crystals of WO_3.   Contrary to the report by Sawada and
Danielson (30) that WO_3 is a p-type semiconductor, Crowder of the Cornell
group has found that it is n-type.   Combining Hall measurements with resistivity
studies on single crystals we find that the carrier mobility approximately follows a
$T^{-3/2}$ dependence, which is designated by the straight line in Figure 4.   The fact
that most of the M_xWO_3 materials, independent of the nature of M and of the
value of x, show the same thermal variation of mobility as WO_3 suggests that the
same scattering mechanism operates on the carriers in the two cases.   The two
chief possibilities for scattering are the "impurity" ions, M^+, and the lattice vibrations of the crystal.   The former would give a direct first power dependence on
temperature; the latter, inverse three-halves power.

At temperatures below 300° K. deviations from linear ρ vs. T behavior may
appear, particularly when the ratio of M to WO_3 is below 0.3.   This has been
observed on single crystals of copper-doped WO_3 (36), silver-doped WO_3 (5),
and low-sodium Na_xWO_3 (20).   It is postulated that a second-order transition
occurs, which is related to the ferroelectric transition in WO_3.   This transition
which occurs in the neighborhood of 220° K. (it is spread over roughly 50°,
probably because it occurs piecemeal as a domain-growth phenomenon), shows
up in pure WO_3 in its resistivity behavior, its Hall coefficient, and its thermoelectric
power (7).   The carrier mobility drops significantly as the temperature is lowered
through the transition, so it is probable that the rather steep rise in resistivity

observed in Cu_xWO_3 and Ag_xWO_3 below 250° K. is due not to a decrease in carrier density as might be true with a conventional semiconductor but to a reduction in carrier mobility. Such a reduction in carrier mobility would not be surprising if, as suspected, the low temperature forms contain tungsten atoms in sufficient misalignment to reduce the $5d$ orbital overlap appreciably.

The semiconductive behavior reported by McNeill for single crystals of $Na_{0.025}WO_3$ appears to be of a different type, since it is not confined to the region around 220° K. but is linear in log resistivity $vs.$ $1/T$ over the whole range of temperature investigated, from 192° to 589° K. Also the apparent activation energy is only 0.02 e.v., considerably smaller than the 0.3 to 0.4 e.v. observed in Cu_xWO_3. Why the 220° K. WO_3 transition does not appear is not clear; because it is a sluggish transition it may have been lost by broadening in a dynamic thermal experiment such as McNeill apparently used. However, there is theoretical reason for believing that a low-energy excitation trap may be formed in M_xWO_3 when x is so small that overlap of trapped electrons is negligible.

Mott (23) has shown that even with localized electrons there should be a discontinuous change from semiconduction to metallic behavior when the localized electrons are close enough together to allow appreciable overlap of the wave functions. Sienko and Truong have predicted for M_xWO_3 that this discontinuity should occur in the neighborhood of $x = 0.25$ and they present magnetic data which are suggestive of some kind of perturbation in band structure at this concentration. It is possible that the 0.02-e.v. excitation reported by McNeill is due to release of electrons from shallow donor sites in M_xWO_3. The donor sites are not necessarily neutral $M°$ atoms but may be, for example, W atoms in the immediate vicinity of the M^+ ions that are interstitial in the WO_3 structure. The absence of donor exhaustion phenomena at high temperature, which if they did occur would give metallic behavior, is surprising but might be attributed to cancelling effects brought about by onset of intrinsic excitation from the WO_3 valence band to the conduction band. Hall measurements to give carrier concentrations would be useful for low sodium content Na_xWO_3. Using McNeill's observed resistivity of 3.05×10^{-3} ohm-cm. at 305° K. and estimating the carrier density as 1.9×10^{20} (from the stoichiometry, there are 4.6×10^{20} Na atoms per cc. of $Na_{0.025}WO_3$; the Boltzmann factor is $e^{-0.022/kT}$, or 0.41), the mobility is calculated to be 11 sq. cm./volt sec., which is the same as that observed for $Na_{0.48}WO_3$.

Magnetic Susceptibilities of Tungsten Bronzes. The high carrier mobilities indicate that the conduction band in M_xWO_3 is appreciably wide—that is, the states are not so closely bunched that the resulting high density of states would mean a very high scattering probability. One might surmise then that the conduction band is rather more like that of an ideal metal than one would expect for a d-banded material. If this is so, the carriers can be treated as quasi-free electrons for which the effective mass approximation is valid. Using the Pauli-Peierls equation

$$\kappa = \frac{4m^*\mu_0^2}{h^2}(3\pi^2 n)^{1/3}\left(1 - \frac{m_0^2}{3m^{*2}}\right)$$

where m^* = effective mass, μ_0 = Bohr magneton, n = carrier density, m_0 = electron rest mass, h = Planck constant, and κ = electronic susceptibility per unit volume, we can calculate the effective mass of the carriers from observed magnetic susceptibilities after diamagnetic corrections have been applied (35). Table II summarizes the results obtained by the Cornell group on the tungsten bronzes that have been measured.

Table II. Magnetic Susceptibilities and Derived Electron Masses for Tungsten Bronzes

Reference	Composition	$x_M \times 10^6$	Derived $\kappa e^- \times 10^6$	n	m^*/m_0
(6)	$Li_{0.05}WO_3$	−15	0.19	0.97×10^{21}	1.2
	$Li_{0.10}WO_3$	−14	0.23	1.9×10^{21}	1.1
	$Li_{0.20}WO_3$	− 5	0.51	3.9×10^{21}	1.7
	$Li_{0.30}WO_3$	− 9	0.97	5.8×10^{21}	2.6
	$Li_{0.36}WO_3$	−10	1.0	7.0×10^{21}	2.5
(21)	$Rb_{0.2}WO_3$	− 1.4	0.69	3.4×10^{21}	2.3
	$K_{0.23}WO_3$	+10.4	0.93	3.8×10^{21}	2.8
	$K_{0.43}WO_3$	+25.2	1.5	7.7×10^{21}	3.5
(19)	$Na_{0.43}WO_3$	+ 3.2	0.80	7.8×10^{21}	2.0
	$Na_{0.78}WO_3$	+14.6	1.2	13.7×10^{21}	2.4

The closeness of the effective mass to the electronic mass supports the essential correctness of the band model. As noted in the first reports on the magnetic susceptibilities of tungsten bronzes, a model following the classical formulation of "mixed-oxide" tungstates, $mM_2O.nW_2O_5.pWO_3$, predicts a magnetic moment considerably higher than the observed. The fact that the effective mass of the carriers is near m_0 at low levels of lithium doping is consistent with the suggestion that the conduction band is not very narrow—that is, the band shape is probably quadratic at its edges, which means a low density of states at low populations. As the density of carriers increases, the effective mass departs from ideality in the direction expected for increasing density of states. However, as metallic systems go, effective masses not much more than twice the rest mass do not represent extreme departures from ideality.

Vanadium Bronzes

Preparation. The sodium and lithium vanadium bronzes discussed below are made by heating V_2O_5 with M_2CO_3 (or with MVO_3) in a 1 to 6 molar ratio in platinum under argon to approximately 800° and cooling slowly for several days. The reaction is extraordinarily complex, since oxygen evolution occurs on the cooling cycle even in the solid state. The over-all reaction, to produce $Na_{0.33}V_2O_5$, for example, can be written

$$Na_2CO_3 + 6\ V_2O_5 \rightarrow 6\ Na_{0.33}V_2O_5 + CO_2 + 0.5\ O_2$$

but this is evidently a stepwise reaction, giving CO_2 evolution from the solid state on the heating cycle, some oxygen evolution from the melt, and finally more oxygen evolution when the melt is cooled below the solidification temperature of 738° C. On recycling, oxygen is partly taken up again on melting and evolved again on cooling. The take-up and release of O_2 have been remarked several times since its original discovery (29), particularly in the intensive phase studies of Flood, Krog, and Sorum (9). Four phases have been reported (α, β, γ, and δ) corresponding approximately to V_2O_5, $Na_{0.33}V_2O_5$, NaV_3O_8, and $NaVO_3$. There is some contradiction as to the homogeneity limits of the four phases, probably because of failure to recognize fully the role of O_2 pressure in fixing composition, but it would appear that the homogeneous regions to x-ray analysis are:

α $Na_{0.4}\ V_2O_5$

β $Na_{0.16-0.36}\ V_2O_5$

γ $Na_{0.92-0.94}\ V_2O_{5.4}$

δ $Na_{1.7-2.0}\ V_2O_{5.85-6.00}$

In all these cases, the oxygen analysis is in doubt. Because crystals of phase β were reputed to be easiest to grow as large crystals, our efforts have been directed to its study as well as to that of the corresponding lithium system. Even so, because of the problems raised by oxygen evolution from the solid state, it has been extraordinarily difficult to get good single crystals for conductivity studies and to obtain reproducible resistivity values that are truly characteristic of the materials and not dependent on the particular crystal investigated.

Figure 5 represents typical results for crystals in the composition range $Na_{0.33 \pm 0.03}V_2O_5$. The behavior is very different from that of the alkali tungsten bronzes, in that the observed resistivities are considerably higher and then generally rise exponentially with inverse temperature. The behavior is ostensibly that of a typical semiconductor, except that on occasion a crystal of apparently the same composition, especially after a protracted series of measurements at elevated temperatures, will show essentially no change of resistivity as a function of temperature. These vagaries, which are not understood, have been attributed to small changes in oxygen content and are currently under further investigation. Preliminary thermogravimetric studies show small but finite weight loss from the solid state at elevated temperatures.

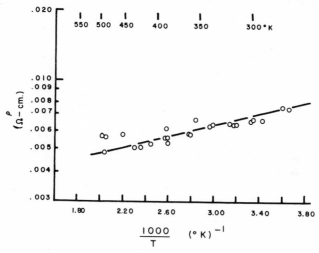

Figure 5.   Resistivity vs. T^{-1} for $Na_{0.33}V_2O_5$

The resistivities we find at room temperature are more than a factor of 10 lower than those reported by Ozerov for a single crystal at room temperature (*26*). Furthermore, our activation energies, 0.02 e.v., are considerably lower than the 0.12 e.v. derived from the data of Ozerov, although his thermal studies were all carried out on powders. Nevertheless, our conclusion is that the sodium-vanadium bronze is normally semiconducting and in this respect differs essentially from the equivalent sodium-tungsten bronzes.

Magnetic Susceptibility of Sodium-Vanadium Bronze.   Using the Gouy technique, magnetic moments of $Na_{0.33}V_2O_5$ were measured at room temperature in order to test the hypothesis that, since $Na_{0.33}V_2O_5$ appears to be a semiconductor, charge carriers might be bound sufficiently tightly to give rise to a localized spin moment. For reasons that will become clear in the following section on magnetic resonance it was believed that these localized electron centers were V^{+4} centers in a V_2O_5 matrix rather than $Na°$ donor centers. At 24° C., the observed (18) magnetic susceptibility per unit volume of $Na_{0.33}V_2O_5$ is 7.6×10^{-6}, which is more than an order of magnitude higher than that observed for the sodium-tungsten bronzes. Also, unlike the tungsten bronzes, it is temperature-dependent, though the thermal coefficient has not yet been determined. (Studies to liquid helium temperatures are now in progress.) The observed value for the molar susceptibility is $+410 \times 10^{-6}$.

This high value of the magnetic susceptibility can be accounted for in the following way. We assume that $Na_{0.33}V_2O_5$ corresponds to sodium doping of a V_2O_5 matrix, and that the sodium atoms are completely ionized to give sodium ions and an equal number of electrons which are bound at localized sites in the V_2O_5 matrix. We assume that these sites are V^{+4} ions, resulting from trapping of electrons at V^{+5} positions of the V_2O_5 structure. The net result magnetically would be that we have 0.33 mole of Na^+, 0.33 mole of V^{+4}, 0.835 mole of unaffected V_2O_5, and 0.825 mole of oxide equivalent about the V^{+4} centers. For Na^+, we use the diamagnetic increment given by Selwood (31); for V^{+4}, we use the spin-only paramagnetism corresponding to a d' configuration corrected by a g-factor of 1.96 as determined from the electron spin resonance studies described in the following section; for V_2O_5, we use the temperature-independent paramagnetic susceptibility reported (13); for oxide, we use the value suggested for a solid-state network (33). Table III gives the molar correction values and the appropriate ones for $Na_{0.33}V_2O_5$.

Table III. Calculation of Magnetic Susceptibility of $Na_{0.33}V_2O_5$

	Molar Value	Actual Increment
Na^+	-6.1×10^{-6}	-2.0×10^{-6}
V^{+4}	979×10^{-6}	$+326 \times 10^{-6}$
V_2O_5	107×10^{-6}	89×10^{-6}
O^{-2}	-9.8×10^{-6}	-8.1×10^{-6}

$$\sum = 405 \times 10^{-6} \text{ predicted}$$
$$410 \times 10^{-6} \text{ observed}$$

The close agreement between the spin-only calculation and the observed value is remarkable, especially since it raises the question: How can there be simultaneously even a modest lability of electrons when the full localized spin moment is effective?

Magnetic Resonance. Both electron spin resonance and nuclear magnetic resonance have been observed in the alkali vanadium bronzes. The details of these investigations have been published (11), but the principal findings can be indicated here.

ESR at 9500 Mc. both at room temperature and at 77° K. gave single absorption lines for lithium-vanadium bronze and sodium-vanadium bronze, centered at $g = 1.96$. The number of spins is roughly one per alkali metal atom. For the lithium bronze, the intensity as a function of temperature suggests a constant number of fairly localized spins. The observed g-factor is the same as that reported for V^{+4} centers in other compounds (1, 12, 17).

The NMR of Li^7 and Na^{23} in $M_xV_2O_5$ was studied with a Varian wide-line nuclear resonance spectrometer and also with a nuclear magnetic pulse apparatus (4). The steady-state experiments, both at room temperature and at 77° K., gave no resonance-frequency shift relative to a MCl solution standard. However, there was significant line narrowing when the temperature of the sample was increased from 77° K. to room temperature. The pulse experiments, which measure the time required for spin-lattice relaxation to dephase an applied resonance-frequency pulse, indicated a minimum in the spin-lattice relaxation time at about 165° K.

In metallic systems, there is frequently observed a shift of the NMR to lower magnetic fields (at fixed frequencies) due to paramagnetic alignment of the excess spins of the electron gas over and above the pairs. At the top of the "Fermi sea," there are some electrons which can be oriented by an external field so as to produce an additional "internal" field to add on interaction with the nucleus. The magnitude of the resonance shift, the so-called Knight shift, is directly proportional to the electron density at the nucleus—that is, the square of the electron wave function at the nuclear position. Absence of a Knight shift in the vanadium bronzes, as in the case of the tungsten bronzes (16), indicates that the conduction electrons have zero density at the alkali nucleus. This can be interpreted as indicating "complete" ionization of the alkali atom or, at a minimum, formation of a conduction band from other than the anticipated s functions of the alkali atoms. Since p and d orbitals have nodes at the nucleus, they could make up the conduction band without contributing a nuclear shift. However, since the s atomic orbitals ($2s$ in Li and $3s$ in Na) are the lowest available, it would be reasonable to suppose their utilization for band formation, if required. Localization of single electrons in atomic orbitals on alkali atoms would give a high local moment.

The line narrowing suggests finite motion of lithium nuclei over a distance which is at least of the order of the lithium-vanadium separation in the crystal; otherwise, dipolar broadening due to Li^7-V^{51} interaction would be significant. It is suggested that diffusional motion of lithium ions through channels in the oxy-vanadium network is responsible for the line narrowing. Such diffusion would be quite in keeping with the tunnel orientation parallel to the b axis postulated by Wadsley to explain his x-ray findings on $Na_{0.33}V_2O_5$. From plots of the induction decay half width *vs.* $1/T$, an energy of activation of 1.6 kcal. is assigned to this diffusional motion.

The minimum in the spin-lattice relaxation time is more difficult to account for. It cannot be attributed to the onset of the diffusional motion, because the jump frequency does not match the Larmor frequency at the temperature where diffusion becomes important. For this reason it is necessary to postulate an additional kind of motion in the lithium-vanadium bronze—a side-to-side jumping from one side of the channel to the other. In the structure there are sites on both sides of the channel roughly 2 A. apart which are equivalent but only one of which is occupied to fulfill stoichiometry. This kind of motion should start at a lower temperature than the above diffusion and lead to a correlation frequency that matches the Larmor frequency at the spin-lattice time minimum. Because of modulation of quadrupolar interaction, side-to-side motion could provide an effective spin-lattice relaxation mechanism.

There was no evidence of sodium motion in sodium-vanadium bronze.

Attempts to study the V^{51}NMR resonance quantitatively have proved difficult because of the large line width of the resonance. No hyperfine lines have been observed in the ESR of single crystals of the alkali vanadium bronzes.

Acknowledgment

The experimental work on which this paper is based is due to the efforts of many colleagues at the Cornell laboratories. Special thanks are given to Julien

Gendell for the magnetic resonance studies; and to Jerome Sohn and Daniel Kudrak for electric and magnetic measurements on sodium vanadium bronze; Sheila Morehouse, on K and RbW bronze; Billy Crowder, on single crystals of WO_3; Paul Weller, on Cu_xWO_3; and B. R. Mazumder, on Ag_xWO_3.

Literature Cited

(1) Bowers, K. D., Owen, J., *Repts. Progr. Phys.* 18, 335 (1955).
(2) Brown, B. W., Banks, E., *J. Am. Chem. Soc.* 76, 963 (1954).
(3) Brown, B. W., Banks, E., *Phys. Rev.* 84, 609 (1951).
(4) Clark, W. G., Ph.D. thesis, Cornell University, 1961.
(5) Conroy, L. E., private communication.
(6) Conroy, L. E., Sienko, M. J., *J. Am. Chem. Soc.* 79, 4048 (1957).
(7) Crowder, B., private communication.
(8) Ellerbeck, L. D., Shanks, H. R., Sidles, P. H., Danielson, G. C., *J. Chem. Phys.* 35, 298 (1961).
(9) Flood, H., Krog, Th., Sorum, H., *Tidsskr. Kjemi Bergvesen Met.* 3, 32 (1946).
(10) Gardner, W. R., Danielson, G. C., *Phys. Rev.* 93, 46 (1954).
(11) Gendell, J., Cotts, R., Sienko, M. J., *J. Chem. Phys.* 37, 220 (1962).
(12) Gerritsen, H. J., Lewis, H. R., *Phys. Rev.* 119, 1010 (1960).
(13) Grossman, G., Proskurenko, O. W., Arija, S. M., *Z. anorg. allgem. Chem.* 305, 121 (1960).
(14) Hägg, G., *Z. physik. Chem.* B29, 192 (1935).
(15) Hannay, N. B., ed., "Semi-Conductors," Chap. 14, Reinhold, New York, 1959.
(16) Jones, W. H., Jr., Garbaty, E. A., Barnes, R. G., *J. Chem. Phys.* 36, 494 (1962).
(17) Lambe, J., Kikuchi, C., *Phys. Rev.* 118, 71 (1960).
(18) Kudrak, D., Sohn, J., private communication.
(19) Kupka, F., Sienko, M. J., *J. Chem. Phys.* 18, 1296 (1950).
(20) McNeill, W., Ph.D. thesis, Temple University, 1961.
(21) Morehouse, S. M., private communication.
(22) Morin, F. J., *Phys. Rev.* 83, 1005 (1951).
(23) Mott, N. F., *Nuovo Cimento* 7, 312 (1958).
(24) Ornatskaia, Z. I., *Zhur. Tekhn. Fiz.* 27, 130 (1957).
(25) Ozerov, R. P., *Doklady Akad. Nauk SSSR* 94, 93 (1954).
(26) Ozerov, R. P., *Kristallografiya* 2, 226 (1957).
(27) Ozerov, R. P., God'der, G. A., Zhadanov, G. S., *Soviet Phys. Cryst.* 2, 211 (1957).
(28) Philipp, J., Schwebel, P., *Ber.* 12, 2234 (1879).
(29) Prandtl, W., Murschhauser, H., *Z. anorg. Chem.* 56, 173 (1908).
(30) Sawada, S., Danielson, G. C., *Phys. Rev.* 113, 803 (1959).
(31) Selwood, P. W., "Magnetochemistry," 2nd ed., p. 78, Interscience, New York, 1956.
(32) Sienko, M. J., *J. Am. Chem. Soc.* 81, 5556 (1959).
(33) Sienko, M. J., Banerjee, B., *Ibid.*, 83, 4149 (1961).
(34) Sienko, M. J., Mazumder, B. R., *Ibid.*, 82, 3508 (1960).
(35) Sienko, M. J., Truong, T. B. N., *Ibid.*, 83, 3939 (1961).
(36) Sienko, M. J., Weller, P., *Inorg. Chem.* 1, 324 (1962).
(37) Wadsley, A. D., *Acta Cryst.* 8, 695 (1955).
(38) Wright, H., *Ann. Chem. Pharm.* 79, 223 (1851).

RECEIVED September 6, 1962. Research supported by the Air Force Office of Scientific Research and by the Advanced Research Projects Agency.

Electrical Properties of the Tungsten Bronzes

H. R. SHANKS, P. H. SIDLES, and G. C. DANIELSON

*Institute for Atomic Research and Department of Physics,
Iowa State University, Ames, Iowa*

The electrical resistivity of Na_xWO_3, Li_xWO_3, and K_xWO_3 has been measured at 300° K. The range of x values was $0.25 < x < 0.9$. All resistivities were characteristic of a metal and lie on a single curve. Extrapolation of the conductivity curve to zero conductivity indicated that the tungsten bronzes should be semiconductors for $x < 0.25$. The resistivities measured for tungsten bronzes with $x < 0.25$ showed semiconducting behavior. The resistivity of Li_xWO_3 exhibited an anomalous peak in the ρ vs. T curve. The Hall coefficient of $Li_{0.37}WO_3$ indicated one free electron per alkali atom, as previously found for Na_xWO_3. The Seebeck coefficient of Na_xWO_3 depended linearly on $x^{-2/3}$, as expected from free electron theory. The implications of these and other data are discussed.

Tungsten bronzes are nonstoichiometric compounds, M_xWO_3, where M is usually one of the alkali metals. Single crystals of these compounds, large enough for electrical measurements, can be prepared with values of x ranging from essentially zero to nearly unity. The tungsten bronzes undergo several changes of crystal structure as x changes, but difficulties in determining quantitative amounts of M have frustrated attempts to delineate the ranges in x over which each of these structures exists. This situation has been a deterrent to studies of the electrical properties of these materials, especially in the low x-value range.

Electrical properties of certain of the high x-value bronzes have been reported. Brown and Banks (1) and Gardner and Danielson (3) both measured the electrical resistivity of cubic sodium tungsten bronze, with x-values ranging from about 0.5 to 0.9, and reported a minimum in resistivity near $x = 0.75$. Gardner and Danielson (3) also reported the results of Hall coefficient measurements which indicated that, in this range of x values, each sodium atom contributed one electron to conduction processes. Subsequently, Ellerbeck *et al.* (2) reported that, when careful attention was given to sample homogeneity, no minimum in electrical resistivity at $x = 0.75$ was observed.

Alkali metal bronzes of lower x value have not been so extensively studied. With the exception of some measurements by Sienko and Truong (8) of the electrical conductivity of cubic lithium bronzes, little of significance has been reported. This publication reports the results of electrical resistivity measurements on several metal-like tungsten bronzes, with x values down to 0.28, together with preliminary results for Hall and Seebeck coefficients, and discusses the implications of these results. Below about $x = 0.25$, all of the alkali tungsten bronzes appear to exhibit properties which are characteristic of semiconductors. Some preliminary results illustrate this type of behavior.

Crystal Preparation

Crystals of the various alkali tungsten bronzes were prepared by electrolysis from a melt of the appropriate alkali tungstate and WO_3. The electrolytic cell consisted of a glazed ceramic crucible, a Chromel wire cathode, and a graphite anode. Crystals were obtained under the following conditions: temperatures of the melt, 750° to 900° C.; current through the cell, 15 to 50 ma.; time of electrolysis, 12 to 24 hours.

For the low x-value sodium tungsten bronzes $(x < 0.5)$, the crystal structure and x values of the crystals obtained depended strongly on the temperature of the melt. The size and homogeneity of the crystals were dependent on both temperature and electrode current. The best crystals were obtained at the lowest temperature at which they could be grown. The optimum current for best quality crystals depended upon x value and crystal structure.

Measurements

Electrical resistivity was measured by a d.c. method using four-probe techniques to avoid problems arising from contact resistance. Pressure contacts were used for both current and potential probes. At low temperatures, the current contacts could be improved by ultrasonically tinning the ends of the samples.

Details of the method employed for measuring Seebeck coefficients have been described by Heller and Danielson (5). The Hall coefficient of $Li_{0.37}WO_3$ was measured by a d.c. method and is therefore subject to error from the Ettingshausen effect. This error is not expected to exceed ±10%.

Electrical Resistivity

In Figure 1, the resistivities of several tungsten bronzes at 300° K. are shown as a function of the alkali metal concentrations. Experimental points are shown for cubic Na_xWO_3, tetragonal Na_xWO_3, cubic Li_xWO_3 [including data from both Iowa State University and Cornell University (8)] and tetragonal K_xWO_3. All these bronzes show metallic conductivity. It is remarkable that the resistivities for all these bronzes seem to fall on the same curve. The metal ions themselves cannot, therefore, be important contributors to the scattering of the free electrons. Rather, the mobility must be limited primarily by electron scattering from the acoustical and optical modes of the WO_3 structure at high temperatures, and from the vacancies at alkali metal sites at low temperatures. The importance of vacancy scattering at low temperatures has been shown by Ellerbeck et al. (2). The conductivity at 0° K. (see their Figure 4) increased rapidly with increasing sodium concentration, owing to a reduction in the number of vacancies which scatter electrons as x increases.

In Figure 2, the conductivities of these same bronzes at 300° K. are plotted against x. These conductivities are simply the reciprocals of the resistivities shown in Figure 1. By extrapolation to zero conductivity, the curve in Figure

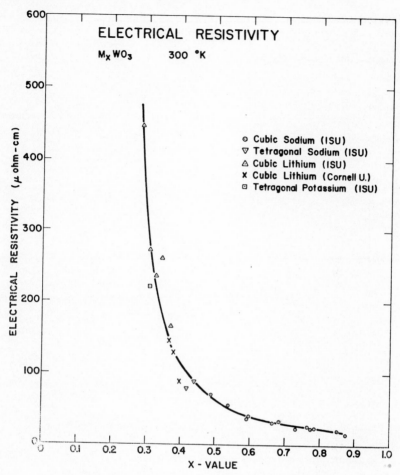

Figure 1. Electrical resistivity vs. x value at 300° K.

2 strongly suggests that all the bronzes will become insulators (or semiconductors) for values of x less than some value in the neighborhood of 0.25. This possibility has been suggested by Sienko and Truong (8) who used the theory of Mott (7) for metal-semiconductor transitions. The experimental data did not, however, show evidence of the discontinuity that would be expected from Mott's theory. If small, the discontinuity may be very difficult to observe experimentally, because of insufficient homogeneity of most available crystals. We have grown a number of tungsten bronze crystals with $x < 0.25$, and have found them to be semiconductors. No crystals with $x < 0.25$ have been found to be metallic in conductivity.

The electrical resistivity of one of these semiconducting bronzes is shown in Figure 3. The crystal is $Li_x WO_3$ with $x = 0.097$. The graph of log ρ vs. $1000/T$ shows the typical behavior of an impurity semiconductor. The activation energy corresponding to the straight line at low temperatures (extrinsic region) was 0.03 e.v., the activation energy corresponding to the straight line at high temperatures was 0.12 e.v. If the straight line at high temperatures corresponded

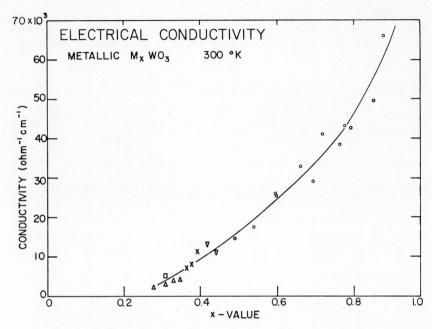

Figure 2. Electrical conductivity vs. x value at 300° K.

○ Cubic sodium (ISU)
▽ Tetragonal sodium (ISU)
△ Cubic lithium (ISU)
× Cubic lithium (Cornell U.)
□ Tetragonal potassium (ISU)

to the intrinsic region, the energy gap for this semiconducting crystal was about 0.24 e.v.

The temperature dependence of the resistivity of Li_xWO_3 is shown in Figure 4. For $x = 0.28$, the anomalous peak was very large and occurred at about 600° K.; for $x = 0.34$ the peak was much smaller and occurred at about 300° K. With increasing lithium concentration, therefore, the peak diminished in size and shifted to lower temperatures. The peak was completely reproducible and x-ray diffraction patterns showed that the cubic crystal structure existed both below and above the temperature at which the peak occurred. However, preliminary thermal analysis measurements indicated some sort of phase change. Mackintosh (6) has suggested the possibility of ordering of the lithium atoms, and neutron diffraction studies of these cubic Li_xWO_3 crystals should be made below and above the transition temperature.

Hall Effect

The Hall coefficient, R, of a crystal of cubic $Li_{0.37}WO_3$ has been measured at 300° K. From this measurement, the number of free electrons per unit volume, n, was calculated from $n = 1/Re$, where e is the charge on one electron. Hence the number of free electrons per mole was obtained. This result for $Li_{0.37}WO_3$ is shown in Figure 5, with similar results for Na_xWO_3 obtained by Gardner and Danielson (3). The straight line corresponds to one free electron per alkali metal atom, and the fact that the point for $Li_{0.37}WO_3$ is very near this line strongly suggests that the number of free electrons in Li_xWO_3, as in Na_xWO_3, is equal to the number of alkali metal atoms.

Seebeck Effect

The Seebeck coefficients (thermoelectric powers) of Na_xWO_3 have been measured over a wide range of x values at room temperature (300° K.). At this temperature, the residual resistance, ρ_0, and thermal resistance, ρ_t, are comparable, the value of ρ_0 being between ρ_t and $2\rho_t$. Nevertheless, one would expect to a first approximation (10) that $S = (1/3)(\pi^2k^2T/e\zeta)$, where S is the Seebeck coefficient, k is Boltzmann's constant, e is the electronic charge, and ζ is the Fermi energy. For free electrons, the Fermi energy $\zeta = (h^2/2m^*)(3n/8\pi)^{2/3}$ where h is Planck's constant, m^* is the effective mass, and n is the density of free electrons. Since n is proportional to x, ζ varies as $x^{2/3}$ and S varies as $x^{-2/3}$.

In Figure 6, the Seebeck coefficient, S, plotted $vs.$ $x^{-2/3}$. The experimental points lie on a straight line which provides evidence of the validity of free electron theory when discussing transport properties of the tungsten bronzes. From the

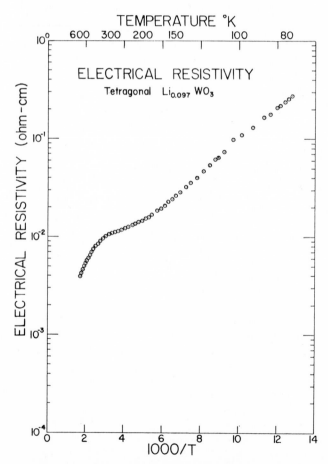

Figure 3. Electrical resistivity vs. temperature for a semiconducting lithium bronze

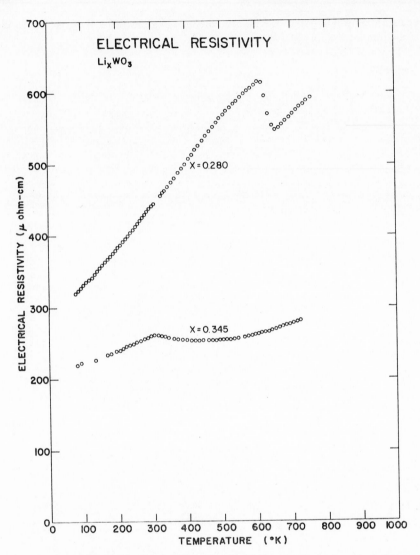

*Figure 4. Electrical resistivity vs. temperature for some metallic lithium
bronzes*

slope of the straight line, the ratio of the effective mass to the true mass of the
electron (m^*/m) was calculated and found to be 3.46, a value about twice that
obtained from magnetic susceptibility and specific heat data (4). [At the Symposium on Nonstoichiometric Compounds, Washington, D. C., March 23, 1962,
this number was reported as 0.035. The error in decimal point was pointed out
to us by B. L. Crowder, Cornell University.]

In Figure 7, S is plotted against the absolute temperature, T. At low
temperatures, where the residual resistance dominated the thermal resistance,
the expression $S = (1/3)(\pi^2 k^2 T/e\zeta)$ should be valid if free electron theory is
applicable. We find in Figure 6 a linear dependence of S upon T at low temperatures, as expected. From the slope of the straight line at low temperatures we

found m^*/m to be 3.72, which is comparable to the value 3.46 found from the straight line S *vs.* $x^{-2/3}$ in Figure 6.

Discussion

The transport properties of the tungsten bronzes appear to agree with the properties which would be expected from a free electron model in which the thermal scattering is caused by the WO_3 and the impurity scattering is caused by vacancies at the alkali metal positions. In particular, the thermal part of the electron mobility is nearly independent of the x value, while the impurity scattering decreases with increasing x value; the Hall coefficient gives the correct number of charge carriers; and the Seebeck coefficient varies linearly with $x^{-2/3}$. The electrical properties suggest that the density of states in the conduction band, $g(\epsilon)$, is given in terms of the energy, ϵ, according to the free electron model, $g(\epsilon)d\epsilon = \epsilon^{1/2}d\epsilon$. The relaxation time of these free electrons in Na_xWO_3 is, at room tem-

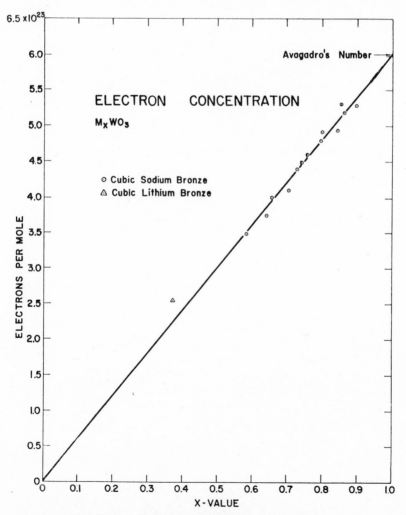

Figure 5.   Electron concentration vs. x-value

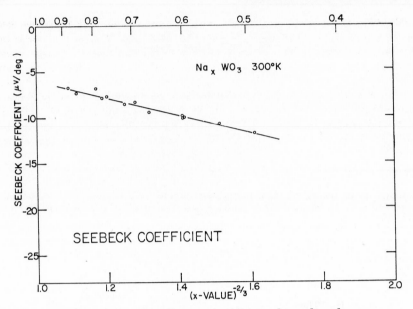

Figure 6. *Seebeck coefficient vs. $x^{-2/3}$ for cubic sodium bronze*

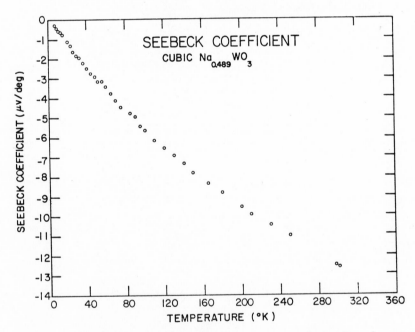

Figure 7. *Seebeck coefficient vs. temperature for a cubic sodium bronze*

perature, not very different from the relaxation time for the electrons in copper (2×10^{-14} second). For example, at $x = 0.7$, $\mu \approx 20$ sq. cm./volt sec.; and $m^* = 3.5$ gives a relaxation time $\tau = 4 \times 10^{-14}$ second.

On the other hand, the thermodynamic properties of the bronzes suggest that the density of states varies much more rapidly with energy than $\epsilon^{1/2}$. Magnetic susceptibility data by Greiner, Shanks, and Wallace (4) as well as specific heat data by Vest, Griffel, and Smith (9) definitely show that $g(\epsilon)d\epsilon = \epsilon^{1/2}d\epsilon$ is not valid; but both sets of data (if we ignore the specific heat data for large values of x) indicate an energy dependence of the density of states which is the same and considerably greater than $\epsilon^{1/2}$. Furthermore, the best fit using $\epsilon^{1/2}$ gives $m^*/m = 1.6$, which is somewhat smaller than the value 3.5 given by Seebeck measurements. These discrepancies suggest that free electron theory must be considerably modified to account for the thermodynamic properties of the bronzes, however well this theory accounts for some of the transport properties.

Literature Cited

(1) Brown, B. W., Banks, E., *Phys. Rev.* **84**, 609 (1951).
(2) Ellerbeck, L. D., Shanks, H. R., Sidles, P. H., Danielson, G. C., *J. Chem. Phys.* **35**, 298 (1961).
(3) Gardner, W. R., Danielson, G. C., *Phys. Rev.* **93**, 46 (1954).
(4) Greiner, J. D., Shanks, H. R., Wallace, D. C., *J. Chem. Phys.* **34**, 772 (1962).
(5) Heller, M. W., Danielson, G. C., *J. Phys. Chem. Solids* **23**, 601 (1962).
(6) Mackintosh, A. R., private communication.
(7) Mott, N. F., *Nuovo Cimento* **7**, 312 (1958); *Phil. Mag.* **6**, 287 (1961).
(8) Sienko, M. J., Truong, Tu. B. N., *J. Am. Chem. Soc.* **83**, 3131 (1961).
(9) Vest, R. W., Griffel, M., Smith, J. F., *J. Chem. Phys.* **28**, 293 (1958).
(10) Wilson, A. H., "Theory of Metals," p. 286, Cambridge University Press, London, 1954.

RECEIVED September 6, 1962.

23

Phase Transitions in Sodium Tungsten Bronzes

A. S. RIBNICK, B. POST, and E. BANKS

Departments of Chemistry and Physics, Polytechnic
Institute of Brooklyn, Brooklyn, N. Y.

The reported structures of tungsten bronzes include cubic, pseudocubic, tetragonal, orthorhombic, and monoclinic distortions of the perovskite-type structure; well-characterized tetragonal and hexagonal structures, as found in the series K_xWO_3; and some unit cells which are reported for isolated phases. This work surveys some of the phases found for various alkali tungsten bronzes. In the sodium bronzes there is a progression of distorted perovskites from $x = 0$ to $x \cong 0.15$, in the same order as the thermal transitions of WO_3 (monoclinic $\rightarrow$ orthorhombic $\rightarrow$ tetragonal). High-temperature x-ray diffractometry shows these phases to go through the same thermal transitions as WO_3, except that two-phase regions intervene. Between $x = 0.15$ and 0.28, two tetragonal phases coexist, the second having a range of homogeneity from $x = 0.28$ to 0.38. This is followed by a cubic (or pseudocubic) range from $x = 0.43$ to 0.95.

Tungsten bronzes have been the subject of many investigations in recent years, because of their unusual electrical properties (5, 7, 8, 10, 29), the occurrence of a number of crystallographic modifications (13, 17), and the existence of broad homogeneity ranges (4, 8, 28), which make these phases ideal subjects for the study of metallic behavior under conditions of controlled electron concentration. Other oxide "bronzes" are known—for example, the vanadium bronzes (19, 30) and niobium bronzes (22). Tungsten bronzes of the alkali metals (3, 8, 12, 16), copper (6), lead (2, 25), silver (26), and thallium (25) have been prepared, and electrical, magnetic, and structural data reported, but by far the most widely investigated members of this group are the alkali bronzes, particularly those of sodium.

The sodium bronzes are the only series where there appears to be a continuous sequence of phases, all having compositions which can be described by a formula of the general type, M_xWO_3, so that they may be considered as solid solutions of the metal in some form of WO_3, whether it is ordinarily a stable phase or not. All of the known bronzes can be described in this fashion, although they usually have narrower regions of existence than is the case with the sodium bronzes. Although a number of different structures have been reported, their ranges of homogeneity have not been completely explored, even in the case of the sodium bronzes.

This paper presents the results of a systematic survey of the structure-composition-temperature relationships for the sodium bronzes. The present work was an outgrowth of the studies reported from this laboratory on the thermal behavior of tungsten(VI) oxide (*20, 23*) and the high-sodium bronzes (*24*). In the latter work, transitions in the coefficient of thermal expansion of "cubic" bronzes were observed between 150° and 250° C. It appeared that, by following the phase transitions in the complete solid solution series, beginning at WO_3, it might be possible to understand the behavior of the "cubic" bronzes. As it developed, we were unable to correlate these changes with the behavior of the phases of lower symmetry. However, we have been able to delineate the ranges of composition and temperature over which various sodium tungsten bronzes exist, at least under the experimental conditions employed.

Experimental

In all of this work, the samples were prepared by "chemical reduction," under conditions where no liquid phase was present and the reaction mixture was completely transformed into a bronze of one or two phases. According to Ingold and de Vries (*11*), such preparations should lie on the pseudobinary join, WO_3-$NaWO_3$, whereas bronzes prepared by methods such as electrolytic reduction may contain oxygen in excess of an oxygen-tungsten ratio of 3.0. Chemical analyses for sodium and tungsten at several compositions indicated that our samples have an O/W ratio of 3.0 ± 0.15. Precision lattice constants of those samples which fell in the cubic range ($x > 0.40$), lay on the same lattice constant–nominal composition plot as reported by Brown and Banks (*4*).

Powdered samples were prepared in sealed, evacuated silica tubes (*4*) at temperatures where no liquid phase was observed. Reaction temperatures were 500°, 650°, or 750° C., at heating periods of several days to a week. The samples of higher sodium content required higher temperatures to effect complete reaction. Sodium was determined by the method of Spitzin and Kaschtanov (*27*).

The bronzes are decomposed in a stream of oxygen and hydrogen chloride at 600° C. The residue of sodium chloride is titrated with standard silver nitrate solution, giving the sodium content of the sample. Tungsten is determined by precipitation of tungstic acid and ignition to tungsten(VI) oxide in the residue from the above treatment. Before analysis all of the samples analyzed were leached successively with concentrated ammonia and hydrochloric and hydrofluoric acids.

This treatment removes unreacted Na_2WO_4, WO_3, and tungsten metal, as well as silica, from the reaction tube. Since all analyses agreed with the "nominal" compositions, this was taken as evidence of completeness of the reactions. Another evidence was the fact that the x-ray patterns of all samples showed the sharp lines of one phase when the composition fell in a homogeneous range, and of two phases otherwise. When several samples fell into the same two-phase region, the positions of the peaks remained constant, but the relative intensities of the two sets of peaks varied continuously over the range.

X-ray diffractometer patterns were taken with a Norelco diffractometer, using nickel-filtered copper radiation. Low temperature patterns were taken by flowing air or nitrogen, cooled by passage through copper coils immersed in liquid nitrogen or dry ice–acetone, over the sample. This technique has been described by Post,

Schwartz, and Fankuchen (21). Above room temperature, the diffractometer attachment described by Perri, Banks, and Post (20) was employed, using a flowing atmosphere of dried helium to protect the sample from oxidation. With this instrument, it was possible to observe rapid reversible phase changes at temperatures up to about 700° C. in samples of very low sodium content ($x < 0.10$). Above this composition, the phase changes occurred at temperatures where sodium vapor is lost rapidly, or transitions are sluggish, or both. For the remainder of the composition range, the transitions were followed by quenching sealed samples from the furnace into ice water. The x-ray patterns of quenched samples were then measured at room temperature.

Results

In all samples studied, the x-ray patterns were sharp and clear; it was possible to identify all phases present; minor phases could be detected in quantities below 5% (better than 1%, in the case of α-tungsten). Five different phases appear, all of which have been described previously, either for WO_3 itself or for sodium bronzes. The "triclinic" (18), monoclinic, and orthorhombic (1, 20, 23) structures have been described only for WO_3. The phase we designate as "tetragonal I" was first reported by Magnéli for $Na_{0.10}WO_3$, while that designated "tetragonal II" was first described by Hägg and Magnéli (9). Its structure was reported by Magnéli (15). Figure 1 shows the relations among the cubic, monoclinic, orthorhombic, and tetragonal I unit cells. All are based upon the perovskite structure, with distortion progressively increasing as the sodium content decreases. The projection on (001) of the tetragonal II structure is shown in Figure 2, which is taken from the work of Magnéli. We have reversed the designations I and II from those used by Magnéli (16). His designations signified the historical order of discovery; we prefer to label these phases in order of increasing sodium content.

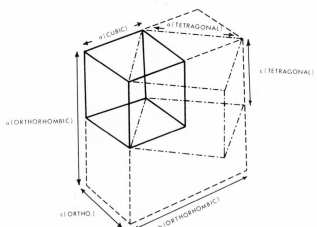

Figure 1.   Unit cells of cubic, orthorhombic, and tetragonal
(I) phases of Na_xWO_3

Figure 3 shows the results of the x-ray patterns taken at various temperatures from samples in the composition range $0 \leq x \leq 0.07$. The phase boundaries at room temperature are represented as accurately as can be determined by preparing samples whose nominal compositions differ by 0.01 or 0.005 (in x). The points shown represent determinations of the transition temperature ($\pm 5°$ to $10°$) by taking x-ray patterns above and below that temperature.

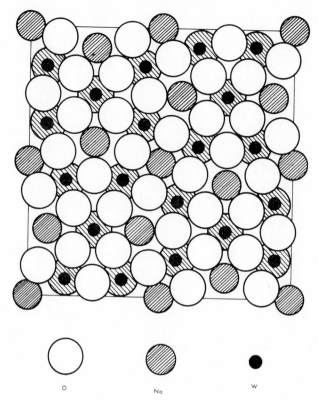

O   Na   W

Figure 2.   Projection of tetragonal II phase on (001)

At extremely low sodium content, a low temperature transition is observed, to a phase of lower symmetry than the monoclinic WO_3 structure, and continuous with the transition in WO_3. The region below this transition has been labeled "monoclinic and triclinic," but we have been unable to establish the nature of this transition, or even whether we are observing two phases. The low temperature transition attains a constant level at $-155°$ C. and $x = 0.012$ (approximately), suggesting a possible eutectoid behavior. It has not been possible as yet to obtain further information in this region.

The transformations above room temperature (monoclinic-orthorhombic, orthorhombic–tetragonal I) are more easily understood. One notes the expected decrease in transition temperature with increasing sodium content, as is found in many alloy phase diagrams. Attempts to observe transitions to a cubic phase at higher temperatures failed, owing to sublimation of samples of very low sodium content ($x < 0.02$) or decomposition at higher sodium concentrations.

Figure 4 shows the observed composition-temperature diagram from $x = 0$ to $x = 0.5$, including the narrow region described above. Above $x = 0.07$, the two tetragonal phases and the cubic phase predominate. Most of the points shown here were obtained by the quenching technique. The diagram shows the single-phase and two-phase regions observed. Few points were determined below $500°$ C., as there were very few phase changes observed below that temperature.

Below $1000°$ C., the phase boundaries do not narrow appreciably, as evidenced by the fact that (with one exception) no single-phase sample was observed

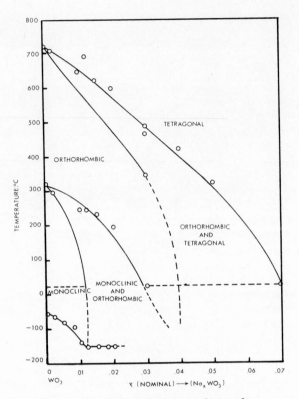

Figure 3.   *Phase transitions in low-sodium bronzes*

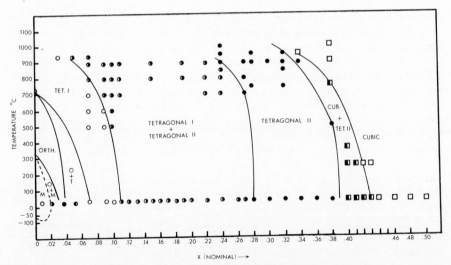

Figure 4.   *Phase diagram for Na_xWO_3 to $x = 0.50$*

to convert completely to a second single phase. Only single-phase to two-phase and two-phase to single-phase transitions were observed, except for $Na_{0.38}WO_3$, which was tetragonal (II) at room temperature and 500° C., two-phase at 750° C., and cubic at 900° and 1000° C. Presumably other samples in that region would behave similarly.

Attempts to carry out quenching from temperatures above 1000° C. led to apparent decomposition of the samples, possibly by loss of sodium. In some cases, samples were obtained which seemed to be mixtures of the tetragonal I and cubic phases. Because of difficulties associated with tube breakage, it was not possible to complete this portion of the investigation at this time.

Discussion

The phase transformations observed at very low sodium concentrations behave in the familiar fashion of numerous alloy systems. These all show lowering of the transition temperature with increasing solute concentration, the appearance of two phases at temperatures intermediate between the regions of homogeneity, and an orderly progression from lower to higher crystal symmetry as the temperature increases.

In the region of coexistence of the two tetragonal phases, the tetragonal II region, and the tetragonal II–cubic region, the transformations were extremely sluggish, precluding the use of high-temperature diffractometry. This is easy to understand in view of the rather drastic structural reorganization necessary for the conversion of the perovskite-like structures into the complex arrangement of Figure 2. In this structure, the WO_6 octahedra are joined at corners to form three-, four-, and five-membered rings, while in the perovskite-like structures, only four-membered rings are present. Hence, transformations from this phase to either of the neighboring phases should be very slow, as observed.

A consequence of the afore-mentioned slow transitions would be a rather strong dependence of the actual structure observed at room temperature upon the previous thermal history of the sample. For example, quenched samples around $Na_{0.35}WO_3$ may be cubic, while slowly annealed samples would be tetragonal (II). Conversely, samples of low sodium content may be cubic if they have been pre-pared by extracting sodium vapor at temperatures of 600° to 700°. The existence of two-phase regions may account for some of the difficulties we (and others) have had in growing single crystals of low-sodium bronzes by the electrolytic method.

The apparent decomposition of samples of various compositions above about 1000° C. could simply be the effect of losses of sodium vapor, which certainly is mobile and does vaporize at that temperature, especially in higher sodium bronzes. The fact that certain tetragonal II phases were changed to mixtures of tetragonal I (sodium-poor) and cubic (sodium-rich) after quenching suggests that there may be a solid-state (or solid-vapor) reaction occurring here which would be of a peri-tectoid type, tentatively symbolized, for a composition in the tetragonal II region:

$$Na_{0.30}WO_3 \text{ (t II)} \rightarrow x\ Na_{0.10}WO_3 \text{ (t I)} + y\ Na_{0.40}WO_3$$

Of course, the correct compositions to be used would be different from those at the boundaries of the respective phases at low temperatures.

In Figure 5, a speculative version of a phase diagram for the system Na_xWO_3 is shown, including the possible peritectoid isotherm. In this temperature region it is clear that the system is no longer pseudobinary, so that verification of the possibility shown here requires some control of the sodium vapor pressure. The "eutec-

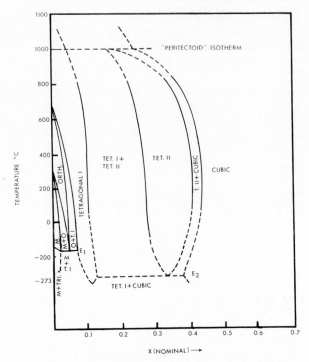

Figure 5.   A possible construction of phase diagram
WO_3-Na_xWO_3 to $x = 0.70$

toid" labeled E_1 has been observed (see Figure 3), but that labeled E_2 is sketched in only for completeness.   Transitions of this type at such low temperatures would surely be "frozen in."

The tetragonal II phase in the potassium tungsten bronzes is reported to have a maximum alkali content of 0.57 (15).   Some experiments done at this laboratory suggest that this phase may have a range only up to 0.50 under certain conditions of preparation.   This may be related to a real difference in the stability of potassium in "pentagonal" and "square" holes.   In the tetragonal sodium bronzes, there appears to be ordering of the sodium positions, leading to the puckering which requires a larger unit cell for the description.   We have attempted without success to find x-ray evidence for such ordering (by structure factor calculations), but the effect on the intensities, if any, was below the limits of error.

These structures, and the hexagonal potassium, rubidium, and cesium bronze structures (14), contain a number of interstices surrounded by trigonal prisms of oxygen ions (0.67 in the hexagonal; 0.40 in the tetragonal).   Recently we have succeeded in introducing lithium into these structures in amounts indicating that some of these positions are being filled.   Further data on these systems will be published later.

Literature Cited

(1) Andersson, G., *Acta Chem. Scand.* **7**, 154 (1953).
(2) Bernoff, R. A., Conroy, L. E., *J. Am. Chem. Soc.* **82**, 6261 (1960).
(3) Brimm, E. O., *et al., Ibid.*, **73**, 5426 (1951).

(4) Brown, B. W., Banks, E., *Ibid.*, **76**, 963 (1954).
(5) Brown, B. W., Banks, E., *Phys. Rev.* **84**, 609 (1951).
(6) Conroy, L. E., Sienko, M. J., *J. Am. Chem. Soc.* **79**, 4048 (1957).
(7) Gardner, W. R., Danielson, G. C., *Phys. Rev.* **93**, 46 (1954).
(8) Hägg, G., Z. *phys. Chem.* **B 29**, 192 (1935).
(9) Hägg, G., Magnéli, A., *Arkiv. Kemi Mineral. Geol.* **19A**, 2(1944).
(10) Huibregtse, E. J., Barker, D. B., Danielson, G. C., *Phys. Rev.* **84**, 192 (1951).
(11) Ingold, J. H., de Vries, R. C., *Acta Met.* **6**, 736 (1958).
(12) Kupka, F., Sienko, M. J., *J. Chem. Phys.* **18**, 1296 (1950).
(13) Magnéli, A., *Acta Chem. Scand.* **5**, 670 (1951).
(14) *Ibid.*, **7**, 315 (1953).
(15) Magnéli, A., *Arkiv Kemi* **1**, 213, 269 (1949).
(16) Magnéli, A., *Nova Acta Regiae Soc. Sci. Upsaliensis* **14**, 3 (1950).
(17) Magnéli, A., Blomberg, B., *Acta Chem. Scand.* **5**, 372 (1951).
(18) Matthias, B. T., Wood, E. A., *Phys. Rev.*, **84**, 1255 (1951).
(19) Ozerov, R. P., *Doklady Akad. Nauk SSSR* **99**, 93 (1954); *Kristallografya* **2**, 217 (1957) (trans. p. 211).
(20) Perri, J. A., Banks, E., Post, B., *J. Appl. Phys.* **28**, 1272 (1957).
(21) Post, B., Schwartz, R. S., Fankuchen, I., *Rev. Sci. Instr.* **22**, 218 (1951).
(22) Ridgeley, D., Ward, R., *J. Am. Chem. Soc.* **77**, 6132 (1955).
(23) Rosen, C., Banks, E., Post, B., *Acta Cryst.* **9**, 475 (1956).
(24) Rosen, C., Post, B., Banks, E., *Ibid.*, **9**, 477 (1956).
(25) Sienko, M. J., *J. Am. Chem. Soc.* **81**, 5556 (1959).
(26) Sienko, M. J., Mazumder, B. R., *Ibid.*, **82**, 3508 (1960).
(27) Spitzin, V., Kaschtanov, L., Z. *anal. Chem.* **75**, 440 (1928).
(28) Straumanis, M. E., *J. Am. Chem. Soc.* **71**, 679 (1949).
(29) Straumanis, M. E., Dravnieks, A., *Ibid.*, **71**, 683 (1949).
(30) Wadsley, A. D., *Acta Cryst.* **8**, 695 (1955); **10**, 261 (1957).

RECEIVED September 6, 1962. Work supported by U. S. Air Force Office of Scientific Research under contract AF18(600)-1193. Abstracted in part from a dissertation by A. S. Ribnick, in partial fulfillment of the requirements for the degree of doctor of philosophy in chemistry from the Polytechnic Institute of Brooklyn.